Also available from Gollancz

Dark Terrors

Dark Terrors 2

THE GOLLANCZ BOOK OF HORROR

Edited by
Stephen Jones and David Sutton

VICTOR GOLLANCZ

LONDON

First published in Great Britain 1996
by Victor Gollancz
An imprint of the Cassell Group
Wellington House, 125 Strand, London WC2R 0BB

The collection © 1996 by Stephen Jones and David Sutton

The right of the individual contributors to be identified as
authors of this work has been asserted by them in accordance
with the Copyright, Designs and Patents Act, 1988.

A catalogue record for this book is
available from the British Library.

ISBN 0 575 06326 8

Typeset by CentraCet, Cambridge
Printed in Great Britain by
St Edmundsbury Press Ltd, Bury St Edmunds, Suffolk

96 97 98 5 4 3 2 1

Contents

About the Editors

Stephen Jones is the winner of two World Fantasy Awards, two Horror Writers of America Bram Stoker Awards and The International Horror Critics Guild Award, as well as being a ten-time recipient of the British Fantasy Award and a Hugo Award nominee. A full-time columnist, television producer/director and genre film publicist and consultant (the first three *Hellraiser* movies, *Nightbreed*, *Split Second*, *Mind Ripper*, *Last Gasp*, etc.), he is the co-editor of *Horror: 100 Best Books*, *The Best Horror from Fantasy Tales*, *Gaslight & Ghosts*, *Now We Are Sick*, *H.P. Lovecraft's Book of Horror*, *The Anthology of Fantasy & the Supernatural* and the *Best New Horror*, *Dark Voices* and *Fantasy Tales* series. He has written *The Illustrated Vampire Movie Guide*, *The Illustrated Dinosaur Movie Guide*, *The Illustrated Frankenstein Movie Guide* and *The Illustrated Werewolf Movie Guide*, and compiled *The Mammoth Book of Terror*, *The Mammoth Book of Vampires*, *The Mammoth Book of Zombies*, *The Mammoth Book of Werewolves*, *The Mammoth Book of Frankenstein*, *Shadows Over Innsmouth*, *The Vampire Stories of R. Chetwynd-Hayes*, *Clive Barker's A–Z of Horror*, *Clive Barker's Shadows in Eden*, *James Herbert: By Horror Haunted*, *Clive Barker's The Nightbreed Chronicles* and *The Hellraiser Chronicles*.

David Sutton has been writing and editing in the fantasy and horror genre for nearly a generation. In recognition of this devotion and achievement in the field, he was honoured with his tenth British Fantasy Award in 1994. From editing his own small press publications and extensive work for the British Fantasy Society during the 1970s, he has been involved in numerous other publications, including the World Fantasy Award-winning *Fantasy Tales*. More recently, he has edited and produced *Voices from Shadow*, a non-fiction anthology celebrating the 20th anniversary of his literary review magazine *Shadow*. Fiction anthologies under his editorship include *New Writings in Horror & the Supernatural* (two volumes), *The Satyr's Head & Other Tales of Terror* and, jointly with Stephen Jones, *The Best Horror from Fantasy Tales*, *The Anthology of Fantasy & the Supernatural* and five volumes of *Dark Voices: The Pan Book of Horror*. Aside from completing four horror novels, the latest entitled *The Land of Shades*, his short stories have appeared in a number of anthologies and periodicals, including *Best New Horror 2* and *7*, *Final Shadows*, *Cold Fear*, *Taste of Fear*, *The Mammoth Book of Zombies*, *The Mammoth Book of Werewolves*, *Shadows Over Innsmouth*, *The Merlin Chronicles*, *Skeleton Crew* and *Beyond*.

Acknowledgements

Special thanks to Nicholas Royle, Dot Lumley, Mandy Slater, Susan Ellison and, especially, Jo Fletcher and Lucy Ramsey.

'Introduction' copyright © 1996 by Stephen Jones and David Sutton.
  'The Comfort of Stranglers' copyright © 1996 by Nicholas Royle.
  'A Really Game Boy' copyright © 1996 by Brian Lumley.
  'Something For Free' copyright © 1996 by Conrad Williams.
  '(Melodrama)' copyright © 1996 by David J. Schow.
  'Absolute Zero' copyright © 1996 by James Miller.
  'Negative Equity' copyright © 1996 by Paul J. McAuley.
  'To This Water (Johnstown, Pennsylvania 1889)' copyright © 1996 by Caitlín R. Kiernan.
  'Out of the Woods' copyright © 1996 by Ramsey Campbell.
  'The Rains' copyright © 1996 by Steve Rasnic Tem.
  'Underbed' copyright © 1996 by Graham Masterton.
  'Animal Life' copyright © 1994 by Clive Barker. Originally published in *USA Weekend*, June 24–26, 1994. Reprinted by permission of the author.
  'Lily's Whisper' copyright © 1996 by Jay Russell.
  'Hell Hath Enlarged Herself' copyright © 1996 by Michael Marshall Smith.
  'Ghost Music: *A Memoir by George Beaune*' copyright © 1996 by Thomas Tessier.
  'The Dead Cop' copyright © 1996 by Dennis Etchison.
  'Where the Bodies Are Buried 2020' copyright © 1996 by Kim Newman.
  'The Museum on Cyclops Avenue' copyright © 1995 by The Kilimanjaro Corporation. Originally published in *Harlan Ellison's Dream Corridor*, Issue Five, August 1995. Reprinted by arrangement with, and permission of, the author and the author's agent, Richard Curtis Associates, Inc., New York. All rights reserved.
  'Hunger: An Introduction' copyright © 1995 by Peter Straub. Originally published in *Peter Straub's Ghosts*. Reprinted by permission of the author.

In Memory of
JOHN BRUNNER
and
BOB SHAW
two Dark Voices now silent.

Introduction

Dark Terrors is one of very few non-themed horror anthology series currently being published. Apparently, most publishers – and presumably the readers themselves – seem to prefer the assurance of anthologies with an obvious 'hook'. Perhaps they provide a kind of cosy familiarity: collections about vampires, ghosts and serial killers or gaming and media tie-ins continue to exploit familiar themes, and low expectations are easily satisfied. However, we trust that you will discover that *Dark Terrors 2* is anything *but* cosy.

This series grew from an earlier incarnation, *Dark Voices: The Pan Book of Horror*, a six-volume series commencing with an omnibus edition reflecting the best of the *original* non-themed anthology, *The Pan Book of Horror Stories*. Pan's paperback series was published successfully for thirty-five years under the aegis of various editors (including ourselves), and along the way it was influential in encouraging many of the best authors working in the genre today.

So perhaps, after all, there is a theme to be found in *Dark Terrors* and its illustrious predecessors. But if so, it is not simply to present a wide variety of tales which can nominally be labelled 'horror' or 'dark fantasy', but to strive to publish some of the very best, most unsettling stories currently to be found in contemporary short fiction.

We believe that we have achieved that objective by assembling an outstanding collection of fine writers, both established names and talented newcomers, with an eclectic gathering of terror tales guaranteed to warp your imagination and disturb your peace of mind with an assault of horrors both visceral and psychological. Whatever you may think of our selection, we are certain that you will agree that 'cosy' is not an appellation which can easily be applied to the diverse *Dark Terrors* that follow . . .

Stephen Jones and David Sutton
April, 1996

The Comfort of Stranglers

NICHOLAS ROYLE

Contracts or something. Release forms. Legal nonsense of some kind. 'Can't I sign them here?' he'd asked, flustered. The voice came back over the line: 'On site, Mr Campbell. On site. That's the stipulation. It's all written down. On site.' Still, there was something to be said for stealing a couple of days.

Paul Campbell sat back, enjoyed the brushed-velvet feel of the head-rest against his scalp. The train skirted the sea, sharp shining cliffs soared arrogantly on the right side of the line. A row of white houses. Platforms. Dawlish. Gone in an instant. Paul wandered down to the end of the carriage, leant out of the window, salty side. It stung his tongue, hair whipping in the vanishing space, head clearing of tiredness as if it were mere foam.

Gina was fucking someone and it wasn't him. He couldn't remember the last time. One minute the way Paul felt, the guy was welcome to her, the next he wanted to kill him. Or her. Or himself. Perhaps if they'd never got married. If he'd listened to the cautionary voice. If he wasn't living in Hampstead Garden Suburb and working for her father. Then it might be easier. He could just walk away. As it was, he had to make do with two days in Devon. She'd offered to come, he'd said no. It was midweek. She was still working, although she had no need to. She liked to keep her hand in, she said. She could have taken the rest of her life off without it making the slightest impact, but she liked to think the modelling industry would grind to a halt if she didn't turn up to jolly along a few hacks. Plus, she'd have two whole nights with Mr Man, whoever he was. Paul didn't really care. It wasn't anyone he knew. He didn't know anybody. Not up there.

The train peeled away from the sea, cut across water meadows, diving through copses, attacking agriculture. Paul went and sat down again, closed his eyes, dreamed of handing in his notice. I'm leaving. You want to know why, ask your daughter.

The ticket guy came round. Paul checked out the features under the cap, tried to feel something. Anything. A sense of coming home. He felt nothing. Nor had he expected to. This was no more his home than NW11. He came from nowhere and was heading the same place. He'd look up Tim, the kid whose folks kept a hotel. He had lived down here, after all, for what, a few years. His teens. Early teens. Then what? These days he never had a chance to sit and think. Maybe that was a good thing. Fragmented memories of growing up all over the place. With this auntie and that uncle, a year or two with Nan and Eric up Southport way. He'd been sent a bag of Eric's silk cravats when the old guy copped it. Couldn't remember where he'd been at the time. They were good people, possibly the only ones he'd known, only ones he could remember, until he met Gina Graham. She was the kind of girl had an abortion while still at school, then grew up over half-term, came back a young woman and left. Went out and got a job she didn't need – father tried to stop her, said she didn't need to work. Made of the stuff. Good commercial head on him, offered Paul a job, fool to turn it down, Gina said. He accepted it. Never looked back, didn't smile much either. Greyhound after the hare.

The train slowed gradually. Totnes. Pretty much as near as it dared get to Salcombe. No one there to meet him. The solicitor was coming down from Exeter, meeting him 'on site' at 2.30. Paul loped down the platform, saw the line of cabs waiting. Driver looked at him questioningly. Paul gave the name of a place outside Salcombe. Checked his watch. He wouldn't have to hang around long.

It was like another country. So far from the nearest railway line you had to go by cab. Not even Scotland was this bad. He scrutinized faces on the road – dog-walkers, cyclists, drivers – looking for signs. Nothing. They looked foreign. The cab driver grunted. Paul paid, got out in the middle of nowhere, started walking.

Grand from the outside, the cottage was a state, as far as Paul could tell peering through grimy windows. No sign of the solicitor. Over there between a dip in conflicting slopes you could see the sea. Just. A powder compact mirror catching the sunlight. Sheep wandered desultorily over the cropped grass. The back door was open. Have a word with the solicitor about that. Anyone could walk in. Though it wasn't the sort of place you passed by chance. Nor was there any purpose here on this false promontory. The interior smelt of dust and old newspapers. Beams high in the black roof space, ceiling absent. Paul stood by the seaward window for a minute – the higher position revealing more blue – before climbing the open steps to the gallery where once there'd been a rough bedroom. He sat on the edge of the upper platform dangling his feet. Looking at the beams. Waiting.

Creeping green tendrils. Tough, wiry. White trumpets with no scent. The watery crunch of soft meadow grass underfoot, his own heavy breathing, pumping chest. Pain in his head, behind the eyes. Sudden sunlight, silhouettes, a blast of pain. Turning, features clear as day, then fade out.

He came round with his head in his hands, perched on the edge. Swaying. He pulled back, gathered his knees to his chin, rocked, blocked the visions. His uncle had lived here alone, apart from the short time he'd fostered Paul. And during those years he'd remained isolated, cold, striking Paul on one occasion when the boy tried to shake him awake, thinking he was dead in his bed. Tim had been Paul's lifeline then. He looked at his watch. The solicitor was late.

Outside the air had freshened – tart, seaweed and diesel. Paul rounded the corner of the cottage, heard the scrunch of tyres before he saw the car. The solicitor had to park some distance away, the cottage having no clear access. He walked,

briefcase in hand, towards Paul. Large black smudges where
his eyes should be, dark snout for a nose. Pain flared up across
Paul's skull, bent him double. A seagull screamed above,
released him. Footsteps now. Paul straightened. The solicitor
took off his aviator sunglasses, pocketed them, offered his free
hand. Prickling with sweat Paul shook it briefly, followed the
man to the cottage.

You may only dream of death so many times before it
becomes a reality.

Shoulders hunched over Paul's uncle's whittling bench, the
solicitor was laying out a number of papers on the only
available surface. Paul scanned them, unpunctuated tracts of
legalese, slight gaps where names had been typed by a
different machine. His uncle's name, Hugh Orr, which Paul
couldn't remember ever having seen written down before.
Not even on a stone in the crematorium. Curious choice, to
be burnt, considering the manner of his death. Individual,
defiant, proud even. Then nothing. Smoke and a handful of
ashes, could be anybody. Any *thing*. Paul hadn't gone. He was
long gone himself. Up north. Somewhere. Anywhere. Away.

'. . . just sign here, here and here, and the cottage is yours,'
the solicitor was saying.

'What if I don't want it?'

'It's yours now.'

No choice. Just like the old sod. Manipulative even from
this distance. Paul signed. The place was his.

'What I want to know is why we couldn't have done this by
post, or in your office,' Paul said, burning up.

'Your uncle's request,' said the solicitor, gathering his
papers together. 'I'll have the deeds in the mail to you by the
end of the week.'

He was already on his way out, fingers at his top pocket,
turning at the door, his eyes black reflective pools once again.
Paul stared after him as the door closed. Remained frozen to
the spot as he heard footsteps recede, car door opening and
closing, engine firing, wheels twisting on gravel. A silence
descended on the dusty topography of the old cottage. A
silence which revealed itself to be composed of the distant

surf, a reedy wind and shrieking gulls. Paul didn't dare make
a sound. He looked up at the beams. Smelt rubber, gas. The
windows were streaked from past rainfall. He knew that in the
far corner of the upper gallery was a big cardboard box the
size of a fridge. He'd glimpsed it before the solicitor's visit.
The south-facing window wouldn't open. Nailed shut. Paul
ran for the door, tore it open, legs buckling as he careered
down the slope towards the gully, the wind peeling tears from
his eyes. He tumbled down the gully, negotiated the awkward
conjunction of soil and sand without care, ended up in a heap
on the beach. Heart thumping in its bone cage, blood
hammering in his temples. Sweat springing to the surface of
his body. The terror. Inescapable terror. He beat a useless fist
on the sand. Looked up through his blurry fringe at the line
of marram grass and sea pinks at the top of the beach. Get it
together. He had to.

Tim was glad to hear from him. 'Come and have dinner,' said
the hotelier. His folks were away and he'd closed up for a
couple of days. 'I've two friends staying, you'll like them.
Come down.'
    Paul threaded the antenna away, stowed the mobile in his
inside pocket. Was there any point locking the cottage?
Feeling of duty. Property owner, after all. It was no luxury
villa, but it was his and neither Gina nor his father-in-law had
anything to do with it. He wandered down the road hoping to
pick up a lift into Salcombe, feeling more relaxed than he had
since he'd boarded the train at Paddington.
    A tractor overtook him, slowed down – there was room on
the trailer – and took off again before Paul caught up. Bastard.
He walked the rest of the way into town. Early in the season
it wasn't very busy in the resort. A few hopefuls in brightly
coloured shorts, carrying balloon-shaped buoyancy aids,
stomped down the main hill towards the sea. The way to the
hotel was a hidden memory which revealed itself corner by
corner. A dog bounded downstairs on hearing his knock,
pawed at the front door while Paul waited for Tim to flounce
down in his baggy shorts and sailor's smock and fling it wide

open. 'Paul. Come in, come in.' Tim shook his hand vigor-
ously, clapped a hand on his shoulder.

Tim took him through to the bar, offered him whatever he
wanted, spreading his arms. 'Beer, wine, cocktails.' There
were dozens of bottles lined up, of all shapes and colours.

'Give him a cocktail, Tim,' said a voice.

Paul swung round. Two women had entered the bar. One
– bright-eyed, wavy-haired, mid-thirties – winked at Paul and
giggled.

'Janet, Loulou, this is Paul.'

Paul stuck out his hand, Janet curtseyed, winked again.
Loulou took his hand, shook it with a man's strength, smiled
grimly. She had a great mop of dark curls. Tim thrust a glass
in his hand. Paul tried to keep up.

'Get that down you,' Janet said with another wink.

'What do you require, Janet?' Tim asked, wiping a fresh
glass.

Janet winked at him, smiled a you-know-what grin.

The four of them gathered in a corner with drinks, laughing, talking easily, as if they'd all known each other for years.
Tim kept folding his long body over the bar to refresh their
drinks. 'Dinner time,' he announced with a flourish after an
hour, maybe two. Loulou offered to help in the kitchen. Janet
stayed and chatted furiously with Paul, winking, fluttering
eyelashes, touching his arm. Half pissed, Paul stopped worrying and had another drink. 'You'll stay here tonight,' Tim
said, smacking a plate of sun-dried tomatoes down on the
table. Janet grinned, her eyes dancing this way and that.
'Ooh!'

Mountains of food, delicious. Paul ate and drank without
restraint. Ten minutes before last orders they rolled out to
the pub, stood shoulder to shoulder, shouted to make themselves heard. Something to say. Anything, dummy copy.
When the lights went out for the last time and the warm,
bright bar finally emptied, they laughed and joked their way
noisily back across the road. 'Room seven,' Tim said to Paul.
'You don't need a key. Don't worry if Betsy visits you in the
night.' Paul must have looked alarmed. Loulou said, 'Don't

worry, love. Betsy's coming in with me.' And she grabbed the shaggy-haired bog terrier round the neck and rubbed noses with her. Janet threw her head on one side and giggled like a spring. Paul said a general goodnight and climbed up through the narrow building to room seven.

There was a tiny en suite bathroom and Paul stripped down to his boxers, did the absolute minimum to his body. Killed the light, jumped into bed. The window was partly open, which was good. Reflected moonlight outlined a couple of items on the bedside table, the last things he saw before he dropped off like a stone – an old-fashioned dial telephone and, like a fat black figure eight, an insomniac's Batman mask.

When he woke, torn from the weight of his dreams like a ring-pull from a can, there were hands at his throat. A figure straddled him, naked except for a gasmask, restlessly struggling, hands closing off his windpipe. He flapped weak arms like fillets of veal, thrashed about. The hands slipped away, moved over his face, stroking hair out of his eyes, resting on his chest. Taking weight. The air being pushed out of him again. He panicked now, finding reserves of strength, bucking his attacker like a bronco with a cowboy. But the hands closed once more round his neck, squeezed, tenderly, some misdirected vestige of affection. Fuck it, he thought, why fight it? As his eyes bulged so did his cock and she rode him all the more energetically, her long wet hair whipping his face. Her eyes remained concealed behind huge black shadows but he knew who she was now. And then she was gone and he was unable to stop himself rolling back into unconsciousness. Bumping and sliding into deep sleep, everything went black. Until the sun splashed his face with golden water and he woke to a pounding in his head. The black eye mask was on the floor. If he half sat up he could see in the wall mirror above the desk. There were faint purple bruises round his neck. Pack and go. Just get the fuck out.

He was halfway out of town before Tim caught up, fell into step beside him, panting. 'Look, Paul. Janet's terribly embarrassed. Apparently she walks in her sleep.'

'And some.'

'She stumbled into your room. Tripped over the foot of
your bed . . . was how she put it to me anyhow.'

'Yes, well.'

Paul didn't stop walking but he had slowed down a little.

The two men fell silent as they reached a kink in the road.
They both knew that down to the left, where the ground gave
way to a scree slope threaded with bracken and thrift, was a
tiny cove hidden from the road. As kids they'd played over
every inch of the coastline round the promontory, negotiating
sections of cliff at low tide that would be inaccessible later in
the day. Approaching the little cove one hot August afternoon
with the tide racing, Paul had been in front, clinging to the
cliff edge some fifty yards ahead of Tim. Paul could still
remember the bite of bitter, salty fear as he realized he could
make it round to the cove and leave Tim behind, but only if
he hurried. The faster he climbed, the slicker his palms
became, the looser their grip on the shale. He stopped once
and decided to go back. It wasn't worth the risk. They'd go
together another time. Tim had got as far as he could and was
shouting for Paul to come back. He looked down as a heavy
wave slapped against the slippy green rock face only a few feet
beneath his trainers. That got him moving, and not back,
because within seconds it had become too late for that, but on
towards the cove. They knew it was there because they'd seen
it from the water, paddling in Tim's inflatable dinghy during
a morning's mackerel feathering. The water splashed his bare
legs and Paul swallowed what felt like a ball of dust and fibres.
His legs turned rubbery and he had to rely on his hands,
sweating now like a tightrope walker's. Just one more corner,
one more ledge. And then he was there.

The cove stretched far enough back for there still to be a
little sand uncovered by the sea, but it was wasting no time.
There was a level path halfway up the slope. Paul trotted
along it. Gulls hung like mobiles in the middle of the cove,
on a level with him, rising and dipping according to the warm
air. Then Paul's stomach turned itself inside out, the hairs on
his arms and neck stood to attention. He shivered quickly.
Blinked, but it hadn't gone away. On the far side of the cove.

It was there. He'd seen it. On the far side of the cove, hanging by the neck, was the body of a man, his clothes in seaweedy rags, his eyes pecked out. The black sockets transfixed the boy, their unblinking stare meeting his gaze across the width of the cove.

Tim got the police out to find Paul, who still hadn't returned by early evening. They found him sitting on the edge of the cliff staring out to sea, thumb stuck in his mouth. He wouldn't speak for a fortnight. The body, it was discovered, had been hung at such a height that the waves would cover it only at high tide. It had been there less than two weeks, they said. He was identified as a nobody, a drifter passing through. Suicide couldn't be ruled out, but the police were treating it as suspicious.

It was the curled lip which had Paul waking in the night, sweat standing out on his forehead like rain on a waxed car. The blackened eye sockets, of course, but also the mouth, the half smile.

'You know, we probably saw him.' Paul looked beseechingly at Tim. 'We probably rowed right past in your dinghy and, if it was anything except high tide, we'd have seen him. Why didn't we do anything?'

Tim spread his hands. 'It's a long time ago.'

'Not as far as he's concerned. It's the very next second for him, just as it has been for the last twenty-odd years.' Paul stared at the banks of nettles at the side of the road which had been laced with convolvulus bindweed like a girl's hair with daisies. 'That didn't use to be there.' He kicked one of the white flowers. 'I've got to get back, Tim. I'll give you a ring.'

He left his old friend still making faces and noises intending to convey that Janet had meant no harm. Whatever comfort the previous night's encounter had provided for her, it had done Paul no favours. He increased his walking pace until his breathing was normal again. When he looked up, the cottage had come into view.

He sat on the edge of the upper level, legs dangling. The big cardboard box was back there in the corner.

Then the box was in the middle of the gallery. In two minds

over what to do, Paul found himself sifting through its dark slippery coils. Eels, angler fish, unknown creatures with huge black eyes. Mucoid lenses. He knelt before the box, arms thrust deep into its damp midst. The overpowering smell of rubber, the sour reek of crushed bindweed.

Paul closed the cottage door behind him. Walked to the road, crossed over, bundled his frame over the farmer's gate. The sun was still high, the sky like rice paper. If he moved his head too sharply in any direction a sharp little tear would appear. An angry confusion of lines scribbled by a lonely child with a 2H pencil. A black jigsaw blade just nosing through into the world. He tried to keep his head still.

He remembered the way from his childhood. It wasn't the kind of thing you forgot. The path unrolled under his feet, a brown carpet. The fence like a necklace, the copse lurching out of perspective like some E-head's huge black panther. The blackened greenery, starved of light, the tiny trumpets of the non-smelling convolvulus. The stars in his head, spinning. Punch-drunk, reeling, he fell to his knees in front of the tough strands of weed that marked the edge of the land. He looked up, into the light, knew what he would see only moments before he saw it. Again.

He got up from the gallery floor, shuffled away from the cardboard box, its contents an oily blur. Stood looking over the edge, flirting with gravity. Giggled to himself. Out loud. Looked up at the beams, strong beams. Thick, solid. They'd have to be. Mainly they went the length of the cottage, others intersected them going the other way. Not so many of them. His uncle, a mathematician, would have enjoyed the geometries.

A chill brushed his arms. He almost overbalanced, drew back and sat down on the edge of the upper platform once more, his heart as leaden as his stomach.

The box cast a long shadow.

*

The white flowers of the bindweed, scattered like gems amidst the velvety undergrowth. He raised his head again. Blinded by the sun he squinted to make out the approaching figures. Their silhouettes rippled, resisted definition, until they reached the gate in front of Paul. They loomed, laughing gaily, an image from an old poster. Mr and Mrs No-mark from Sussex, they use the train when it suits. Mr No-mark smokes a pipe. Mrs No-mark's cardigan buttons up the back. Their two children are never a nuisance.

Post-war fantasy figures, Britain getting back to her feet. Thanks to families like these. Mr No-mark's Fair Isle sleeveless sweater had been knitted by his good wife, who whetted those knife-edge creases in his trousers. Mr and Mrs No-mark both wore gasmasks, the children also; their laughter was tinny but heartfelt. They swung the gate open, beckoned to Paul. His knees popped as he stood up, sweating at the temples, breathing in shallow draughts. They looked so contented, so free. *Join us*, everything about them seemed to say. Paul followed them into the field where a path soon materialized. The children skipped either side of it but never strayed far. Mr and Mrs occasionally held hands, looked back to reassure Paul. He was becoming light-headed, losing it, white flowers bursting silently in the air in front of him. Tiny fairies coalesced out of the pollen, danced, mingled with the grass ahead of the two children who stamped them into the earth.

The grass grew shorter, the flowers less frequent, until the path was a pavement and the houses alongside were bay window semis. An Austin Seven in every drive. Catmint and red-hot pokers in each herbaceous border. Ropes hanging from every landing balustrade, dangling a noose in each darkened hallway. The comfort of stranglers.

An open door, a swinging rope. The smells of rubber and leather overpowering the mothballs and iodine. Not an antimacassar out of place. Paul went in, fingered the coarse rope, felt something somewhere tighten.

*

He tipped up the box, rummaged, mentally catalogued. The gasmask, full-length leather coat, rubber salmon-fishing waders, assorted rags and ties, the rope. They said it was suicide, whispered it in the Devon pubs, the post office queue. No one knew. Even *normal* sex was not spoken of here. Paul tried to picture his uncle's face without the gasmask. It was blank. He slipped the rubber strap round the back of his head, undid the buckle on his trousers. Would this help exorcize the memories? Cause the nightmares to disintegrate like smoke in a sudden breeze?

The coat might have been tailored for him. Would the door open and his uncle walk in? Himself? It was too easy, as if the beams had been nailed into place according to a set of instructions, an auto-erotic's manual. Paul slipped the noose over his head, gathered the slack.

Light filtered down through the dust-sparkly air between rope and windows, a chance twist of angles illuminating a distant corner of the mahogany hallway. Mr and Mrs standing stock still, eyes like flies', snouts of undiscovered beasts. Children dead on the floor at their feet, cold as January's turkey carcass, school caps obscuring pecked sockets.

His legs protruded from behind the door. Paul closed it. The fallen rope, the contorted legs, the wooden splinters under the fingernails. His uncle in a gasmask, the rope an extravagant tie. The open coat revealing more than his physical nakedness. Paul bent down to pull the coat closed, opened it wider instead and crept underneath. His uncle was still warm. Had he come back earlier ... With his cheek resting on the floor he saw his uncle's final message on the bare wooden boards only inches from his face. Its marble pallor spoke only to him and he answered it. The last drops of ink from his uncle's pen spelled a word too private for anyone to read. He ate it.

It was easier that way. By committing an act he would forget for decades he allowed the world to believe that a suicide note had simply been missing.

*

He was dimly aware of the scrunching of gravel as the rope tightened, comfortably. He felt hot, then very cold. He remembered the word. Imagined his head as a balloon being blown up almost to bursting point then tied with string. Saw a million flies hovering, their eyes pilots' goggles. The dead children. Goodbye Gina and fuck off. The blissful ease of resting the entire body in a hammock of lint, stained vermilion, flecked with petals and pearls. The salty splash of the sea over the sightless face. The greedy wheel of the gulls. Either he lost feeling in his feet or they slipped from the gallery floor. Swinging, his head a whirlpool of lights, a spinning galaxy, bloody feathers. Then a rush of strange sudden light, bitter seaweedy stench, a laying on of hands. Something wet on his face. A dog barking. Soft hands at his throat.

Nicholas Royle followed his 1995 début novel, *Counterparts*, with *Saxophone Dreams*, published by Penguin in Britain and White Wolf in the USA, while a collection of short tales entitled *The Crucian Pit & Other Stories* is forthcoming. The new novel he is working on stems from ideas he has been developing in such recent short stories as 'The Lagoon' (from *Dark Terrors*), 'Lacuna' (*The Best New Horror 7*) and 'The Matter of the Heart' (from *The Third Alternative*). He is the award-winning author of more than seventy horror tales, several of which have been selected for *The Year's Best Fantasy and Horror*, *The Year's Best Horror Stories* and *The Best New Horror* series, as well as many other anthologies and periodicals, the most recent including Stephen Jones' *Shadows Over Innsmouth*, Ellen Datlow's *Twist in the Tail* and Poppy Z. Brite's *Razor Kiss*. Also recently published are two Royle-edited anthologies: *A Book of Two Halves* (Gollancz), containing all-new stories about football but featuring a number of genre writers, and *The Tiger Garden: A Book of Writers' Dreams* published by Serpent's Tail. The author offers the following explanation to describe the evolution of 'The Comfort of Stranglers': 'Some sort of occult, alchemical power surely exists, but whether it resides in space or in time, or in people, is a mystery. Possibly born out of the right conjunction of all three – a case of being in the right place at the right time. Or the wrong place at the wrong time.'

A Really Game Boy

BRIAN LUMLEY

Yes, you're right, Sheriff, Willy Jay *is* a real game boy, and I counts myself lucky he's my friend. And I really do 'preciate the point that he ain't been home for more'n a week (a whole week! Dun't that beat all?), but iffen we was to stop him now – why, he'd never fergive us!

As to the folks sayin' *I* got somethin' to do with him bein' missin' – why, I really dun't believe that. Everyone knows how much I love that boy! He's the onliest kid 'round here has anythin' to do with me. Hell, most o' the kids is even a mite scared o' me! Well, they shouldn't do the things they do and then I wouldn't git mad.

And you know as well as I do how many heads Willy's rattled 'cause he heard them a-callin' me. *That's* how close Willy Jay and me is, Sheriff, and you can believe it. And that's why I cain't tell you where he's at.

Now listen, Sheriff, you dun't scare me none. My Paw says that iffen I dun't want to talk to you I sure dun't have to, and that dang him but it might be best iffen I dun't say nothin' anyhow. And anyways, Willy made me promise.

See, it's kind o' a endurance test – that's what Willy called it, a endurance test – and he wouldn't thank me none for lettin' you break it up. Not now he's gone this long. Sure is a game boy, that Willy . . .

Tell you all about it?

Well, I s'pose I could. I mean, that's not like tellin' you where he's at. See, I cain't do that. 'Cause iffen you stopped

him he'd surely blame me, and I values his friendship too
much to lose it just 'cause I shot my mouth off to the town
Sheriff. I mean, Sheriff – what did you ever do for me, eh?

Hey, I knows you laugh at me behind my back. Paw told
me you do. He says that you're the two-facedest Sheriff he
ever knowed.

What's that you say? Well what's that got to do with it,
Willy bein' just thirteen and me eighteen and all? He's a real
big kid for thirteen, and he treats me just like a brother. Why,
I could tell you secrets me and Willy knows that would—

—But I wun't . . .

There you go again, blamin' me for that little Emmy-May
kid what drowned. You think I did that? Why, it was me drug
her out the water! And Willy with me. It was a *accident* she
fell in the crick, that's all, and I never did take her clothes
offen her like some tried to say I did. That was just Willy
foolin' about with her. He didn't mean her no real harm,
but—

Aw, see? I promised him I'd never say a word 'bout that,
and there you go trickin' me into shootin' off my mouth
again. Well, okay, I'll tell you – but you got to promise me
you'll never tell Willy.

Okay . . .

It was like this:

See, Willy took a shine to that little Emmy-May girl and
he wanted to sort of kiss her and do things. Aw, shucks,
Sheriff, you *knows* what sort o' things! Anyways, she bein' a
Sunday school girl and all, he figures maybe she ain't much
for that kind o' thing. So bein' a game boy and all, and not
lettin' nothin' stop him once he's set hissen mind on somethin', Willy works out a little trick to play on her. So this
Sunday Willy gets re-ligion and off he goes to Sunday school.
When it's over and all the kids is a-leavin', he catches up to
Emmy-May and asks her iffen he can see her home. See, she's
seen him hangin' back, and she's sort o' hung back too, so
maybe she's taken a shine to him like he has to her.

Anyways, their walkin' takes 'em close to Fletcher's Spinney
where the crick bends, and this was part o' Willy's plan. I was

a-waitin' in the spinney, all crouchin' down and out o' sight like he'd told me to be, and I seen and heard it all.

'I knows a secret place,' says Willy, his face all eyes and teeth and smiles.

'Oh?' says Emmy-May, and she laughs. 'You're just foolin' about, Willy Jay,' she tells him. 'Why, there ain't no secret places 'round here!'

'Is so,' he says. 'C'mon and I'll show you – but you got to keep it a secret.'

'Sure thing!' she says, all big-eyed, and they runs into the spinney. Anyways, sure 'nough there is a secret place: a clearin' where the grass is kind o' cropped under a big old oak that leans right out over the crick. Me and Willy had fixed up a rope there and used to swing right out over the crick and back. And sometimes we'd take our clothes off and splash down into the water off of the rope. O' course, me and Willy can swim like we was born to the water . . .

So there they are in the secret place, and me creepin' close in the shrubs and listenin' and a-watchin' it all. 'See,' says Willy, 'this here's my secret place. And that's my swing. Why, I can swing right over the crick on that there rope!'

'Can you really, Willy?' says Emmy-May.

'Sure 'nough. Watch!' says he. And he takes a run at the rope, grabs it and swings right over the crick and back. 'Iffen I'd a let go I could've landed on the other side,' he says. 'Would you like to try the swing, Emmy-May?'

'Oh, no!' she holds back. 'I cain't swim, and iffen I fell—'

Willy, he nods and lets it be. 'Anyways,' says he, 'it's just a pre-caution, is all.'

'A what? What sort of precaution, Willy?' she asks.

'Why, the rope!' says he. 'In case I got to run.'

'From what?' she laughs. 'Ain't nothin' here'bouts to be a-feared of.'

'Oh?' says he. 'What about wood spirits, eh? Surely you knows about them? My Paw says your Maw and Paw is full o' superstition from the old country.'

'Oh, I *knows* about them,' she answers, 'but like you say,

them's just old wives' tales.' But still she looks around the clearin' real careful like.

By now they's a-sittin' under the old oak and this is where I'm to play my part in the joke. See, Sheriff, Willy had it all figured out. I just rustled a bush a little and let out a low sort o' groan, like a hant might make.

'What was *that*?' asks Emmy-May, and she creeps real close to Willy and puts her arms around his neck.

'Did you hear 'im?' says Willy, actin' all s'prised. 'Ordinary folk dun't hear 'im, mostly.'

'Hear who?' she whispers, her blue eyes big and round.

'That mean old wood spirit,' says Willy. 'But dun't you worry none. Oh, he's ugly and he's mean, but iffen you're a good friend o' mine he wun't hurt you. He's only ever real bad on full moon nights.'

She hugs his neck tighter. 'Tonight's a full moon, Willy Jay!' she whispers.

'Is it?' Again he looks s'prised. 'Why, so it is! But that's okay. Just be still and quiet. As long as you're with me he wun't hurt you none. We gets along just fine, me and the wood spirit – mostly.' And he gives her a kiss full on her mouth.

Now she pulls back from him and stands up – just like he'd told me she might. I rustles the bush some more and makes a angry sort of grunt, and Willy says, 'I *told* you to stay still, Emmy-May! Dun't you know them wood spirits is dangerous? Now come back down here.'

So she gets down again, all shivery like, and Willy pulls the bow at her neck and loosens her buttons. Well, Sheriff, by now I'm all excited. I mean, me? – I'd never *ever* dare do any sech thing, but dang me iffen Willy ain't the gamest boy. But . . . that Emmy-May is sort o' game, too. She slaps him real hard. And me, watchin', I sees his face go all red from the slap.

'So,' he says, breathin' real hard. 'That's how it's a-goin' to be, is it? Well, I warned you, Emmy-May.' And he calls out: 'Wood spirit, you see this here girl, Emmy-May?' I gives a big grunt and shakes my bush. 'Well, she dun't like me and

she dun't believe in you. There,' he says to her. 'Serves you
right, Emmy-May, for slappin' me. Your folks'll sure miss you
tonight!'

That was my signal to make some real angry growlin' and
snarlin', and to beat on the ground with a fallen branch. And
I set the bushes a-shakin' like they was full of rattlers as I
crept closer, pantin' like a wild animal.

'Call 'im off, Willy Jay!' Emmy-May cries. She hugs Willy
tight and sobs, and this time when he kisses her she dun't
protest none. And when he puts his hand up her dress she
sobs a little but she dun't stop him none. Then he stands up,
real slow like, and takes off his clothes, every last stitch. And
his pecker is big as my own, Sheriff, I swear it. He's a real big
boy for thirteen . . .

'What you a-doin', Willy Jay?' she says, all breathless like.

'Wood spirit,' he calls out, 'iffen she's good to me you just
stay quiet – but iffen she ain't . . .'

Emmy-May starts in a-sobbin' real loud.

'And iffen she dun't stop her snivellin' right this minute –
then she's all your'n!'

'Willy! Willy!' she cries, crawlin' to his feet.

'Take off your clothes,' he says, his voice all broke up like.
'All of 'em, and do it slow.'

'But Willy,' she gasps, 'I—'

'Wood spirit!' he calls, and I gives a real loud howl, so like
a wolf it scares even me!

So she takes her clothes off and stands there all pink and
sweet and shivery and a-tryin' to cover herself up with her
hands, and even the hot summer sun comin' through the oak's
branches cain't warm her none. And Willy, he lies her down
in the grass and touches, pokes, strokes and kisses her here
and there and everywhere, and—

Well, I'm a-*comin*' to that, Sheriff!

Finally, he's all worked up and his face is red and his hands
a-shakin'. He says: 'Open your legs real wide, Emmy-May,
so's I can put my pecker in you.'

'I'll tell, I'll tell!' she screams, and she jumps up.

Quick as a flash Willy yells: 'Sic 'er, wood spirit – sic 'er good!' But she ain't listenin' none.

That was when the accident happened. See, she made a run at the rope, jumped, fell—

Well, I sprung up out o' hidin' and was all fixed to dive right in after her, but Willy grabs me and says: 'Dun't fret yourself, Zeb,' he says. 'She swims real good . . .' Only he was mistook, 'cause she couldn't. And the crick bein' pretty fast water just there and all . . .

Down she went and swept away, and her head bobbin' in the current as she's whirled out of sight. Willy, he tosses her clothes in after her and gets hisself dressed real quick. 'C'mon, Zeb,' he says, 'and I'll tell you what we'll do. We'll say we was walkin' by the crick and we saw her in the water. Mind, we dun't know as to how she got there.'

Then we races near a mile to the big swimmin' hole where the kids is all splashin' and a-yellin'. And Willy shouts, 'There's a girl in the water, comin' down the crick! We seen her!' And as Emmy-May comes driftin' into view we both go in full-dressed and drag her out. But by then she's a goner.

So you see, Sheriff, it were a accident. Just Willy's little trick gone a mite wrong, is all.

Now I done *told* you he ain't run away! What, because o' what happened to Emmy-May, you mean? Shucks, why that weren't nothin' compared to the other things. I mean, it were a accident. But then there was your prize hens, and—

Oh, my! I didn't *ever* mean to mention them hens, Sheriff, I surely did not. Well, you shouldn't whacked his ear that time he gave Jason Harbury a bloody nose. That really made him sore, Sheriff. Oh, it were Willy, all right. He pizzened 'em good! And then there's Old Miss Littlewood . . .

Why sure, Sheriff, I knows she's dead.

Well, see, Willy had this thing he'd do with worms. It tickled me pink and made the girls all throw up, and Willy – heh! heh! – such a *game* boy, that one!

See, he'd find a big, juicy worm and pop it in his mouth, then let it just sort o' dribble out, all wrigglin', when someone'd stop to speak to him – 'specially girls.

One day he'd trapped Old Miss Littlewood's cat and tied a can to his tail, then let him loose over the old lady's fence. Why, that cat was madder'n all hell! Finally she grabbed him and got the can off of him, and she came over to the fence where we was hidin' in the bushes.

She sees us and says: 'Zeb, I just knows you wouldn't do a thing like that. But *you*, Willy Jay – 'bout you I ain't so sure. You are one mean, cruel, unpleasant boy, Willy – and you'll end up in a sorry mess sure as shootin'!'

And Willy, he just stands up all slow like, and he opens his mouth and grins, and a big fat worm glides over his bottom lip and falls plop on to the grass!

Well, she screams! She really screams! – and Willy just standin' there laughin'. Until she reaches across that fence and brings him such a smack as I never heard. That did it. Willy bein' such a game boy and all, he wa'n't a-goin' to let no old spinster lady get away with that! No sir!

We spent the next hour or two diggin' out the biggest, fattest, juiciest worms we could find, and when Old Miss Littlewood left her house and walked off down the street and into town with her basket, then that Willy he snuck into the house and put worms in her bed, and her kitchen, in her preserves, her butter, her milk! . . . worms everywhere!

T'ward dusk she comes home, goes in, lights her lamp, and for a while we can her her a-hummin' through the open window. Then – she starts a-screamin'. And she keeps right on a-screamin', each scream higher'n the last. Woke all the neighbours, and all their lights goin' on, and me and Willy watchin' the house and a-sniggerin' fit to bust. Then she comes staggerin' out in her nightdress, trips and falls in the garden – and lies still. Me and Willy, we gits out o' there fast!

Yes, I know folks said she'd had a stroke or heart attack or sumthin', and so she did. But what *caused* it, eh?

Now, Sheriff, I allow I didn't much care for that one. I mean, when I saw Willy next day and he laughed at her bein' dead and all. But when he saw I wa'n't too happy 'bout it he soon dried up and said yes, I was right. But it had been a accident, just like Emmy-May, and iffen folks found out I'd be in real trouble 'cause I helped him dig them worms. But, him bein' my friend and all, he said not to worry my head none – he wouldn't tell on me. I was just to fergit the whole thing . . .

Now Sheriff, I done told you already I cain't—

What?

Just tell you what the endurance test is all about? Well, I suppose that'd be okay. So long as you dun't ask me where it's at.

See, Willy has this thing 'bout ropes and climbin' and a-swingin' – a reg'lar Tarzan, he is. Well, one day we was at – the place. No, sir, not the secret place in Fletcher's Spinney, the place o' the endurance test. And there's this rope a-hangin', see. And Willy says, 'Hey, Zeb, you're pretty big and strong. Iffen that rope was round your feet, how long you reckon you could hang up there, all upside down like, afore you had to stop?'

'Why, I really cain't say as I knows that, Willy Jay,' says I.

'I reckon,' says he, 'I could beat your time whatever.'

'Now Willy,' says I, 'you're a real game boy and no question, but I beat you at runnin', swimmin', wrestlin' and swingin' – so what makes you think you could outlast me on that there rope?'

Willy, I dun't think he liked bein' reminded I could beat him at them things. He got that stubborn look on his face and said: 'But I could beat you *this* time, Zeb, I knows I could.'

'Willy, you're a real winner,' says I, 'and my onliest true friend, too – but I'm older, bigger and stronger'n you. Now you think real clever and no question, but you're just thirteen and—'

'I can beat you!' he says.

'Okay,' says I, 'I believe it.'

'No,' says he, 'that ain't no proof. This here's a endurance test, Zeb, and we got to try it out.'

'Now, Willy,' says I, 'I got a good many chores to do for Paw. Iffen I'm not home an hour from now, he'll—'

'You first,' says Willy.

See, it makes no matter nohow arguin' with him when he's

in that there stubborn mood o' hissen. So we climbs up and hauls up the rope and he ties it round my feet in a noose. Then I climbs back down and lets go and swings to and fro 'til I'm all still, and Willy Jay sits up there lookin' down at me and a-grinnin'. 'There you go,' says he, and he keeps the time.

Now then, Sheriff, after 'bout an hour or so Willy says, 'Hey, Zeb! You all right down there?'

'Sure,' says I. 'My ears is a mite poundin', and I got pins and needles in my legs – but I'm okay, Willy Jay.'

'Sure?'

'Sure I'm sure!'

'Well, enough is enough,' he says, soundin' a bit sore at me. I can't say why he's sore, but he sounds it. 'You better come on up now, 'cause it's time you was a-startin' home to them chores o' your'n.

'But what about the endurance test?' says I.

'Well, we'll finish it another day,' he says.

So I clumb up – but truth to tell I nearly didn't make it, my arms and legs was so stiff and all. And I got the rope off and staggered about and stamped my feet 'til I could feel 'em again. 'How long'd I do?' I asks.

'Oh, an hour and three and a half minutes,' says Willy, sort of half-sneerin' like.

'Hey!' says I. 'I could go a lot longer but for them chores. Why, I could go another ten or twenty minutes easy!'

'Oh, sure!' says he. 'Listen,' he says, 'I beat you hands down, Zeb. I could stay up that there rope a whole week iffen I wanted to . . .'

Now that was boastin' pure and simple and I knowed it. 'Willy,' says I, 'ain't nobody – but *nobody* – could do that! Why, you'd git all hungry, and how'd you sleep?'

'Hell!' he says. 'There's meat enough on my bones, Zeb. I'd not crave feedin'. And as for sleepin' – well, bats do it, dun't they? They spends all winter a-hangin' and a-sleepin'. Hell, I bet I could do that too, iffen I put my mind to it.'

'Well all I knows,' says I, 'is that I'm real glad I'm down after only one hour, three and a half minutes, that's all.'

'You're you and I'm me, Zeb,' he says, 'but I can see you

needs convincin'. Okay, how long's them chores o' your'n a-goin' to take?'

'Oh, 'bout an hour, I reckon.'

'Okay,' says he. 'I'm a-goin' to tie up my feet right now and hang here 'til you gets back.' And he did. And hangin' there, he says: 'Now this is stric'ly 'tween you and me, our secret. Dun't you dare tell a soul 'bout this, hear? See, I'm a-goin' to stick my thumbs in my belt, like this—' and he did, '—and just rest here easy like. And I'm a-goin' to concentrate. Now dun't you go breakin' my concentration nohow, Zeb, hear?'

And I said, 'Okay.'

'Iffen I feels like hangin' here a week, you just let me hang, right?'

'Right,' says I. But o' course, I dun't believe he can do it.

'So off you go and do your chores, Zeb Whitley, and I'll be right here when you gits back.'

'Okay,' I says again, and I scoots.

Well, I was late home and Paw gives me some talkin' to. Then I did my chores – chopped firewood, fetched-'n'-carried, this and that – until I figured I was all through. A good hour was up by then, but Paw saw me a-headin' off and says: 'Hey, boy! Where you a-goin'?'

'Why, nowheres, Paw.'

'Danged right!' says he. 'You was late, and so you can do some more chores. I got a whole list for you.' And he kept me right at it all evenin' 'til dark come in. After that – well, I ain't allowed out after dark, Sheriff. Paw says he dun't want no trouble, and people bein' ready to lay the blame too quick and all, it's best he knows where I'm at after dark. So off I goes to bed.

But when I hears him a-snorin', up I jumps and runs to . . . to the place o' the endurance test. And wouldn't you know it? There he is a-hangin' in the dark, quiet as a bat, all concentra-tin', his thumbs tucked in his belt just like afore. And Lord, he's been there all of five or six hours! And him so quiet, I figures maybe he's a-sleepin' just like he said he could. So I just tippy-toed out o' there and snuck home and back to bed.

Anyhow, next mornin' Paw gets a note from Uncle Zach

over the hill, sayin' please come and bring big Zeb, 'cause
Uncle Zach's a-clearin' a field and there's work a-plenty. And
hey! – that was excitin'! I mean, I really do like Uncle Zach
and him me. So Paw hitches up the wagon and off we goes,
and we're all the way to Uncle Zach's place afore I remembers
Willy.

By now he'll be down off of that rope for sure and madder'n
all hell, I reckon, 'cause I wa'n't there to check his time. But
heck! – he beat me every which ways anyhow . . .

And we was at Uncle Zach's six days.

This mornin' we comes home, and soon's Paw's done with
me I gits on over to . . . to the place o' the endurance test,
and—

That's right, Sheriff! Now how'd you guess that? Sure
'nough, he's still up there. Nearly a week, and that spunky
boy still a-hangin' by his feet. So I goes up to him – but not
too close, 'cause it's all shut in and hot and all, and the
summer flies is bad and the place stinks some – and I says:
'Willy, you been here six days and seven nights and some
hours, and you sure beat the hell out o' me! You see that old
clock out there over the schoolhouse? It's near noon o' the
seventh day. Dun't you reckon you should come on down
now, Willy Jay?' And I reaches up and gives him a little prod.

Sheriff, are you okay? You sure do look groggy, Sheriff . . .

Well, I shouldn't have prodded Willy like that 'cause I
guess it spoils his concentration. Down comes a arm real slow
and creaky like, and it points to the door. He's a tellin' me to
git out, he ain't finished yet! So off I goes, and I'm a-comin'
up the street when you grabs me and—

Why, yes, I did say I could see the schoolhouse clock from
the place o' the endur—

Aw, Sheriff! You're just too danged clever for your own
good. You guessed it. That's right, Old Man Potter's livery –
and him away visitin' and all. His old barn, sure – but dun't
you go disturbin' Willy none, or—

Okay, okay, I'm a-comin' – but I just knows there'll be
trouble. He told me not to say a word, and there I goes
blabbin' and a-blabbin'. And he wun't thank me none for

bringin' you down on him, Sheriff, and that's a fact. Okay, I'll be quiet . . .

Oh, sure, I knows the door's shut and bolted, Sheriff, but there's a loose board there, see? Yes, sir, you're right, it is a danged hot summer. And did you ever see so many flies? Only quiet now, or you'll disturb Willy.

See him there? Yes sir, Sheriff, I knows it's gloomy, but—

Hey! Lookit them flies go when you touched him! And . . . Sheriff? Are you sure you're feelin' okay, Sheriff?

What?

The rope was too tight 'round his ankles? His blood pooled and swelled up his belly? His belt got wedged under his ribs, you say, and trapped his thumbs? And he's . . . he's . . .

No! You must be mistook, Sheriff Tuttle. Just give him another little shake and you'll see how wrong you are. Why, he'll go up that rope like a monkey up a stick, all a-laughin' and—

But he *cain't* be dead, not Willy! He's just a-concentratin', that's all. Maybe he's a-sleepin' even, like them bats do. What, Willy Jay – dead?

See! See! I'm right. I done *told* you, Sheriff. See what he's a-doin' now? That there's his worm trick!

Dang me, Willy Jay, but I never seen you get *that* many in your mouth afore – you really *game* boy!

Brian Lumley began writing in the 1960s with stories and, later, novels set against the backdrop of the 'Cthulhu Mythos' created by H.P. Lovecraft. After producing a number of books in this vein, in the 1980s he turned his attention to more contemporary horror with a trilogy, *Psychomech*, *Psychosphere* and *Psychamok!* During this period he also published *Demogorgon* and *The House of Doors*. His best-selling, multi-reprinted 'Necroscope' series, *Necroscope*, *Wamphyri!*, *The Source*, *Dead-speak* and *Deadspawn*, continued in the 'Vampire World' spin-offs: *Blood Brothers*, *The Last Aerie* and *Blood Wars*, plus two volumes of *Necroscope: The Lost Years*, stretching the saga into ten massive books and some half a million words. A selection of the author's short stories can be found in such recent collections as *Fruiting Bodies and Other Fungi*, *Return of the Deep Ones and Other Mythos Tales*, *Dagon's Bell and Other Discords*

and *The Second Wish and Other Exhalations*. Also planned is an updated, revised and extended reprint of his book of poetry, *Ghoul Warning & Other Omens*, and readers interested in some of Lumley's earlier work will be pleased to learn that his American publisher will be issuing his six 'Titus Crow' novels in two omnibus volumes, plus two further collections of short stories. 'A Really Game Boy' was originally written in 1981 but remained unpublished until now, as the author reveals: 'It was laid aside and forgotten, and only came to light among a pile of old manuscripts when the editors asked my agent if there was anything available.' With what we imagine is a monstrous grin, he adds: 'Now we find ourselves wondering what else may be in there – "rotting down", as it were – among those old manuscripts . . .'

Something For Free

CONRAD WILLIAMS

'Look,' Isobel said, yanking open the mouth of her Budgens' carrier bag. 'Pears, from a house on Ornan Road. They were just sitting on the wall with a piece of paper next to them. "Please help yourself," it said.'

Her fiancé, Peter, looked up from the deep box in which he had been rummaging. His expression had not changed since yesterday evening: his 'removal' face, as Isobel had described it, all folded up and wrinkly, as if it had just been fed through a mangle. 'Hmm,' he replied. 'Are you sure they're all right? Might be poisoned or something.'

'Oh Peter. This isn't Warrington now, you know. This is Belsize Park. People wear hats and scarves here. People go out for breakfast!'

'Hmm,' Peter said again, and went back to his box. 'Well I don't want one. They look a bit sour for my liking.'

Isobel swallowed down her remark that he looked as if he had eaten a few already and went to the kitchen, which she was already beginning to infuse with her own character. It wasn't quite how she wanted it but at least inroads had been made on the ghosts of the previous owners. Dried flowers on the windowsill, her huge spice rack on the wall and her prized range of Le Creuset pots hanging from a beam by the cooker – all of this, especially in the honeyed morning sunlight pouring through the window, cementing her belief that it was the best decision they had ever taken.

Warrington had become too anonymous for her recently, a

New Town more concerned with the ugly spread of 'sardine can' offices in the business parks which surrounded the centre. She couldn't recognize it any more. All the pubs had gone over to chrome and neon, catering for a youth which had never known anything different. The fish market and green-grocer's she had enjoyed visiting as a child had been subsumed by the siege mentality of the shopping mall. She was itching to get out but only realized how much when Peter mentioned a possible move south and she had almost begged him to make it happen.

Everything was new here. A perfect start for their family. She let her hands follow the distended bulk of her belly and she smiled as Toby (it was a boy, she could tell without having a scan) kicked out in response. Any day now, the doctors had said. This, she felt, was a fine place in which a baby could grow up.

The next day she rose early, and drank a glass of orange juice by the bedroom window, watching the confusion of cars at the junction of England's Lane and Primrose Hill Road. The forbidding sky was pregnant with its own offspring, but how long it would be before the rain came, she couldn't tell. Peter moaned in his sleep. Poor thing, he had shouldered all the pressure of their move: shifting boxes and furniture while she made him cups of tea. She could tell in his moods and mannerisms that he was less effusive about their uprooting, even though he was the main reason for it. He would come round. She would make sure of it.

In the street she saw mothers pushing prams. When they caught sight of Isobel, a warm and secret smile passed between them, as though she were soon to be allowed into a secret society that only women could know about. It was a fortifying illusion and she hardly felt the first spits of cold rain, so engrossed was she in this invisible umbilicus which connected her with those who had already experienced giving birth. By the time she reached Belsize Village and its little sprawl of craft shops, delicatessens and restaurants, her hair was plastered to her forehead but she didn't regret leaving her umbrella behind.

'Hear the rain, Toby?' she whispered, covertly rubbing the area where she believed his head might be.

She bought croissants, milk and strawberries for breakfast and popped into the florist's where she chose a spray of white lilies. From the gift shop, she bought a mirror with a thick, rough-hewn wooden frame. Pleased with her purchases, and the short time it had taken her, she headed towards the main road where she planned to catch a bus for the trip into Hampstead Village; browse in Waterstone's for ten minutes and perhaps have a lemon tea at the café.

Outside the house on Ornan Road she saw two pairs of woollen booties and a fabric sling wrapped in clear polythene along with a note, its ink leaching into the paper from the rain:

PLEASE FEEL FREE.

As she went to pick up the package, her eyes flicked to a window which shivered with pale light. A thin globe in one of the panes, smeared with a bluish tint, slipped out of sight: a head, Isobel suddenly realized. Someone had been watching her. She felt guilty now, as if what she was involved in was theft rather than accepting a freebie. Nevertheless, she bagged the items and hurried away, all thoughts of books and lemon tea fleeing too. In the window, as she took a frantic glance back, a shadow remained, as if whoever it was had stained the glass with their presence.

'What's with you?' asked Peter, as Isobel barrelled into the room. 'You shouldn't be dashing around like that. You'll do yourself a mischief.'

'It's raining. I didn't want to get wet.'

'Wetter, you mean. You're bloody drenched. Get those clothes off and have a hot shower before you and the baby catch pneumonia.'

Under the hot spray, while Peter set about breakfast, she tried to wash away the irrational fear that had cloaked her. 'What is wrong with me?' she hissed. But by the time she was towelling herself dry, her panic had subsided and she could even giggle over her rash action. 'Silly cow,' she sneered at the mirror. It must have been some deep, involuntary protection mechanism: she was scared for the baby, that's all, even though the person who spooked her was merely curious about who was picking up his or her gift.

The rest of the day they spent tooling around the flat, doing little and feeling vaguely directionless. Most of the major work had been completed; now there were few things that could be done until they'd decorated and they couldn't make a start on that until tomorrow, when they had planned a trip out to choose paint and wallpaper. Towards evening, their impotence lessened and they began to unwind. They tried the Indian restaurant and had a drink at The Washington, the pub on the corner, just across from where they lived. Lots of people smiled at her and winked at Peter and asked them when the 'event' was due. Isobel was glad to see her husband relax into the evening and, when he leaned over to whisper in her ear how much he loved her and how he really believed they would be happy here, she felt like bursting into tears with exhilaration.

As they left, she caught a glimpse of faint blue as a head moved back into its seat and her blood quickened, but then Peter was ushering her across the road, laughing as the wind buffeted them against each other.

Later, in front of the TV, she began to feel strange. Peter was stroking her thigh but it didn't feel right. She thought that, at any moment, his fingers would sink into her flesh and cause the meat of her leg to fall away from the bone. She tried to tell him, but the words turned to wool in her mouth and were then cut off by a tremendous bolt of pain which tore through her loins. She ripped feverishly at her skirt and knickers, upon which a red flower was already blooming.

'Oh Jesus God, Peter!' she managed to cry, as her vulva swelled and split. When she turned to look at him, his mouth was open wide and he was howling with laughter – so forcefully that his cheeks were purple, his eyes bulging. Ropes of saliva connected his lips. His tongue squirmed in its juices like a shucked oyster. 'Pe-ter,' she stuttered, her breath stitching. She looked down at the blue, waxy head as it erupted and, through the pain, couldn't believe the gnarled aspect of its face. At the same time, its eyes and mouth flew open and she didn't know which was worse: the small knives arranged in its gums or the ancient, awful wisdom which fastened her with its stare.

'Toby!'

Blackness folded around her and she grew swiftly aware of the slick of sweat which coated her; the distant, somnolent sound of traffic; Peter, as he drew her to him and hushed her and whispered that everything was all right now. She listened to the sprinting heartbeats inside her and couldn't even begin to work out which one was hers.

'You're new, aren't you?'

'I'm sorry?' Isobel turned to find an old woman peering at her but was unsure whether she had been in the charity shop all this time or had just entered. She placed the child's toy back on the shelf, knowing that this was the woman from the house in Ornan Road: her blue-rinse hair, tucked up like a pie crust on her head, was proof enough of that. Now that the stranger was exposed, Isobel felt ridiculous for having ever felt nervy about her.

'I mean, you're new to this place aren't you? Just moved in?'

'Yes. We arrived a few days ago.' When the old lady didn't respond, resting her gaze instead on her belly, Isobel felt compelled to continue. 'We're very happy.' She made to leave but the old woman stopped her with a remarkably firm grasp.

'Come and have some tea with me, my dear. I'll pay. I'd love to talk to you.'

'Oh thanks but I really can't—'

Her smile split the grey dumpling of her face. 'I in*sist*,' she said. 'By the way, my name is Eva.'

*

Eva had lived in the house all her life, it transpired. Over cups of Earl Grey, they chatted about this cosy corner of London and the friendliness of the people, almost as if it were a pocket which was protected from the bustle elsewhere in the metropolis. And then, so seamlessly that Isobel found herself trying to work out when the change of subject had occurred, Eva was talking about children. Isobel learned, without asking anything of the older woman, that she was a mother too, although her apparent comfort at talking of such things was belied by a glazed look which stiffened her face whenever the conversation strayed too far into detail.

'So these things you leave outside, the booties and the carrying sling, it's stuff you're getting rid of now?'

Eva nodded. 'Yes. There comes a time when you have to, I don't know, throw off this feeling of being a mother. Sometimes, when they leave the coop, they leave for ever. They never return and you stop being a mother. There's no reason to worry any more because you've got nothing solid – no address, no knowledge of what your babies are up to – to worry about. But it takes such a long time to go through all the boxes. I'd leave the whole lot outside if it wasn't for the fact I might find something I didn't want to give away.'

Isobel couldn't stop herself from reaching out and touching Eva's wrist. Her skin was so soft, despite its blotchiness and the blue veins scoring the surface. The physicality of her action seemed to awaken something in Eva's eyes and they blazed with wetness and colour.

'You're very close, aren't you? To your special day? I can smell your milk.'

Suddenly, Isobel felt constricted, as if her privacy had been impaled by the older woman's stare. Silly, she reasoned, as they moved apart and Eva beckoned the waitress over; asked for the bill. She's just remembering how it was. She was pregnant too.

In the street, Eva pressed her hand for a moment against Isobel's bulge and she leaned over to whisper something against her blouse before straightening and flushing with colour. 'Sorry, dear. Just . . . just saying hello, giving the little one my blessing.'

She turned to go, then flapped a hand as if she'd forgotten something very important and blatantly obvious. 'I meant to say, you must come round some time and have a look at some of the things I've got. You could help me sort them out. Take what you like, of course, save you from trolling past my front door every now and then on the off-chance.'

She waved goodbye and Isobel watched her move away, slowly but with a fluency that suggested she could be more swift and elegant if need be. Isobel's tummy tingled where she'd breathed against her blouse. It felt as if she'd been stung.

Isobel bathed late that night, hoping that Peter would be asleep when she finally climbed into bed. Her stomach was really quite beautiful, she decided. Her breasts too, the areolae swollen and dark. Inside her slumbered the magic of her love for her husband: the thought that she would see Toby soon excited rather than relaxed her, and she towelled herself dry feeling like doing something more energetic than sleeping.

She walked towards the clutch of lights at the far end of Belsize Park Gardens. A large rocking horse in the window of one of the houses on her left made her uncomfortable, perhaps because of its complete lack of motion and the vacant black stare with which it favoured her. She pushed her mind to more agreeable things, imagining Toby in its moulded saddle, laughing as Peter nudged the horse into gentle motion. This was better. By the time she had reached the end of the street, she could picture the horse's mane and the thin muscles in Toby's arms shifting in rhythm, while a golden fire painted them into a dreamlike blur. It revitalized her, the way she had supplanted an upsetting image with a more pleasing one and that by the sheer force of her will. It had been the same with Eva. It would be the same with anything that threatened her or her family. She would press it all into a manageable shape that she could look at without flinching. Maybe, she thought, as she turned into Ornan Road, that was what becoming a mother meant. Maybe that was the secret gift that all mothers received with their firstborn. An allaying of fear.

Outside Eva's house, by pleasing symmetry, minutely rocking in the breeze: a little toy horse, painted in faded primary colours, its tail knotty and denuded. The note flapped, caught beneath chipped hooves:

FOR BABY.

Behind the stained glass of the door, light shivered. If she looked up at the landing window and those even higher, she could see its mischief as shadows playing against the walls. What she first took to be the newel post in the top-most window turned out to be Eva's head: it sank beneath the sill and Isobel watched her progress as she descended.

'Come in,' she said, opening the door an inch or two so that only a slice of white face and the glister of an eye could be seen. 'It's freezing out there. Come in and have some tea, won't you?'

Isobel hesitated by the rocking horse, her hand resting on its immovable withers. A needle stitched the inside of her womb and she winced, but the discomfort was gone almost as soon as she had recognized it.

Carrying the horse, she followed Eva through the chilly hall into the kitchen. She envied the older woman its lived-in charm and clutter. Dried flowers, old letters, photographs and mugs filled with Biros vied for space with the more conventional kitchen paraphernalia. While Eva boiled water, clucking on about the weather and the toll on her back that hunting through boxes was having, Isobel studied the top picture in a sheaf of photographs. A woman stared out from the sepia. She wore a sleepy smile as she pointed at her own stomach. Isobel knew two things immediately, though neither was obvious: that the woman was Eva (no traces of this young creature had travelled to the older incarnation, except maybe, for the almond shape of her eyes) and that she was pregnant – a couple of weeks only – but she knew.

'You?' she said, as much to break the silence as confirm her suspicion.

'Of course,' replied Eva, tartly, plucking the photograph

from Isobel's fingers and tossing the whole batch into a drawer. 'A long time ago.'

They moved to the living room, negotiating islands of packed boxes. All of the photographs on the walls were of Eva. Eva with men or Eva alone. Eva playing the piano. Eva swimming or skiing. Isobel almost felt the loneliness emanating from her.

'Do you not have any pictures of your daughter?' she asked, biting down on another, more acute, stitch. She swallowed some tea. Better.

Eva looked flustered by the questions. *So let her squirm*, Isobel thought, and was unashamed by her cruelty. *She wanted me here. She wanted to talk.*

'I . . .' the older woman began, her gaze flitting anywhere but Isobel's face. When at last she settled on Isobel's stomach, her anxiety drained away, softening her features. She stood up, almost spilling her cup. Tea sloshed into her lap but she remained unfazed. 'I'll not be long. Why don't you have a rummage in that box, see if there's anything you can use. I don't need any of it.'

Isobel followed her to the doorway and peered after her as she moved slowly away down the hall, her bluish hair close against her skin and looking, in this half-light, like a caul. She was humming some tune, a nursery rhyme, but Isobel could not determine which.

The box was a tea chest stuffed with ancient, childish fancies. Here was a doll, discoloured by time, its left eye refusing to open while the right blazed with a light that seemed unworthy of plastic. Here, a linen bag containing pieces of a jigsaw puzzle and the soiled beauty of an ormolu music box. Her hand fastened around what felt like a curl of tightly wadded bandage near the bottom of the chest. At first, she thought it was a novelty soap but the texture was wrong, not so much waxy as scabrous, much like holding an unpeeled prawn. It was familiar, but the accelerating pains in her midriff would not allow her thoughts to coalesce. It was old, that was for certain, and she was considering calling Eva in order to sate her curiosity when its clenched shape was at last identified by the nagging in her head.

How could she not have known. Even as she was recoiling in shock, her hands were turning the desiccated foetus this way and that, her fingers tracing the spindly limbs, the pale nubs where its eyes had begun to surface.

'Say hello to Laura . . . my daughter,' came the even voice behind her.

Isobel lurched away from the chest and felt a similar lurching within, accompanied by a deep, scything agony which felt as if it would cleave her in two.

Eva stepped into the room, a thin filleting knife clasped by her side. 'All my gifts . . . all the things I gave you. Isn't it time you gave me something in return?'

Backing away, her heart thumping, Isobel felt another great shift inside her. She mewled with pain and dropped to her knees as her waters broke, splashing her thighs and the carpet beneath as a shadow engulfed her.

'Don't worry, my sweet,' Eva sang, softly. 'I will deliver you.'

Conrad Williams is a freelance journalist whose short stories have appeared in such anthologies as *Darklands 2*, *Sugar Sleep*, *The Science of Sadness*, *Northern Stories 4*, *Last Rites & Resurrections*, *Narrow Houses 3* and *Cold Cuts II*, among others. His tale 'The Bone Garden' was selected by the late Karl Edward Wagner for inclusion in the prestigious *The Year's Best Horror Stories XXII*. Williams is the winner of the 1993 Littlewood Arc Prize and the British Fantasy Award for Best New-comer. Another story, 'Ancient Flavours', was nominated for the British Fantasy Award in 1994. 'I got the idea for "Something For Free",' explains the author, 'when I walked past a house in London's Belsize Park and saw, on the wall, a pair of boots with a note which said HELP YOURSELF. I thought, "How very nice. How very Belsize Park." But by the time I'd reached my flat I was starting to have my doubts. I found something quite uncomfortable about it – like being offered a bag of sweets by a leering stranger.'

(Melodrama)

David J. Schow

Monstrous, was the countenance staring back from the mirror at Robert Blake. Its colourless mat of hair resembled a scrap of shag throw in which rats had nested. A glob of scar tissue occluding the left eye had stratified into layers, like wax melting floorwards to fuse with the cheekbone due south of a black eyepatch. There was beard stubble and burnflesh and gapped, rotten teeth; spiderwebs were hung up in the hair and lingered on the funereal clothing.

The left shoulder drooped to accommodate some spinal inadequacy, and a shabby three-quarter cloak failed to conceal or contour the hump that bulged there, like some failed, half-metastasized twin on the back of Robert Blake, who smiled, as the monster smiled back. It was all part of what had become a personal, private ritual. He did the Gravely Grimace. Maybe some more blackout stick for the teeth, but overall, not bad for a fifteen-minute job by an amateur.

Perfect.

Sherry dropped off formatted pages for the prompter and Blake watched her ass in the mirror as she slid sideways into soundstage blackness. The pages were part of the ritual: he would hand over his scrawl on yellow legal sheets (always neatly carved from the notebook perforations, never torn free in haste), she would transcribe his shotgun cursive into machine jive, and her printer would burp out real words in readable English. Nobody used formal script style for a gig such as this. In the half-hour before they got the use of the stage, she would drop off his so-called 'script' without a word; her silent delivery, in turn, helped Robert Blake, programme director of KSLA-TV (and her boss), ease into the persona of Gravely, late-night host of the station's *Friday Night at the Frights* – a more blatantly avuncular role which permitted all sorts of safe, defanged innuendo between them, as sort of a private fringe benefit never incorporated into his job summary.

He doubted whether Sherry could ever appreciate the subtlety of their relationship-by-default. He paused to ponder, instead, whether her brassières appeared several sizes too small on purpose; whether that low-slung, saucy lope was unconscious or calculated. She was quite the anatomical masterwork, despite being a gum cracker and what was called a 'bottle blonde' in the fifties. Her mien and manner screamed *sex* no matter what she actually intended or did. She was at least thirty years younger than Robert, yet still over two inches taller. The *concept* of women bigger than him was still a pleasant surprise. His late wife, Marion, had remained a neat five-one until the cancer had shrunken, then stolen her . . . about the time sweet Sherry Malone had been celebrating her sweet sixteen.

Had Sherry been a virgin at sixteen? Was anyone still unplucked at that advanced age, any more?

Eyes in the mirror. Contacts are too uncomfortable, too costly. The nose is fake; he had bought the very first one mail order. Later jazzed up in latex by a kid whose ambition was to change the world with makeup effects – fired, long ago. Robert had not seen the boy's credit anywhere lately. Ever.

His wobble had always been a mimic of poor old Karloff's arthritic gait. Awaiting him onstage was a two-camera setup a handbreadth shy of local access. Sherry usually loitered long enough to see Gravely do his stuff for another week. She never watched the movies. Reverie on that topic was like a foreign language to her.

Wilson, at Camera One, handed him his cigarette in its trademark long-stem holder. Show intro was a bit of tape featuring clay animation of a zombie-looking critter clawing its way out of a mulchy plot. When the camera went live, Wilson would reach around and slide back a foreground model gate with gargoyles on it. It was on top of a stack of milk crates right in front of the lens. Through the viewfinder – and onscreen – the POV would appear to push into the cemetery set as an *enormous* iron gate withdrew to frame left; it was cheesy but effectively atmospheric, and sound effects helped sell it. Above them, in the spiderweb of the light rigging, a KSLA gofer named Will Folke waited to drop a prop tentacle, his historical precedent being Groucho's duck on *You Bet Your Life*. The teleprompter began to scroll Sherry's rearranged text. On the cue, Robert was gone and Gravely was live-on-tape, in a world where he knew monsters personally and whatever outlandish supernatural pun he uttered referenced something real.

(*roll / gate / cue Gravely*)

'According to my ghostwriter's his-and-hearse horror-scope – he's in the spook-of-the-month club, don't you know – our venue this week is drama. No, not the living ends of a fairly grim tale, like *Jerk the Giant Killer*, or a gameshow like *Tooth or Consequences*, but a classic – you know, like *Sales of a Deathman*.'

(*cackle / puff cigarette*)

'We received tonight's fright feast COD – Corpse on Delivery. Part of the die-nasty of some son-of-a-witch who slipped me this philtre-tip.'

(*puff / cue Will F. / tentacle uncoils from the ceiling / sign on tentacle reads: NOT ME / Gravely Grimace*)

'No, Dora dearest – not you.'

(*pat tentacle / tentacle retreats*)

'Before you could say, "Dig that crazy grave," I became the soul proprietor of an edifice complex.'

(*pat nearby tombstone / muffled voice says: 'LET ME OUT!'*)

'Tonight, haunters of the dark, I would love to show you Lon Chaney, Jr. in *The Wolf Man* . . . but that never had the chance of a ghost.'

(*fling film can / OS 'crash' / Stump howls*)

'The play is the thing, as some Brit once said, eh, Stump?

And our play is also the Thing – *The Thing That Wouldn't Die*, dug up for your midnight pleasure here on *Friday Night at the Frights*.'

(*puff / Gravely Grimace / DISSOLVE to bumper*)

He squinted past the glare of key lights aimed at his face, past the boundaries of Gravely's domain, this gutter-budget boneyard of papier mâché. Past Wilson and Camera One. They'd sail through the whole routine a second time, top to bottom, half an hour from now, which was how they managed cutaways with only one cameraman. Sherry had already left.

By the time they wrapped, it was past 11.30. And, while they had not been looking, Robert Blake and Gravely had missed two decades of change, and all of a sudden the fans of films fantastic or horrific or science fictional had become much younger – a generation of such youth that *Star Wars* was both a watershed and a fond memory of early childhood, a vast crowd who could access obscure movies via rental tape or cable or dish, and conduct searches for rarities on something called the Internet. Unseen, they *watched*, staring at screens for everything important to them, to whom Gravely's antique medicine show was a curiosity, a byte of pop kitsch to be ridiculed and forgotten by people to whom the TV tripe of the sixties counted as nostalgia, or worse, culture.

'I can still remember when we actually got the movies shipped in on reels,' Wilson told him, during their post-show ritual of shots in the imaginary graveyard. Robert, in Gravely drag, sat on one side of an enormous fake sepulchre engraved with the name TALBOT. Most of Gravely's repertoire was spun from behind this prop, which provided a 'surface' to fill the bottom of the frame and permitted him to produce or exhibit other wild bits of business. Just now, it made an excellent bar. Wilson poured Old Crow into paper cups. No ice, no water; everything beyond the phony cemetery gate of balsa-wood and spray-paint was, give or take, straight-up. 'Getting those Mexican cheapies from the film rental joints for fifteen bucks a feature. Tossing up a PLEASE STAND BY card while we spliced the breaks in the film manually.'

'Jesus,' Robert muttered, Gravely. 'What I remember was that *The Brainiac* held the all-time record for on-air breaks—'

Wilson finished the line for him: '—because the reels were full of hot glue splices that had dried out and turned to brown dust that looked a lot like heroin. It got all over the projection bed.' He smoothed his palm back over the dome of his head until he hit what little hair he had left. Robert could only see the whites of scoop lamps, sharply reflected in the lozenge-shaped lenses of Wilson's glasses. Wilson was the only person at KSLA-TV who still wore new plaid shirts, and two innovations of the seventies to which he had really cottoned were hi-tech running shoes (for work) and fanny packs worn frontwise (for gear related to work). He held in his free hand a VHS cassette – the air check of tonight's taping, cut as a regular courtesy to Robert. 'You know, I wouldn't take away tapes and laserdiscs and cable and all of it from anybody. But you know something?' He waved the cassette; Robert's eyes followed its arc. '*This* is too damned easy.'

'I like movies,' said Robert, sipping. 'Moreover, I like film. I mean the actual printed filmstock. Spooled on reels. Any gauge. I like looking at reels of film, whether they're being projected or not. I enjoy holding the damned reels, Wilson. They have weight and substance, a heft that suggests what you're holding is not just a representation of a movie – like a book of plot synopses, or that videotape – but the movie itself. Every foot of every 16-millimetre film contains three little pictures per inch; forty per foot. Presume a 90-minute movie and that's somewhere in the neighbourhood of 130,000 tiny photographs, and you can hold each one of them up to the light and see it without the help of a videocassette player, which is basically an interpreter of rust . . . that is, iron oxide particles stuck on plastic.'

'Like I said,' said Wilson, toasting semi-obliviously. 'Too damned easy.'

'I am attempting, my good man, to elucidate a passion most irrational and increasingly obscure, yet not without arguable merit.' He burped softly; the whiskey burned in his gorge.

'Thank you, Gravely.'

'You know, people are going to look at old movies a hundred years from now and be totally lost. They won't comprehend *Frankenstein* because they won't be able to see what product the movie was pushing.'

'Know what happened to the stock-in-trade of your scare show, since the bad old days?'

'Do tell. No puns, please.'

'It all got legitimate.' Wilson paused in his pronouncement long enough to pour new doubles and encompass Gravely Manor and the Gravely Grounds with a sweep of his hand. 'All this. Monster movies. Scary actors. Special effects. Cruise your ass over to World Book and News and check out how many individual magazines there are on aliens and monsters and recycled serial junk from the dawn of cinema time.' He performed the expansive gesture again, looking rather lordly. 'It got legit. What was once fringe has now been assimilated, my friend, into the mainstream. And lo, there shall come forth a day when even Gravely – much as I love him – won't be able to compete with some bimbo in Vampira drag with deep-dish cleavage and double scoops.

'So get over it.'

'Doom-crier,' Gravely said, gravely.

'Simple truth, then,' Wilson countered. 'Half the films made before 1950 *don't exist* any more, and that's strident, but it's a fact. Every collector enjoys the delusion that they are insurance against apocalypse. That's why you hang on; it's the way one rationalizes any collecting obsession – the gentle lie that you are the last hope, the only one who genuinely cares.'

'Except, in my case, I don't have the collection to prove it.'

'It's there.' Wilson pointed at Gravely's head. 'In your case, it isn't a physical thing, or quantifiable, but it exists because you keep it alive, and I help you do it.'

'I was wondering why we enact this desperate pageant every week, unto death.' Robert was joking, of course.

It was all part of the ritual, such talk between them after shows. Two men in the process of aging beyond their youthful exuberance, trying to figure out how to ride the waves that crashed towards them. Generally, Wilson wrapped first, pleading wife, kids, chores, obligations, leaving Robert, as Gravely, to kill the last lingering lights, prime the alarms and lock down. Just a back-end task performed by rote by any other programming director moonlighting as the station's resident ghoul emcee. It was Robert's habit to sit quietly in the imaginary cemetery by himself, using up his store of contemplation points. Funny – he always removed the Gravely makeup and costume last. Every time.

Tonight, when Wilson slapped on his ballcap and bid the empty stage adieu, he joked about how maybe Robert should clear a space in his living room for that big TALBOT tombstone soon ... for the second time. Once, it was a rib. Twice, and it was some kind of obscure point *maybe* Wilson would get around to specifying in the next week or so ... *if* Robert was wily enough to ask the right question, the right way.

Robert finished his whiskey and scrutinized the monument. He could see the flaking seams and patches of paint-over. Black-and-white would not have forced it to pass such severe muster. A drum of the fingertips would betray it as hollow, untenanted. The moony pall of his good-old-days reveries lingered suffocatingly, thick as Spanish moss on a humid evening. Moving through Gravely by rote had begun to leave a repellent tang of decay in his mouth. Wilson was gone. Sherry had left the building. Will F. the tentacle-boy and that nameless makeup maven were history. Robert Blake felt like spitting. Instead, he would lumber home and pop a sleeping pill, which was the only way he could guarantee himself more than twenty minutes of uninterrupted slumber. Each day was an arc of pills, from the round headache tablets in the morning to the medications and vitamins taken with or without meals, and terminating in two oval sleeping pills at bedtime. Pills dried a person out. Perhaps that was why he could work up no spit.

He decided to answer the letter he had received. Just one; the only component of his end-of-week mail stack that did not bear a corporate return address or a cellophane window. The correspondent was one Master John Sheldon, aged eleven, and he was writing to thank Gravely for showing *I Married a Monster from Outer Space* two weeks ago, and that movies that weren't in colour were sometimes pretty good.

Oh, yes, and did Gravely have an e-mail address?

According to custom, Master John Sheldon would receive an autographed Gravely 8×10 and a handwritten note on Gravely stationery. The task was not that time-consuming; very few fan letters came in at all these days. What Robert needed was some way for Gravely to thank this young stranger for the note of hope on which he had closed – time marched on, and there were still some people who believed in the romantic, and kids weren't all aliens, and sometimes movies in black-and-white could be, well, pretty good.

Robert flicked on lights as he returned to his office, unconsciously maintaining the lop-sided Gravely gait. It was so quiet the fluoro tubes could be heard to hum. He slotted this week's air check on to the bookshelf with its fellows. In the file drawer of Gravely stuff he discovered that the folder of 8×10s was empty. He had mailed off the last one a long time back – so long that if he were to order another 100 printed, it would probably come out of his own pocket.

There were clippings in that drawer, stirred in amid crumpled promo posters, press releases, and the odd video – a whole history of the cadaverous wiseass named Gravely, from the heyday of the Screen Gems *Shock Theatre* package in the late fifties, to the last gasp period, late seventies, when the nation's eccentric, weird and just plain regional TV horror hosts dropped out of sight more quickly than shooting gallery targets. Born amid shameless hype, Gravely and his fellows were an anachronistic hangover, ill-designed to outlast the explosion of microchip media. Robert Blake understood evolution, especially natural selection.

In the eyes of someone like the ebullient Sherry, he thought, *all* his days were halcyon. No wonder she had left. Nobody relishes hanging around a funeral when the ghoul is bombing. The world had no need for him as a repository of classic fright film lore; his goldmine of myth had petered into common coin. Even Wilson could see it.

He wanted to pretend that Master John Sheldon's fan letter was a message from the past – a telegram bearing special powers from a time that mattered.

There came a thud on the office door, accompanied by a clotted voice: '*Master!*'

Robert tried to stand and turn all at once, but his hump constricted him. He had been genuinely startled since, as had been established by the worst of slasher flicks, he was supposed to be alone. He smiled the first honest smile of the night. *How about that; I'm having the horror movie host version of a Nam flashback.*

'*Master!*'

It was impossible not to recollect the character of Stump, since Stump seemed to be speaking to him from the distant past. Stump was a furball, one of the tamer breeds of lycanthrope, pudgy, savvy enough to cross the street if the traffic wasn't too fast, rather like Michael Landon's Teenage Werewolf in the wake of a decade of bad chow (Gravely Train, of course) and two of senescence, utterly devoted to Gravely's needs yet only capable of fulfilling entry-level monster sidekick duties. If there was a gruesome gag to be had at someone's expense, the all-purpose butt was always Stump, so-called because of the bear trap incident. His right hand was a big coathook attached to a leather wristlet, and yes, Stump had chewed off his own hand after waking up that night in Tijuana with a brand-new wife-wolf.

Stump had been portrayed on *Friday Night at the Frights* by Jim Kjelgaard, by day a KSLA accountant whose deep operatic basso kept him in à la carte announcing gigs, as well. If you had ever heard a KSLA public service announcement, then you had experienced Jim at his most resonant. Stump had been phased out in June of '78, during the budget tightening. Kjelgaard had moved to Hawaii and, as far as Robert knew, was still using his voice to make a living.

'*Master!*' Thud-thud-thud.

It was so much like the old routine that Robert automatically responded in the Gravely voice. 'Oh, who goes there, a wolf?'

'Not there-wolf, Master. *Were*-wolf!'

'Were? Ware?'

'Right here, Master.'

'Oh, what is it, you flea-bitten nincompoop!?' Automatically, the corn was flying.

The door was nosed open, and there stood Stump in his perpetual half-crouch, as though undecided between biped and quadruped. 'Master! I have it! I have brought it for you!' Stump held out a stack of linen-grain writing notecards emblazoned with the Gravely Crest. 'For the epistle you so needed to dispatch!'

'For Christ sake,' Gravely muttered, still in character. 'Who sent you – Wilson or Sherry?'

Stump cocked his head and scratched, using his hook gingerly. A flea popped. 'You needed paper, Master. And the photographs.' From his lupine armpit Stump shook an equivalent stack of fresh Gravely glossies.

Standing up abruptly forced a plunging vertigo to slam through Gravely's eyes and sinuses. How much of Wilson Kane's Old Crow had he pounded down? It was never in his interest to actually count shots. He steadied himself against the desk and succeeded in making the action resemble an executive point-making gesture. 'Look—'

Stump went *yipe*, turned tail and fled in a cloud of floating stationery and photos.

Robert was disgusted. It didn't even make sense as a practical joke; the references were too stale. He yanked the door open, expecting a boo! and getting none. 'Come *on*,' he said, more to establish presence than ask questions.

The cemetery and Gravely Grounds were full of fog. He could see the vapour swirls of Stump's hasty passage towards Gravely Manor. The fog was damp but it did not have the distinct odour of the CO_2 stuff.

All right, Gravely thought. *Actual real fog has invaded our stage. Accidentally.*

Three steps in, he added, *Keep your wits. You don't know everything. You CAN be tricked.*

Stump was capering in little wee-wee circles before the iron (plywood) door of the Film Vault (styro veneer and spray aging). 'It's time, Master, it's time! Time to choose!'

The normal show routine would have Gravely selecting some sterling-silver horror classic – *Frankenstein*, say, with all the cut footage restored. He would hold the film can to his breast, sigh wistfully ... then toss the movie aside – *(crash)* – in favour of some spool of schlock that classified as a movie only because it had sprocket holes and used up ninety minutes of airtime. At the offscreen impact of the discarded classic, Stump would always howl.

Since its inception, this gag had been Gravely's backhanded dig at KSLA, which would rarely budget for monster movies of genuine pedigree. Instead, Gravely's imaginary Film Vault filled up with the leftovers of barter deals and low-end booking. It had not been much different in 1957, when the first *Shock* package of Universal Studios' horror films had been unleashed. Over 600 of the studio's pre-1948 films went hunting for TV adoption, and to get the scary stuff an enterprising programmer had to eat a generous portion of turkey. Just the year before, a TV broadcast of *King Kong* pulled in viewership at a whopping ninety per cent of the people who owned television sets. *The Chiller Theatre*-style shows that sprang up in response to the *Shock* and *Son of Shock* film packages could have *Dracula*, *The Mummy* and *Man-Made Monster* ... if they also took *Sealed Lips*, *Destination Unknown* and *Danger Woman*.

Gravely's joke on KSLA had been to first name the film he would *prefer* to screen, then plod onwards with the business of what he was *forced* to screen, whatever creature feature they'd been able to dig up for cheap *that* week.

Stump eagerly pushed open the vault door, which shrieked on corroded hinges – a tape effect Robert Blake had selected and dubbed personally.

Had he promised to dance this dance for someone's birthday, was that it? Certainly never on the for-real set, there were insurance risks to consider. Maybe it was *his* birthday, that was the gag, and everyone was going to leap from the fog and scream surprise, causing him to remember that it was actually his anniversary or something. Maybe Sherry would slither up out of a cake, wearing only diet frosting.

'Master! Time to choose!' Stump danced around. Up close he smelled, well, like a wet police dog needing a bath and breath-freshening biscuits. Gravely's eyes itched. He sneezed, once, twice, concussively. He had not suffered an allergic reaction this strong and swift since Marion's boxer, Lefty. Lefty had last made Robert Blake sneeze a very long time ago.

The whiskey was still stroking the furrows in his brain, permitting him to indulge whatever madness this might be. But it had just crossed over into being irritating.

'Look, Stump, or is it . . . it can't be Jim Kjelgaard, I mean, whoever you are—'

Gravely got an eyeful of what was revealed when Stump swung the Film Vault door full back, squeak and all. He executed a mid-course correction in his speech: '—holy fucking *Christ*, what have we got here?'

This made Stump jolly. He proceeded to doggy-dance around the interior of the Vault . . .

. . . which was lined with cubist ranks and files of films, films on reels, well-maintained and labelled films on reels. *Good* films, on reels. *Attack of the Mushroom People* and *Doctor Death, Seeker of Souls* were nowhere to be glimpsed, even by accident.

'This wasn't here.' The Film Vault was a false front with just enough room for Gravely or Stump to reach inside. It had no interior; it ended a foot short of the background cyclorama for the cemetery, which featured a painting of Gravely Manor in the far distance, at the end of a winding uphill path dotted with tilting headstones.

'Always was here,' countered Stump, who cringed at the appropriate moment. Best not to contradict the Master. 'You are the Master! Only you choose!' Stump waved his hook towards the film racks, which looked to be mahogany, and twelve feet high. The gesture reminded him of Wilson's, in another life. 'You give them a home, take care of them, only you, like you take care of Stump!'

Gravely was ignoring his mascot, gazing at the spines of the film cans. He extracted one. No corrosion. In black ink, in a steady hand – the way his handwriting *used* to look – was the title: *London After Midnight.* It was on two big 2000-foot reels and one smaller pickup reel. Gravely slid it back.

Odd.

Since entering the Film Vault he had not looked back, nor bothered to reassure himself of his own passage into this hallucinatory state. Now he turned around. Where Camera One had been an hour earlier was now just a tombstone, and more fog. He could not recall passing either camera. When he looked up he saw no lights and no rigging. Just a full moon, costumed in cirro-cumulus.

The next logical conclusion at which a man like Robert Blake would arrive was: *I've tipped over,* or, in Gravely-speak, *I'm marble-less. I've gone insane and out-sane.*

Time-delay extrapolation slapped him in the side of the head. *London After Midnight* was a silent. No way KSLA would ever permit it to be shown . . . not even with a laugh track.

He shook his head. Stump had apparently lit off to pee on Dora the Tentacle's prop tree.

Being intended for short hauls only, Gravely's patience was already crashing into its spoilage ceiling. Normally the mystery resurgence of Stump would have already used up most of an entire show.

Gravely's weekly assignment was to occupy ten minutes per show, which in theory left 90 minutes for the movie and twenty for commercials. When KSLA decided to bunk-bed the ad blocs during each half-hour bridge (after 10 p.m. nobody gave an honest damn about ratings and focus polls), they cut Gravely down to five minutes per show for *everything* – intro, outro, shtick and viewer mail, plus a set of bumpers to book-end the commercials. If that wasn't enough, then the movies were easy to shave. Ridiculously easy.

Apart from Stump and Folke, the tentacle operator, the closest the show got to actual guest appearances could be

counted on two fingers. In early 1974, Forrest J Ackerman
had done a walk-on, toting an issue of *Famous Monsters of
Filmland* featuring the Creature from the Black Lagoon on
the cover. In 1976, Jim Kjelgaard had busted his leg, and so
for four shows in a row his Stump duties were handled by an
East Coast monster delinquent named Jarvis; Gravely could
not recall a first name. On the spot they conceived the twisted
saga of Stump's courtly cousin, Count Ludarca, supposedly a
bluesman from the Transylvania bayous. They coasted the
rest of the way, gooning Lugosi.

Then whatsisname-Jarvis lit back to New York to endure
some sort of comic book job, and *Friday Night at the Frights*
commenced its twilight period.

'Enough.'

That was remotely decisive. It was too easy to get lost in
the maze of past events; too easy to distract his attention from
the precipitous weirdness of Stump, bounding out of the past
to dog him. He marched towards the head of the cemetery
path – downframe, cameras or no – repeating 'enough' to
himself, keeping his eyes on his feet and the tamped earth of
the trail.

He almost collided with the flagstone wall, which had not
been there before, either. The only place there had ever been
such a wall was in the imagination of Robert Blake, when
idealizing how the Gravely Grounds would look, given proper
funding. This wall was supposed to lead to a vast mausoleum,
where Gravely was known to picnic. If memory served, the
concept included a vaulted arch of skulls, decorated with bone
grotesques.

Inside, he found a corridor of marble, dark, cool, mono-
chromatic. One of the plaque-stones at eye-level read:

COLLIER YOUNG

HE SCREWED UP BIGTIME

He remembered when he had first proposed that inscription
for one of the foamcore tombstones on the Gravely Grounds.
KSLA had shot him down on the grounds that 'screwed up'
was invective too harsh for what the affiliate considered a

kiddie show. Next from on high would come the objection
that Gravely's smoking sent a bad message to the kids. That
sort of anal, blinkered complaint could burrow beneath the
skin of his conscience, to fester. It was all kid stuff, no matter
how it was dressed up. Wilson had been right about its
legitimization; the youngsters who liked it simply grew up
and found a civilized way to hang on to it – the imprimatur of
camp. All through the sixties, the tale had been different.
Monsters were sub-par entertainment, derided as spook fests,
always cited with that knowing elbow-to-the-ribs. *TV Guide*
listings told the tale whenever it subheaded Gravely's weekly
offerings not as drama, horror, thriller or suspense, but as
melodrama – meaning extravagant theatricality, plot and
physical action over characterization, sensational trifles aiming
for the gut rather than the head. Such flip categorizations
caused a special alchemy to start bubbling away, independently, in its own secret corner, where responsible grown-ups
could not watchdog. It happened when that word, *melodrama*,
suddenly shape-shifted to mean *monster movies*. If you were a
kid reading any programme listing and your eyes skidded past
that magic word, you knew without looking further that you
had hit paydirt.

Gravely heard noise from the far end of the mausoleum.
A clanking of chain-links echoed, a soft, almost porcelain
sound.

Scrolled, wrought stanchions held black tapers. Gravely
lifted the nearest one to see.

Sherry, she of the Ilona Massey bosom and endless legs,
goddess of lipstick-by-the-pound and watermelon-flavoured
sugarless gum, was shackled to the far wall, clad in the
nightgowny rags of a serial heroine after about four chapters
of thrills, her artfully-shredded clothing precariously close to
non-existent.

'Oh, Master, it's you, Stump told me you would come, you
never forget your Lenore, I'm so happy, you don't know how
happy I am, how I look forward to your visits.'

Whatever else cascaded through his mind at that moment,

it was handily conquered by this clear vision of a woman in heat.

'Sherry—' He faltered. Bad form. Try to be strong. 'Eh . . . Sherry, this is way beyond what either of us would call irregular—'

'Sherry, yes!' she overrode him. 'I'll be Sherry for you tonight. Any name! Just promise me the cat, after the movie!'

'The – *what*?'

'And the leather paddles, yes, and promise your Sherry you'll use the quirt and the signal whip! Save the strop for my ass, and I'm yours, darling!'

It was totally berserk, but so was the erection inside his spacious Gravely trousers. The temperature in the mausoleum seemed to be skyrocketing. Hot wax from the candle stung his wrist. Pheromones were zizzing around his body like bubbles in seltzer, dissolving his inhibitions in fast-forward.

'Master! The movie! The movie!' It was Stump, back at the arch with a film can crooked against his hook.

Gravely turned and shuffled towards the arch, imagining his enrobed penis slicing through the heavy atmosphere like the prow of a clipper through choppy seas. 'Can't you see I'm *busy*, dog breath?!'

Stump flinched. 'Yes, Master! But they're all waiting.' He numbly indicated something outside.

'Get out of my way.' He shoved past Stump, who was accustomed to the casual abuse. He looked out into the cemetery. In terms of the extremely limited set, he would be looking roughly from the Camera Two position towards the Gravely Manor backdrop, with its painted extension of the cemetery.

He saw thousands and thousands of headstones. No, not headstones, but *heads* – a whole Woodstock of milling people seen only in shadow, but for the calm glow of their waiting eyes. The crowd began in the darkness beyond the Film Vault, stretched unbroken to the top of the hill, and kept going, like all the armies of Rome on standby, all awaiting him.

Gravely's first response was to recoil. He took an involuntary backward step, away from the mausoleum. Conceivably, he could just limp away doubletime, if not run like hellfire. But the gate was closed. It was solid wrought iron, and the topmost spikes jutted five feet higher than he could reach on tiptoe. The gargoyles were full-sized, as menacing as his conception of them had originally been.

He moved for the TALBOT sepulchre from which all of his presentations had emanated. Even though he was on the opposite side, facing the wrong way, it felt right and spurred his courage. It had always been his rock, his anchor.

'Unholy smokes!' he belted out. 'I won't say the movies are in a bad way, but Garland has wilted, John has waned, and Andy's no longer very Hardy, either. Tonight's fear-feast might have been the immortal—' he paused to peer at the film can Stump had handed off— *'Thanksgiving VII* – so called because it's the sequel to six other turkeys. The producer lit off to Bermuda to make some shorts, and in view of the cow flops he squeezes out, we can only hope the future is better than the pasture!' He flung the film can in the prescribed manner, and Stump jitterbugged when it splashed down and was engulfed by quickmud.

Vamping here, now, was no more difficult than the average *a cappella* personal appearance at some supermarket opening, and he had sailed through plenty of *those* during his tenure. Dora's tentacle dropped in at the appropriate moment for Gravely to deploy the 'tree's a crowd' gag.

Right on cue, Stump slammed the big Strickfaden knife-switch home. Contact. Blue neon sparks leapt away from the prongs as an unseen projector started to grind celluloid. A fan of mote-laden light sprayed over the multitude, and every single head turned to watch it. Comparisons to religious mob behaviour were unavoidable.

Stump panted. Gravely saw him at ease near the sepulchre, as though awaiting the command to sit.

'Who are they?'

'Master?'

He gestured. 'All of them. Those watchers in the darkness.'

Stump shrugged exaggeratedly, inadequate to the demands of plot arcs or pinpoint irony. 'They just come.'

'Why?'

Stump brightened. Here was something he could answer. 'Because of . . . that!' He pointed at the projection light with something like beatific idiocy softening the point of his snout. His hook indicated the Film Vault. 'Because Master is the only one who . . . you are the keeper. Only you.'

Stump was mesmerized by the flicker, the only kind of light that would ever matter in a realm such as this. Gravely took advantage of his distraction to snatch his hook, which came free like a leather chap off a wooden leg.

'Master!' Stump instantly cowered, his furry arms crossed before his face. At the end of one was a black-nailed were-hand. Only one.

'Sorry, Stump, it's okay.' Fortunately, as well as his other canine attributes, Stump had the guilt-span of a puppy, and by the time Gravely had reattached the hook and patted him on the head – which cost him another wet sneeze – all feelings were bandaged. 'It's all right, boy.'

He leaned against the rough granite, graven with TALBOT for as long as he could remember, and, for the first time in quite a long time, he was fulfilled and content. Yonder waited Lenore. But Gravely still had a performance to get out of the way.

He returned to the office and took his seat before the mirror. This was a private ritual for him – the way he sat, the order in which his cosmetics remained arranged from the previous session, the mirror he promised himself he would wipe clean before the next time.

He re-did his nose with care. Spirit gum was used to attach it, then he smeared a base-coat for the preliminary blends. Unlike his earlier application, this was no fifteen-minute quickie. The custom-made dentures had to be specially bonded. Once his wig was affixed, he combed loose strands to hide the clips. He stowed the long-stemmed cigarette holder in a jewellery drawer.

Perfect.

Then he rose, just as the sun was doing likewise, to be the

first person into work, as Robert Blake, programme director of KSLA-TV.

David J. Schow is busy these days with multiple scriptwriting projects for television and feature films. Earlier screenplays include *Leatherface The Texas Chainsaw Massacre III*, *Critters 3* and *4* and *The Crow*. He has also written many short stories, some of which can be found in the collections *Seeing Red*, *Lost Angels* and *Black Leather Required*. A fourth collection, *Look Out He's Got a Knife!*, was delayed and will now be expanded. Schow's novels are *The Kill Riff*, *The Shaft* and *Liberators* and he has recently completed the text for the revised second edition of his non-fiction guide, *The Outer Limits Companion*. Having written a mammoth run of forty instalments (around 80,000 words) of his 'Raving and Drooling' column for *Fangoria* magazine, he now hopes to find time for more short fiction. About his contribution to this anthology, the author says: '"(Melodrama)" is dedicated to Jeff Rovin, my friend of some twenty years, and owes its existence to a number of others, some of them imaginary – Robert Downey, Hattie the Witch, Tom Weaver, Dennis Daniel, Jeepers Keeper, John Bloom, John Stanley, Bob Stephens, Vincent Di Fate, Jack Jacobsen, Bill Warren, and kindly, loveable Dr Scar. Grateful acknowledgement is also made to Elena M. Watson's *Television Horror Movie Hosts* (McFarland, 1991). The story also provides the third act to a trilogy written over an eight-year period. The two previous pieces investigating variants on the same arc are "Monster Movies" (1988, in *Lost Angels*) and "Last Call for the Sons of Shock" (1990, published in *The Ultimate Frankenstein* and *The Mammoth Book of Frankenstein*). But most of all, those who pay attention to what they read will realize that this story belongs to Robert Bloch as well. Besides the obvious referents (all the players except Gravely himself being named after Bloch's assorted pseudonyms and alter-egos) or the abstract homages (think *structure*), much of Bloch's cunning punnage, from story titles to odd quotations, has been worked into (or wreaked upon) the dialogue directly.'

Absolute Zero

JAMES MILLER

Carol sat on the edge of the bed, watching Daniel. He was standing by the window, wearing only his pants, and indifferent, it seemed, to anyone who saw him. She finished pulling on her clothes and hurriedly lit a cigarette to try and take away the hung-over taste in her mouth. Her head ached, her thoughts felt thick and sticky.

'What are you doing?' she asked.

Daniel turned away from the rain-streaked window. Carol thought his body looked faintly ridiculous now, with his long, thin arms and legs and the tiny nipples that punctuated his slim, hairless chest. His skin shone in the moist dawn light. She felt no desire, not any more. Just tired and cold, and dirty. She thought about the long hot bath she'd have when she got home.

'Somebody will see you,' she said, exhaling a thin cloud of smoke.

'I doubt it,' Daniel replied, his voice dull and indolent.

Carol knew he was probably right. The houses opposite were abandoned, their windows blacked in with boards, the skin-pale walls cracked and split. In the evening, clouds of pigeons would flock to their rooftops. She would often stare at the houses as she waited for Daniel to come back and imagine that something was trapped inside those big, raw rooms, scratching frantically at the walls with bleeding fingertips, desperate to break out. But she knew there was nothing inside them, nothing at all. Just the wretched emptiness of shadows and dust-heavy spider webs and wallpaper peeling down like flaps of dead skin and lingering, lonely memories. Ghosts too pale to be seen. She shivered, sucking hard on her Marlboro. It was too early to be awake. Far too early.

Daniel lived in one of those eerie, lost quarters of the city, neither residential, nor commercial, nor industrial, but a curious confusion of all three. Its streets of ugly warehouses and workers' yards and untenanted offices were broken up, here and there, by black shards of derelict land. The few residential roads had a shabby, pathetic feel to them, the old terraces split into bedsits, their gardens choked with brambles and dirt. Daniel lived in one of those barren streets where there was always silence, always closed doors, never people. Travelling home, Carol would see the city leached of colour, reduced to the stark darkness and blinding light of open doorways and broken windows. Her eyes would close against a sky of shattered glass and achingly empty concrete. It wasn't until she reached the reassuringly normal terraces of North London that the feeling would begin to fade.

Carol stubbed out her cigarette. Soon she should go. Daniel was in one of his introspective moods. It didn't matter what she said to him, because everything would be greeted with the same sullen expression. He was probably still thinking about Stephen. She had hoped that once the police had found his body Daniel would stop brooding about it, but now he seemed even worse.

She watched him, standing by the kettle, still wearing only his pants.

'Do you want anything?' he asked

He had a nice back, she thought, very long and smooth; a bit spotty around the shoulders, but still, very nice.

'I'd like a cup of tea, I guess . . . but I should be getting back.'

She lit another cigarette and tried to think what to say. She hated these derelict moments, these pauses. They made everything seem so pointless, so lonely. It was cold in the flat.

'Have you heard from Stephen's family?' she asked.

'No . . . nothing.'

'What about his friends?'

'A couple came round yesterday. Wankers ... didn't seem to know what they wanted.' Daniel pulled on a T-shirt. He walked over and she took her tea. Stephen had been Daniel's flatmate, and his friend, of sorts. Except she could hardly remember them speaking to each other, and they never used to go out together. Now he was dead. She'd never known him at all.

Daniel walked out of the bedroom and on to the landing. Carol followed him. They went into Stephen's bedroom.

'Have the police ... did they say if he was murdered ... yet?'

Daniel didn't turn around to speak to her. 'I don't know ... no. Nothing. I just identified his body. That's what I did. They wouldn't even tell me where they'd found him.'

Daniel rummaged in a box of video cassettes by Stephen's bed. He took one out and went over to the TV.

Carol had been in Stephen's room a couple of times before, but the contrast with Daniel's room always surprised her. Where Daniel's was slovenly and impersonal – bed, armchair, clichéd Nirvana poster, dirty ripped curtains – Stephen's was crowded with things. The walls were covered with prints of Surrealist paintings: Dali, Ernst, Magritte, and maps of London, and architectural drawings and photographs culled from magazines and newspapers. Plush rugs were spread over the floor. If it wasn't for the fact that Stephen was dead and Daniel had seen his naked body stretched out on a slab in the morgue, the room would be cosy and relaxing.

'What are you doing?' Something about Daniel's attitude disturbed her. It wasn't right for him to be going through Stephen's things like that. 'Daniel?' He pushed the tape into the video and stood back.

'You're spilling ash,' he said.

'What?'

'Your cigarette. Ash. On the carpet.'

'Oh?' Carol turned away. She wanted to go. It felt wrong to be standing there, in a dead man's room. She felt unusually tense, as if everything had gone on for far too long.

'But what are you doing?' she asked again.

'I just want to see something,' he muttered, not looking at her.

'Daniel ... look, he's dead. This is his room. There's nothing we can do.'

'Isn't there?'

Carol stared into his brown eyes, blank and fixed: as featureless as a concrete precinct, a stretch of motorway. She was shivering. She turned away and looked at herself in a mirror wedged between a de Chirico and a large-scale map of Clerkenwell. Her black hair hung down over her face. And she was so pale. She tied back her hair and gazed intently at herself, at the dark rings under her eyes. She heard Daniel fiddling with the video. There was a faint pain in the back of her neck. making her eyes sting.

'Daniel.'

'Um.' He looked up from trying to work the video.

'You remember the story about Paris and the Greek goddesses?'

'What?'

'Which one would you have chosen?'

'What do you mean?'

'Which one. I mean, would you have gone for Hera, Aphrodite or Athena?'

'You say some funny things, Carol.'

'But which one?'

Daniel sat back on his heels, smiling at her. 'Well, I guess it would be hard to resist Aphrodite ... but I suppose I should really go for Athena.'

'Why?'

'Well, Aphrodite might have promised the most beautiful woman on earth ... but Athena offered ultimate wisdom ... didn't she? So, that way, I could have got Helen without having to go through all the Trojan wars as well.'

'Yeah ... that makes sense.' Carol nodded.

'But then ... with ultimate wisdom ... I could have become a fucking god myself.'

And he hit play on the VCR.

For a moment the screen was blank.

At first the picture seemed to be out of focus. Carol couldn't work it out, everything was hazy and pink. Then the camera drew back and all at once she could see what was happening.

A woman lay on a crimson bed. Her legs were spread open and she was rubbing herself with one hand, her red fingernails moving in and out. Her legs were twitching.

'Daniel . . . Jesus. What the fuck is this?'

'Hey, don't look at me. It's Stephen's. And anyway, this bit doesn't last long.'

'You mean you've seen it before?'

'Loads of times. This is nothing. Anyway, Stephen made it or wrote it or something.'

'He made it!' Carol gasped. She couldn't think what to say.

'It's not a porno.'

'Yeah . . . right. What is it then? *Art?*'

'Just be quiet and watch it!' he snapped aggressively. 'I have to know.' He sounded edgy, biting his nails as he spoke, as if something vital was taking place before him. 'I have to find out what happened to Stephen . . . he was on the point of something. . . something he couldn't . . . couldn't bring himself to tell me. *Look!*'

Now they could see the whole woman. Her face was covered with a black silk scarf. Her left hand cupped her breasts. Her nipples had been painted red. Her whole body was trembling and flexing in mock ecstasy. She looked very pink and shiny and fleshy. With her face hidden she didn't seem real. The camera lingered over the scene, giving them time to absorb every detail. Carol lit another cigarette.

'Look, Daniel, if you want to watch this shit then that's fine. I'll go home and you can have a nice wank in peace, okay?' He ignored her.

The picture shifted upwards, moving through a window. Then, suddenly, the film changed to black and white. It seemed to be shot from a moving car. Inner city streets. Building sites. A house being demolished. A canal clogged with black water. A headless statue covered in bird shit. The images were faintly familiar.

Daniel turned up the volume. A woman's voice, panting and gasping. A man's: moaning, a long ugly groan. Other noises, muffled, in the background. The woman's voice peaking, shrieking to orgasm. Then dead cows moving through a slaughterhouse, metallic blades slashing strips of meat. And more and more moaning.

'I've got to go.'

'Sorry . . .?' Daniel glanced back at Carol. Something about his cold, almost vacant expression unsettled her. It made her think of the ruined shop fronts that lined the main road, waiting to be pulled down. 'Okay. Look . . . um, I'll ring you.'

'Fine.'

'Bye then.'

'. . . yeah . . .'

The street outside was streaked with silvery puddles. Rain fell from the closed sky. Carol was annoyed that she'd let the film get to her so badly. It was just art school crap about capitalism or something similar. But leaving Stephen's room she'd caught one last glimpse of the screen: fragmented black skeletons of derelict warehouses stark against a barren white sky. And now, as she stood waiting for the first bus of the morning, she could still hear those moaning voices, driven, it seemed, with a desire that could only hurt and hurt again.

Carol drifted uneasily, depressed by the shop fronts and apartment blocks that flanked the road, jolted out of her thoughts each time the bus swerved into a stop. Cold blue light submerged the city, washing away all other colours. Droplets of rain splintered her hollow reflection. Streetlights disintegrated like drowned stars in the concrete sky.

Carol wished she could get closer to Daniel, but there just didn't seem to be any way that they could ever really understand each other. She remembered his face again, caught in the flickering light of the TV screen; his eyes . . . distant like the silhouette of a tower block. And how his arms around her, as she woke up that morning, and his body, even though it was pressed against hers, had still felt cold. Like embracing an emptiness, a space. She wondered what he thought about

when their conversation faltered and she would light a cigarette and stare wistfully at the ceiling. And he would sit, and
wait for her to say something else. She was always the one
who broke the silence, always.

The bus paused outside an old church, stained and faded
with pollution. Carol noticed an iron chain around its doors.
She wondered if it was there to keep people from getting in,
or to stop something else from getting out. Sometimes she
was convinced that the city was disintegrating, its barren,
derelict areas spreading like a cancer, corroding whole streets
and districts. Everything would collapse into a blackness, a
pit. In the sunlight the buildings would dissolve, the people
evaporate. She yawned. Away from Daniel and the strange
brooding tension that kept her on such an edge she could feel
herself . . . slipping. Dreams lapped against the waking shore,
layering their images together. The bus jolted on, passing a
shiny new office block, its mirrored windows catching the
rain. Then a garage choked with wrecked cars, or was it some
kind of museum, an exhibit? She recalled reading somewhere
about new statues being set up around the city, that resembled
cranes and gas silos and huge iron spikes and burnt-out buses.
The images on the billboards reminded her of an exhibition
Daniel had taken her to see at the Tate. She couldn't guess
what was being advertised. Then all she could see were neat
rows of Victorian houses, sleepy and hooded by the dawn.

Carol closed her eyes. She remembered walking back home
one Sunday morning, London hidden under soft white mist.
All alone. She'd come to a small park and sat on a bench wet
with dew. Beyond the hazy outline of trees the sky had burned
gold, like a fire blazing out above the clouds. Glistening leaves
had left wet smears on her skin as she wandered languidly
through the undergrowth. And, between the trees, bright
white statues, of naked men and women. Elegant and beautiful, like Greek gods ('which one do you choose?'). And the
silence of a city holding its breath. She had wanted to sit
among the statues, until the mist burned away and the sun
drew the moisture from their perfect stone bodies. But instead
she had opened her eyes to find Daniel shaking her, his lips

kissing her, his hands touching her. The dirty white ceiling of his room was fractured and cracked.

The bus stopped at the end of her street. Carol walked slowly back to her flat, letting the rain run through her hair and down her cheeks like tears.

'Daniel, why did we come here? What's going on?' said Carol accusingly. They stood on a footbridge, half engulfed by the roar of traffic from the dual carriageway beneath them. Daniel was turned away, looking down at the road. 'Why won't you give me a straight answer?'

Daniel muttered something but she couldn't hear him against the traffic. On one side of the bridge was a bleak industrial estate of warehouses and empty carparks where she'd followed Daniel as he'd trudged from one site to the next, going to the places marked out on one of Stephen's maps. Over the bridge was a huge council estate, tower blocks and lower, slab-shaped buildings linked together by concrete walkways.

Carol was sick of it. Daniel had called her up this morning. He'd sounded lethargic, mumbling his words together, his sentences trailing off into vague dead ends. He'd whispered to her about clues and paths and secrets hidden in Stephen's maps. 'Stephen was close,' he'd kept saying, 'he was close to something.' She'd found Daniel in Stephen's room. Maps of London were spread over the floor, certain parts highlighted. Daniel had been trying to piece them all together, standing on the bed to look down at them, as if he could find evidence of a larger pattern. Another video had been running: pictures of kids dancing around a bonfire at the base of an electricity pylon. More surrealist prints and drawings – maybe Stephen's – had also littered the floor, spread around the maps. And amongst these, something else ... more photographs or ink drawings? Carol hadn't wanted to look too closely. And she'd shivered as Daniel gazed at her with his wide hollow eyes. His own room had seemed emptier and lonelier. The windows had been blurred with condensation, one of the curtains hanging down forlornly, like a dissected eyelid.

'*What is it that you want?*' she shouted at him. She felt tired and ill. The pain at the back of her head was worsening, as if something had pierced the back of her neck and sucked at her spinal fluid. Gritty flakes of sleet blistered down from the cloud-chilled sky. Everything was grey and dead. 'What do you think you're trying to do? I'm not doing this all day.' Then she pointed at the estate, the next place marked out on Stephen's map. 'There's nothing in there. There are no hidden truths to be found, it's just a fucking council estate! Hey, if we're lucky we can get mugged by a drug addict. Do you want that? *Will that suit you?*' She stopped. She hated shouting. She hated all this. Last night she'd been shaken from a dream by sirens. She'd been wandering through a quiet old town, a place from her childhood...? She couldn't remember, but it had been haunted, haunted by an orange light that shone in shop windows and was always ahead of her.

Daniel turned away from the road. His nose and ears were red from the cold, his hair tangled and damp from the wind. 'Stephen was close to something...' he said.

'What do you mean?'

'If I knew I wouldn't be here, would I!' Daniel stood up close to her. He was taller than Carol and she looked at his thin neck, at the stubble on his chin. 'Look, one night me and Stephen went out together. We were in a strange mood, both of us. Angry, in a sense. We rode the tubes until they all stopped. Then we just walked about through these fucked-up, empty forgotten bits of the city. Neither of us really spoke ... didn't say why we were doing this or anything. We just felt compelled. At one point some guy, he was drunk, came up and started harassing us, wanted the time, wanted change for a phone, that stuff. We lashed out at him. We kicked the fuck out of him. He ran off, screaming abuse at us. It was weird. I was shaking all over afterwards. I felt sick, but we kept going. And there was something else there, something with us. Always behind us ... or just ahead. Where we couldn't quite see it.' Daniel glanced down, pausing.

Carol waited, the roar of a passing truck momentarily engulfing her thoughts. Then he continued.

'You've heard the stories, about the gangs of youths that live underneath the motorways, in abandoned factories, empty office blocks, places like that. I've heard they build temples in these places, where they sacrifice animals ... maybe even children, to their own fucked-up gods.'

'So what, Daniel? Just stories ... they don't necessarily mean anything.' Carol knew what he meant. Rumours and myths that hovered on the point of becoming fact, becoming just something else that everybody gradually accepted, like the fear of being burgled, or raped, or involved in an accident. The first time she'd heard about it, as more than a rumour of something half seen and so easy to forget, she'd been shocked. Then it became nothing special. It was like the first gang killings, or chemical dumpings; the first police with machine guns and CS gas. For a moment the media, the politicians and everybody's conversation was full of it. Then it passed. Then it was just something else that happened. Like being burgled. Like getting raped. It was accepted.

'This city ... it's ... it's an amazing thing. It's the greatest work of art ever created. If we could only understand the whole system ... grasp it all at once ... I want to see where it's leading us ... what it's pointing towards...' Daniel paused, clenching his fists. 'It's like language, it's all we have to communicate ... I don't know ... it breeds itself, destroys itself.'

Carol could see the confused pain and anguish in his face, the tension straining behind his eyes. She wanted to reach out and put her arms around him and let him rest his face on her shoulder, and close his eyes, and let everything be all right again. But she felt the distance, like a stretch of concrete spreading out between them. The city was dividing, falling away, its blackness and decay spreading through the streets and into them: a disease, a vacant lot, a waste. In Stephen's video she'd seen dead cats strung up on telegraph poles and strange, beggar-like people scavenging through tenements flooded with sewage. The black lines of a wire fence had pressed against the screen and behind that had been something grey, unfocused and amorphous. Something new and almost alive, growing and waiting . . .

Daniel's mouth was moving up and down, but the noise of the traffic had swallowed up his words. She wanted to touch him, but she was always the first one to make a move, to fill the spaces with her voice.

Daniel came closer. 'The things he told me . . .' he said, 'the night before he disappeared . . . he was trying so hard to . . . like . . . trying.' The traffic was a single rushing scrape, the desperate exhalation of a huge metallic beast. A death gasp over everything. 'I didn't understand him . . . then . . . he said we should escape, that was the word he used . . . escape . . . but I didn't . . . find out . . . I need to, Carol . . . don't . . . help me . . . I need you . . .' His words splintered against the traffic's roar.

Carol walked over to the end of the bridge. She glanced back and he was still standing there, in the middle. He seemed to be trying to look at something, something she couldn't see from where she was standing. She tried to look at the expression on his face. She thought, for a moment, that he was screaming. But she couldn't be sure. The top of a warehouse on the opposite side of the bridge framed him. Its hard outline made a pleasing shape against the wispy grey sky.

Carol wandered down some steps that led into the estate. She saw two boys, thirteen or fourteen, crouching down on a step, sharing a joint. As she walked by one of them stood up in front of her. She felt a momentary stab of panic and tried to pass them, hoping they wouldn't follow her and didn't want anything. The boy made a strange, twisted sign with his hand. 'You're a dead person,' he hissed in a razor-rough voice. 'Dead lady, dead lady, dead lady dead.'

She hurried by and didn't look back. But she heard them: 'Fucking bitch cunt fuck,' and laughter like the sound of bottles breaking.

Carol went back to Daniel's bedsit. She stood in the middle of his room, unsure what to do, or where she should go. She lit a cigarette, but, hands shaking, dropped her lighter on to the floor. It bounced underneath the bed and, as she reached down to grab it, her fingers brushed against something. She reached forward and pulled out a filing box.

She picked it up and sat on the bed. She held the box in her hands for a long time, thinking and waiting. She finished the cigarette, stubbing it out on the floor. Rusted nails poked up between the floorboards. Daniel must have ripped up his carpet one night. Sighing, she lit another cigarette.

When it was almost dark she got up and switched on the light. She hadn't noticed before but there was only a single, weak bulb hanging down to illuminate the room. She saw that Daniel's Nirvana poster had fallen down leaving behind a skin-pale square on the wall.

When Carol opened the box she found that it was full of love letters, several years old, to Daniel, from a girl she'd never heard of. She carefully lifted each letter out of the box, smoothing them with her fingers as she did so. She began kissing the letters, then pressing them against her face, as if they could drown her. She listened to the scratch her eyelashes made against the paper, rubbing them over her nose and mouth as if she could detect a trace of the girl's perfume. The letters were inarticulate and inexpressive, scrawled in Biro on large sheets of notepaper. She wondered if Daniel still felt their words; if, alone, late at night, he went through them, carefully re-reading each one, thinking about her all over again. And, somewhere else, there must be another box, filled with his letters, his crude words; the paper yellowing, the ink fading. And, no matter how hard he'd try, the memories would decay, dissolving into the present.

Carol put the letters back and went into Stephen's room, where it was warmer. She kept thinking about herself and Daniel. She imagined their naked bodies lying together in his bed, like two dead fish floating on the surface of a stagnant lake. She shivered. Sometimes it seemed as if the only thoughts she had were bad ones. She sat up all night, smoking, drinking coffee and watching videos.

The morning was cold, but bright with wisps of cloud blown against a hard blue sky. Daniel still hadn't come home.

Carol thought about waiting for him or using the maps to try and follow him. But she wouldn't do that. She remembered what he'd told her about stalking through the city with Stephen, both follower and followed. She imagined dark shapes, like dust and fallen leaves, drawing together inside the derelict houses, pressing against the walls and bricked-up windows.

Carol knew she had to leave the city.

On her way to the bus station she thought about returning to the bedsit. She would sit on the floor and see how much paracetamol she could swallow before her stomach turned and she vomited. Or for how long she might be able to stand in the shower, watching as her blood mingled with the water, before panicking and trying to call an ambulance. All the buildings seemed empty, all the windows shut tight on dark and silent rooms.

Only when she reached the bus station did she begin to relax. As she queued for her ticket, Carol noticed an ordinary-looking couple giving out flyers. She took one dumbly as they walked down the queue. She only looked at it as the bus pulled out of the station. Underneath a picture of a small child was the message: *Have you seen our son?*

Carol held on to the flyer as they sped on to the motorway. For some reason she couldn't bring herself to throw it away. They drove northwards out of the city. She stared, fascinated, at passing service stations, factories and gas works. Rows of houses, hidden beneath double-glazing, were pressed so close to the motorway that Carol felt she could almost reach out and touch them. She felt drawn to the symmetrical arrangements of tower blocks and pylons on the horizon. As they travelled further out into the suburbs she leaned back, watching them until they drifted out of sight. The sky beyond was split by thick grey clouds and sharp orange light. The clouds seemed to be falling behind, revealing a bright and distant sky shimmering above the trees and silvery aeroplane trails.

Carol closed her eyes and tried to sleep. She wished she could go back to her old dream again, to the statues in the park. *Which one do you choose?* She wondered if there would be anything left when she returned to Daniel's flat. Perhaps she would find the door padlocked shut, the windows all broken, cracks from the walls spreading over the pavement and on to the road. And she saw herself turning and walking away through shattered empty streets, filled with nothing but her fading memories.

James Miller's first story publication was 'The Outpost' in the small press magazine *The Third Alternative* in 1995. Since then he has been featured in *Last Rites & Resurrections, Dreams from the Stranger's Café, Violent Spectres, Time Out* magazine's *Net Books, Psychotrope* and several others, plus he has a story in Nicholas Royle's mainstream anthology, *A Book of Two Halves*. "Absolute Zero" was painfully and slowly written over several months,' the author reveals, 'and is partly a result of my interest in modern art plus many lonesome hours spent walking around London, another of my great fascinations.' He is currently studying English at Oxford University and includes among his favourite writers Milton, Blake, Dostoyevsky, Kerouac and Moorcock. 'I don't think of myself as a horror writer,' he adds, 'and I try to expand and subvert concepts and assumptions of genre in my work.'

Negative Equity

PAUL J. McAULEY

Caroline and Mark had to give up a lot for their dream house, but they both agreed that it was worth it. They needed a 250K mortgage, true, but Mark worked in the bond trading department of one of the big four banks; his base salary would cover the repayments, and they could live off his end-of-year bonuses – and the in-house interest rates were *very* competitive. And so what if the house had required, as the estate agent put it, a little cosmetic updating (damp-proof course, new roof and staircase, ditto wiring and plumbing and windows, treatments to get rid of woodworm and deathwatch beetle, and dry rot in the cellar and kitchen). The cost of all that went on the mortgage.

And so what if the house was due east of Norwich, and Caroline and Mark's friends greeted the move with jeers of derision? Norwich, for Christ's sake! Hicksville UK! Full of couples called Kevin and Sharon, with kids called Krystal and Wayne. Babies born there, confided one of their friends, an up-and-coming consultant also employed by BUPA, invariably had three letters added to their medical records. NFN. Normal for Norwich. You might as well move to Birmingham. To *Humberside*! And the price of the place, that necessary 250K nut which had to be serviced every month . . . They would, their friends assured them soberly (for this was about money, and money was serious, just after the Crash of '87), go down the tubes. They'd never recoup.

But Caroline and Mark knew what they were doing. They

were lifestyle commandos. Style warriors. They saw what they wanted and went for it, by fair means or foul. They had bought their one bedroom flat in Crouch End just before the property boom started, while their friends were still renting, and then had traded up to a pinched house in Islington with no garden but a fantastic location (a quiet cul-de-sac off Upper Street, just two minutes' walk from the Angel tube station). Prices had been rising at 40 per cent *a year* for most of the decade. The profit they had made simply by staying put meant that not only could they afford a substantial deposit on the new house, but also a fire engine red Porsche 911 for Mark and a nippy Peugeot 205 GTI for Caroline. Trading up to a more expensive house meant a bigger mortgage, and not all the money went on the new house. Everyone did it. As Mark pointed out, it freed up money and kept the engine of the economy turning over which meant that house prices kept rising. No one lost.

And despite their friends' misgivings, Norwich had just been nominated top-of-the-league in EEC quality of life tables. The train service was fast and uncrowded, and rising prices in London were forcing commuters further afield. People had always commuted in to London from Kent and Surrey and the Sussex coast; now they were coming from Oxford and Bristol and Bath, and as far north as Hebden Bridge in Yorkshire.

And best of all, the house had the potential to be a grand country house in the style of the new country house hotels to which frazzled City dealers flocked for sybaritic fantasy weekends, weekends that emulated the *Brideshead Revisited* lifestyle, but with central heating and reliable plumbing. Caroline and Mark would be living that *all the time*. They had to gazump someone to get the house, and Caroline had to give up her job as secretary for a PR firm because her salary was less than the season ticket, but that didn't matter. Her biological clock was ticking: she had always known that her job was only a stop-gap until it was time to start a family. Besides, renovating the house was a full-time job in itself. And (40 per cent a year) it was worth it, deathwatch beetle and all.

'You'll be living like a lord,' their solicitor told Mark on the day they exchanged contracts. 'Lord of the manor. And Lady too, of course,' he said, leering at Caroline.

This was Piggy Roberts, one of Mark's rugby chums, a ruddy-faced young man whose belly was already straining the waistcoat of his Savile Row three piece suit. Most of his business was obtaining work permits for the American computer programmers and systems analysts who were needed in ever increasing numbers in the City, and he was doing Mark and Caroline's conveyancing as a favour. He had opened a bottle of champagne, and couldn't stop looking at Caroline's legs.

'There's even your annual rite,' he said.

'Right? Like right of way?' Caroline was suddenly alert, alarmed that a snag had surfaced to puncture her dream.

'Nothing to worry about,' Mark said. 'Just some silly clause in the deeds.'

'Land rent,' Piggy said. 'But don't worry. You have freehold because the owners are long dead and lost. Happens a lot of the time with these big old houses.'

Caroline was still alarmed. She looked at her husband. He smiled. 'Don't worry, darling. It's just a legal technicality. The house is ours, free and clear.'

'You find all kinds of conditions in these old deeds,' Piggy said. 'Odd ground rent fees, like a red rose, or a shoat. Never seen something like this, but—'

'More shampoo,' Mark said firmly. 'Don't you think?'

'Like beating the bounds,' Piggy said, and buzzed his secretary for another bottle of Bollinger.

Caroline forgot about the moment. There was suddenly so much for which she was responsible: she and Mark had dreamed, and now the dream had come true. The house was, quite literally, huge. A late Victorian monster built at the edge of a small, utterly dear little village less than a mile from a long shingle beach, and thirty minutes from the railway station. Ten bedrooms, five bathrooms, eight receptions (one as big as a ballroom – they put a grand piano in it, how could they not?), a vast kitchen, an equally vast wine cellar.

Never mind that the house hadn't been decorated in years – all those yummy period details which counted for so much these days hadn't been ripped out or covered in woodchip and painted with brilliant white gloss. And the grounds: three acres of lawn and mature garden (in other words, utterly overgrown; as soon as they could afford it, they'd have to have a man in) and woodland, and a lake. A lake! And a drive that described a wide loop in front of the house, surfaced with small blue pebbles that made *such* a satisfactory clucking sound under the wheel arches of Caroline's new Peugeot as she drove in convoy behind Mark's Porsche and the pantechnicon.

Of course, their possessions didn't even begin to fill the place, and the rest of their money went on a new Smallbone of Devizes kitchen, and V&A reproduction wallpaper and drapes throughout, and a four-poster bed from Viscount Linley's firm, and furniture from Heals and the Conran Shop. Even then most of the rooms were empty and the rest only half-full. Maybe they shouldn't have bought the sixteenth century refectory table Caroline just had to have in the kitchen (they'd been into auctions when there had only been dealers and interior designers to compete with), and perhaps the Ron Arad floor lamps and concrete-cased stereo had been a *little* extravagant, but the important thing was to make a statement. Compared to the cramped Islington house, even the empty rooms were a statement.

And so, for the first year, Caroline and Mark were both blissfully happy with their decision. Caroline bought a Persian kitten, Mark a bouncy six-month-old labrador which he took for long walks around the lake (there were ducks on the lake and perhaps he could get a gun and teach the dog to retrieve). They held a housewarming party to show their friends what a prize they had won: the party cost five thousand pounds, what with wine waiters and maids, and the hot air balloon and the dodgem ride, and the clay pigeon shoot in the afternoon. Piggy Roberts used champagne bottles for target practice, getting broken glass all over the terrace and shooting out one of the french windows by mistake, and there was a minor scandal concerning a couple of Mark's chums and one of the maids, but nothing a little cash couldn't fix. Someone was sick in the grand piano, and the sixteenth century refectory table in the kitchen had to be french-polished to remove the obscene sketch someone had scratched into its surface, but the statement the party made was worth all the expense and trouble. No one made derogatory remarks about Norwich after that. Even their lovemaking improved, and Mark no longer flinched when Caroline talked of babies. There was a room under the eaves just right for a nursery . . .

Not even a couple of small unpleasantnesses could spoil their bliss. Soon after they moved in, the local vicar called, suggesting that they might allow the village fête to be held on their lawn. Caroline was half-taken with the idea, Lady of the Manor and all that, but Mark put his foot down. He didn't want a bunch of country oiks gawking through his windows, digging ruts in his drive with their rusty Capris and Marinas. He explained politely but firmly that it would be too much trouble so soon after moving in. When they had settled, then, well, perhaps. Of course the vicar, a deaf old coot with a red veiny face and white hair growing out of his ears, didn't like that one bit. He started on about tradition, about community values, but Mark cut him short and said that was all very well, but he wasn't a charity, and he agreed with the Prime Minister that there was no such thing as society, only individuals engaged in free-market decisions. That shut the old coot up. He went even redder, then clapped his shapeless black hat on his head and wobbled off down the drive on his black old bicycle without another word.

The next day, the woman Caroline had found to 'do' the place phoned up and said she couldn't come, and that her husband had had a think and, no, the garden would be too much trouble for him. Mark shrugged it off and went ahead and found a landscape gardener and an agency in Norwich that did contract cleaning. Caroline stopped using the village shop soon after; she heard someone say something about incomers as she was leaving, and there was mean laughter.

Well, that was their loss. There was a perfectly good Sainsbury's not twenty minutes' drive away, and so much cheaper. Nothing was going to disturb her sense of satisfaction with the house.

Nothing at all, until she found the hole in the cellar.

It was a couple of months after the kitten had disappeared. Foxes, Mark said. He'd get some pals around; they'd have a shoot. Only he never seemed to have enough time.

It was the middle of the beginning of Lawson's property crash, and people were beginning to realize that the magic carpet ride they'd enjoyed in the '80s was over. Money had suddenly become more important, and more difficult to find. It no longer flowed.

What the Chancellor of the Exchequer had done was close a loophole. Unmarried couples buying a property would no longer be able to get double tax relief on their mortgage. That September there was a last frantic boom as people scrambled to get on the property ladder before it was too late, and then it was over. Suddenly, people found that they couldn't sell their houses any more, and this was six months after someone paid 60K for a broom cupboard in Knightsbridge – admittedly with a view of Hyde Park from the minuscule shower room, but still a broom cupboard. People couldn't sell, and lowered their prices, and still couldn't sell. Those who had taken out 100 per cent mortgages in the boom years suddenly found that their debt was higher than the value of their house. There was a new, sinister phrase in the air: negative equity. Mark claimed that it didn't affect them. He'd fixed it, he said. A little deal, nothing for her to worry about. They'd done well to get out of London. Houses like theirs, country houses with traditional virtues, would never lose value. He'd made sure that their luck would hold.

His end-of-year bonus was the biggest yet. Money still flowed in the City, like stormwater through a conduit. It flowed from all over the world, passing through the City on its way to everywhere else. But their own finances were still tight: that 250K nut; the painting Mark bought Caroline for

Christmas; their holiday in the Seychelles and a mad weekend in New York; replacing the old lead plumbing. Caroline wanted to help. She dreamed of finding an old master or a set of Chippendale chairs or a bottle of vintage wine in the cellar. But there wasn't anything valuable, of course, just junk and mouldering old newspapers, piles and piles of them, and sheets of filthy cobwebs.

And the hole.

It was near the stone stairs that led down to the cellar from the kitchen, and she didn't see it until she was about to go back up. A few bricks had been pushed out, and the ones around the gap this made looked, well, *chewed*. Coated with something black and tarry. Caroline shone her powerful torch in the cavity but couldn't see anything, then put her hand in to see how deep it went.

And felt something, and pulled it out, thinking *treasure*. It was the body of the kitten, rotten and alive with maggots.

Rats, Mark said. He was quite calm. He told Caroline she shouldn't go in the cellar again. He'd get an exterminator in.

'We're in the country. Old place like this is bound to have a few problems. Nothing we can't fix, darling.'

Caroline was scrubbing her hands under a gush of scalding water, scrubbing and scrubbing. She had somehow fixed the evening meal and was washing the smell of fish from her hands. Mark lounged at the big refectory table, toying with his glass of Australian Chardonnay. He looked sleek and smug in his striped shirt and red braces.

'Poison will get rid of them,' he said. 'I'll phone an exterminator. Should have had it done when the roof was treated.'

He had to take a day off in the end, to show the exterminator what had to be done. Not much more than a teenager really, with blow-waved dyed blond hair and tight stone-washed jeans, but he seemed to know his stuff, and left little trays of blue pellets around, with a top-up supply just in case.

But it was soon clear that the poison wasn't doing any good. The rats were eating it all right – they'd even gnawed into the plastic bag containing the extra pellets which Mark had left at the top of the cellar stairs – but if anything, the poison only encouraged them. There were noises at night, in the dark spaces of the house. Lying on her four-poster bed in the cold master bedroom beside her sleeping husband, Caroline was kept awake by noises. Scrabblings behind the walls. Something walking over the keyboard of the grand piano, making a ghostly arpeggio. Max, the Labrador, would come and scratch and whimper at the bedroom door until Caroline got up and let him in.

The next spring, Max disappeared. Run off, Mark said. He said that he'd get another dog, but he never did. He was very busy in the City, and talked about getting a flat and staying overnight Monday to Thursday. They had a fearful row about that, and although Caroline won, Mark sulked for days, and from that day on would find ways of reminding her who earned the money.

There was still plenty of money. Maggie was suddenly deposed in a bloodless putsch, but privatization was in full swing, and people in the City were earning huge amounts of money from inside knowledge about the switch from public to private monopolies. Caroline signed documents for huge tranches of shares which Mark sold on. The garden was landscaped. Decorators stripped the V&A wallpaper, repanelled the walls of the ballroom and painted them deep red with gold leaf highlights, resurfaced the ballroom floor, brought in crates of leatherbound books, bought in bulk at auction, to fill the bare shelves of Mark's study. There were Persian carpets to match the new paintwork, new sofas, a Flemish tapestry. The Ron Arad lamps went into the basement, replaced by huge table lamps with bases of beaten copper and silk shades. The redecoration cost as much as the first mortgage on that tiny one bedroom flat in Crouch End.

Then Mark began to worry about money again. He wouldn't let Caroline see the bank statements, and he didn't question the bills that flooded in, but she knew that there were problems. In the evenings and at the weekend he spent a lot of time in his study, shouting down the telephone or running documents through the fax. It was a liquidity problem, he said, the market was getting nervous because there was a chance Labour might get elected; the new man, Major, wasn't filling Maggie's shoes very well.

Something went wrong with the drains, and a sour reek filled the house. The septic tank was replaced; the lawns were ripped up to check the drains. One day Caroline found trails of transparent slime all through the ballroom and Mark's study and the hall, drying into curling translucent sheaves, like cellophane passed through some obscene chemical transmutation.

Then Caroline became pregnant, and Mark was furious. More blazing rows. He blamed her. She thought that he was seeing another woman and went through his credit card bills, even hired a private detective for a week. What she found was that Mark had lost his job. Every day he set off as he always had, but spent his days tramping between employment agencies and interviews. She couldn't let him know that she knew. She couldn't take away his pride.

Caroline lost the baby one sunny day in April. She was three months pregnant. She'd had cramps all morning, and suddenly started bleeding when on the toilet. It was over very quickly. It looked like nothing much more than a bigger version of the bloodspot you sometimes find in free range eggs, floating in the toilet bowl amongst strings of blood and mucus. Her baby.

Mark was very good about it. Caroline had been unable to flush the foetus away. She hunched miserably in the sitting room, watching soft evening light fade in the tops of the trees beyond the wide green lawn, listening as her husband set about clearing up. He stripped the bed where she had lain all afternoon and put the blood-stained sheets in the washing machine. Doors were opened and closed. He was down in the cellar for a while. He cooked supper. Everything would be all right, he said. A week later, John Major won the election. Mark brought back copies of the *Sun* the next day, yesterday's edition with its picture of Kinnock's freckled face distorted into a lightbulb, today's edition with its gloating headline.

'"It Was The Sun Wot Won It,"' Mark said. 'If only they knew.'

After that, things were very good. Mark got a new job as senior commodities broker at a private bank, the oldest in Britain, at double his previous salary and with huge year-end bonuses. The Porsche was replaced by a Bentley; Caroline's Peugeot by a sleek Mercedes SL200. Mark was wary about trying for another baby, saying that it was all a question of timing, but in the end he gave way. Caroline signed up with a gynaecologist on Harley Street, and her second pregnancy was trouble-free. She stayed in the private ward with her newborn daughter for a week, came home to find Mark had decorated the nursery and turned the box room beside it into a bedsitter for the nanny.

The house was quieter now. No more mysterious night noises. Every summer, Caroline and Mark had a huge party, with a marquee on the lawn and a jazz band on the terrace. Some of their old friends still came, but many of the guests were connected with Mark's business, or his new links with the local Conservative association. At one party, a brace of Arab princes turned up, like exotic birds of prey; at another, Andrew Lloyd Webber (Mark had bought large numbers of shares in *Cats*) and the balding pop star who had made millions with his versions of old Motown songs. There were always minor TV personalities, afternoon chat show hosts, weather girls, presenters of game shows. The crowning moment came when Jeffrey Archer spent an hour mingling with his admirers and signing huge numbers of his books. Caroline got to know the wife of their MP quite well, and the wives of prominent Conservatives and local businessmen. Mark became a member of two nearby golf clubs and the Round Table. He was developing an adorable bald spot right on top of his head, and hated it when Caroline kissed him there.

It became their custom that when Caroline and the nanny and little Emma went off to St Lucia, or Antibes, or skiing in Austria, Mark would join them after a week or so. Even then he couldn't relax and spent most of his time on the phone or on his portable computer. They slept in separate bedrooms now. Caroline had her suspicions about another woman, but this time she didn't follow them up. There was talk of Mark standing in a safe seat at the next election, and Caroline had learnt from her new friends that after a certain length of time what mattered most in every marriage was its public face of loyalty and unity.

In November, Caroline was on holiday with Emma and the nanny, in the farmhouse Mark had just bought in Tuscany, when the news about Caroline's mother came, early one morning, conveyed by her sister across a crackling line. Caroline's mother was in hospital after a sudden collapse. The surgeons had opened her up, but it was hopeless. The cancer had spread everywhere.

Caroline had not seen her mother for a year. Her family, old-fashioned liberals, her father a GP, her mother a retired teacher, had never really taken to Mark. The last time Caroline had seen them all together had been when her father had died two years ago.

She found three first-class seats on the next flight from Florence, helped the nanny pack, and in five hours they were airborne. Mark was not due to join them for three days and he had not left the answer machine on. Well, she would tell him when she got home; it wasn't as if he would want to go to the funeral.

They took a taxi from Heathrow across night-time London, Emma tired and fractious and mildly sunburnt, caught the last train out of King's Cross, then a taxi from Peterborough to the house. Wisps of freezing fog drifted amongst the stripped branches of the trees; the lawn was dusted with frost. Lights burned in the windows and Mark's Bentley was parked outside the front door, its boot open. While the nanny took Emma up to bed, Caroline went to find her husband.

She found his Armani suit draped over one of the kitchen chairs and a sea of newspaper spotted with rust-brown stains littering the quarry tile floor. And found Mark in the cellar.

He was naked except for Calvin Klein boxer shorts. His hands red and wet, his face a stranger's mask turning towards her. She couldn't take in the thing on the floor. White goosepimpled skin like a plucked chicken carcass. An arm ropey with blue tattoos. White strings inside the cut throat. Mark had caught the blood in a shiny blue washing-up bowl and was using a two inch paint brush to splash it around the hole in the wall.

The hole was bigger than Caroline remembered, framed with layers of stinking, clotted black blood. Newspaper photos stuck around it: photos of Maggie and Reagan and Bush; of the *Antelope* going up like a firework in the dark Falklands sea; of oil wells burning furiously under a black sky; of gassed Kurdish children. Glossy photos from porn mags and the *Innovations* catalogue. Flyers for *Cats* and *Starlight Express*. Expired Amex and Visa cards. A signed photograph of Michael Portillo.

Worse than this, worse than the corpse on the floor of the cellar, worse than the stink of blood, was Mark's reasonableness. It was as if he was relieved that he had been caught. He wanted to explain, he wanted to share this with Caroline. He'd tried to stop, he said, but things went wrong when he did.

'It started with the kitten, and poor Max, but then animal blood wasn't enough. I tried to stop, darling. But there was Lloyds. The Gulf War. The ERM – poor Lamont and those fags and cheap champagne! I have to keep going, darling, it keeps wanting more. No one misses them. They're detritus. Rent boys, runaways from the north. A fiver in advance, the promise of another fiver. That's all it takes. No one's surprised when they vanish. No one cares. No one even *knows*.'

Caroline was very calm. The calmness gripped her like a season. She spoke out of her calmness. She ordered Mark to clear up. She ordered him to leave, and to stay away from her, from her daughter, from the house. She said that if he didn't do as he was told she would let the press know everything. He had his job, he had his political career. She would not get in the way of any of that as long as he went away and never tried to come back.

Mark argued, but it was from a weaker position. He pleaded, he wept. But Caroline knew he would not kill her, and he knew it too.

She buried her mother, standing alone amidst her relatives in Nicole Farhi black, little Emma in black crushed velvet weeping hot tears for her Gramma. Caroline put a restraining order on Mark, had the house transferred to her name. The rest he could keep as long as he kept up the very reasonable maintenance payments. She started divorce proceedings, citing irreconcilable differences.

Caroline heard about the bank collapse from Mark. He phoned her in the middle of a Sunday afternoon late in February, three months after she had ordered him out of the house. He was nearly hysterical. He wanted to come back. He said that he wanted to make good. He said that it was the only way. There was still a chance that the Bank of England might step in, but if the chance was missed then it could only get worse.

'Just a simple payment. That's all it takes to change our luck. I can do it right now, darling. It's so easy. Sheep to the slaughter. They *want* to die.'

Caroline let him talk, then put the phone down and turned on the TV. It took a while for the story to come out. She got most of it from TeleText. The bank, the oldest merchant bank in England, the Queen one of its depositors, had been bankrupted by one of its dealers in the Singapore stock market. The dealer was what Mark used to call a council house oik, the kind who had done well with quick wits and stamina and hooligan aggression. He had bought millions of dollars of futures on the Tokyo stock market, and the yen had dipped and left him exposed and he had made a run for it. The bank was bankrupt. Caroline's husband was out of a job, and then he was dead.

The police brought her the news on the day that the rogue dealer was caught in Frankfurt, smirking under a baseball cap.

Mark had driven to St Andrews, where he had gone to university, had parked amongst sand dunes overlooking the North Sea. He had run a hosepipe from his Bentley's exhaust into the cabin, and switched on the engine.

Very few people came to the funeral. It is not money that makes connections, but the flow of money, the potential of movement. For Mark, that had ended. For Caroline, too, it seemed. The insurance policies were voided by his suicide. The place in Tuscany was taken back; Mark had only leased it, it turned out. The Bentley and the Mercedes were leased too, in his name. Most of his money had gone into making himself a Lloyd's Name, and the syndicate he'd joined owed vast amounts of money to workers in the asbestos industry.

Caroline had to let the nanny go. All she had was the house, and the unpaid mortgage on that was worth more than the house itself.

Piggy Roberts was one of the few who came to Mark's funeral, and Caroline made an appointment to see him the next week. Piggy had aged badly: too much brandy and champagne, too many post-prandial Monte Cristo cigars. His hair was frazzled and receding; his ruddy complexion was splotched with broken veins and the rims of his nostrils were reddened. Cocaine, probably: coke was making a comeback. Caroline saw all this with her new, clear, unforgiving vision. She saw the frightened little boy peering out of Piggy's fleshy face, trapped in the gross adult body. She saw the way he still snuck a peek at her legs when he thought she wasn't looking.

Caroline made him show her his photocopy of the deeds of the house, show her the clause he and Mark had joked about all those years ago. No, less than ten. How far they'd come! How high they'd flown!

Piggy Roberts tried to make a joke of it. 'A bit different from a red rose as ground rent every year, but just as cheap. Maybe there was a Saxon temple there a thousand years ago, midsummer sacrifices and so on. Corn gods. These old relics can live on, in law . . .'

He offered to take her out to dinner, a feeble attempt at a pass that Caroline squashed instantly. 'Anything you need,' he said, as she got up to leave, 'anything, just ask. I tried to be a good friend to Mark. He loved that house, you know.'

He meant well, but Caroline knew she had to do it alone. She spent a week planning. She found some of the equipment Mark had used: neat coils of nylon rope; a brown bottle of pharmaceutical grade ether; a snaptop freezer bag with a dredging of brown granules, like cane sugar, labelled *heroin* in Mark's neat hand; squares of aluminium foil and a cigarette lighter; a roll of plastic disposable syringes and a box of sterile needles; a pair of handcuffs. Caroline had her hair cut short and bought a secondhand Volvo estate. She put blankets and Mark's gear in the back of the car, with a half bottle of whisky and a cosh she'd made from the leg of an old pair of tights and ten pounds' worth of pennies, had Emma stay over with one of her friends.

Caroline knew what she had to do. She had given all she had for the house. She would make any sacrifice to keep it.

Paul J. McAuley recently quit his job as a professor at St Andrews University in Scotland to write full time, although he had his first major success back in 1988 when he won the Philip K. Dick Award for his début novel, *Four Hundred Billion Stars*. Later books include *Secret Harmonies*, *Eternal Light* (shortlisted for the Arthur C. Clarke Award), *Red Dust* and *Pasquale's Angel*. His latest novel is *Fairyland*, from Gollancz (which won the 1996 Clarke Award for best science fiction novel published in Britain the previous year). The same publisher has also recently issued a collection of short stories with a biotechnological theme, *The Invisible Country*. Other works include an earlier collection, *The King of the Hill; In Dreams*, an anthology edited with Kim Newman, and his short story 'The Temptation of Dr Stein' (from Stephen Jones' *The Mammoth Book of Frankenstein*), which won the 1995 British Fantasy Award. As the author explains, he began writing 'Negative Equity' in the late 1980s: 'When everyone was talking about nothing else but how much more their house was worth this week. It was as if they were . . . possessed. In its embryonic form, the story was overtaken by the Lawson boom/bust in house prices, but a recent television documentary series hosted by the egregious Peter York brought back the full horror of the decade of cruise missiles, yuppies, Gordon 'Greed' Gekko and Wham!, and gave me a way of bringing the story up to date.'

To This Water
(Johnstown, Pennsylvania 1889)

CAITLÍN R. KIERNAN

Hardly dawn, and already Magda had made her way through the forest into the glittering frost at the foot of the dam. When the sun climbed high enough, it would push aside the shadows and set the hollow on fire, sparkling crystal fire that would melt gently in the late spring sunrise and drip from hemlock and aspen branches, glaze the towering thickets of mountain laurel, later rise again as gauzy soft steam. Everything, ice-crisped ferns and everything else, crunched beneath her shoes, loud in the cold, still air; no sound but morning birds and the steady gush from the spillway into South Fork Creek, noisy and secretive, like careless whispers behind her back.

Winded, her breath puffing out white through chapped lips and a stitch nagging her side, she rested a moment against a potato-shaped boulder, and the moss there frost-stiffened too, ice-matted green fur and grey lichens like scabs. Back down the valley towards South Fork, night held on, a lazy thing curled in the lee of the mountain. Magda shivered and pulled her shawl tighter about her shoulders.

All the way from Johnstown since nightfall, fifteen miles or more since she'd slipped away from the darkened rows of company houses on Prospect Hill, following the railroad first and later, after the sleeping streets of South Fork, game trails and finally the winding creek, yellow-brown and swollen with the runoff of April thaw and heavy May rains. By now her family would be awake, her father already gone to the mill and twelve hours at the furnaces, her mother and sister neglecting chores and soon they would be asking from house to house, porches and back doors.

But no one had seen her go, and there would be nothing but concerned and shaking heads, shrugs and suspicion for their questions and broken English. And when they'd gone, there would be whispers, like the murmur and purl of mountain streams.

As the sky faded from soft violet, unbruising, Magda turned and began to pick her way up the steep and rocky face of the dam.

This is not memory, this is a pricking new thing, time knotted, cat's cradled or snarled like her sister's brown hair and she is always closing her eyes, always opening them again and always the narrow slit of sky is red, wound red slash between the alley's black walls and rooftops, pine and shingle jaws. And there is nothing left of the men but calloused, groping fingers, the scalding whiskey soursweetness of their breath. Sounds like laughter from dog throats and the whiskery lips of pigs, dogs and pigs laughing if they could.

And Magda does not scream, because they have said that if she screams, if she cries or even speaks they will cut her tongue out, will cut her hunkie throat from ear to ear and she knows that much English. And the big Irishman has shown her his knife, they will all show her their knives, and cut her whether she screams or not.

The hands pushing and she turns her face away, better the cool mud, the water puddled that flows into her mouth, fills her nostrils, that tastes like earth and rot and the alcohol from empty barrels and overflowing crates of bottles stacked high behind the Washington Street saloon. She grinds her teeth, crunching grit, sand sharp against her gums.

And before she shuts her eyes, last thing before there is only raw pain and the sounds she won't ever shut out, Magda catches the dapper man watching from the far away end of the alley, surprised face peering down the well. Staring slack-jawed and light from somewhere safe glints coldly off his spectacles, moonlight on thin ice.

The demons growl and he scuttles away and they fold her open like a cockleshell.

By the wavering orange oil light, her mother's face had glowed warm, age and weariness softened almost away, and she had been speaking to them in Magyar, even though Papa said that they'd never learn that way. And she had leaned over them, brushing her sister Emilia's hair from her face. Her mother had set the lamp carefully down on the wobbly little table beside their bed, herself in the wobbly chair, and it had still been winter then, still dirty snow on the ground outside, the wind around the pine-board corners of the house, howling for its own misfortunes. And them bundled safe beneath quilts and rag-swaddled bricks from the hearth at their feet.

Magda had watched the shadows thrown across the walls, bare save for knotholes stuffed with old newspapers and the crucifix her mother had brought across from Budapest, blood-dark wood and tortured pewter. And the lamplight had danced as her mother had spoken, had seemed to follow the rise and fall of her words, measured steps in a pattern too subtle for Magda to follow.

So she had closed her eyes tight, buried her face in pillows and Emilia's back, and listened to her mother's stories of childhood in the mountain village of Tátra Lomnitz and the wild Carpathians, listening more to her soothing voice than the words themselves. She knew all the old stories of the house elves, the hairy little *domovoy* that had lived in the dust and sooty corner behind her grandmother's stove, and the river people, the *Vodyaniyie* and *Rusalky*; the comfort her sister drew from the fairy tales, she took directly from the music of timbre and tender intonation.

'And in the autumn,' her mother had said, 'when a fat gander was offered to the people who lived under the lake, we would first cut off its head and nail it to the barn door so that

our *domovoy* would not know that one of his geese had been
given away to another.'

And then, sometime later, the lamp lifted from the wobbly
table and her mother had kissed them both, Magda pretending
to sleep, and whispered, her voice softer than the bed, '*Jó
éjszakát*,' and her bare footsteps already moving away, sounding hollow on the floor, when Emilia had corrected her,
'Good night, Mama.'

'Good night, Emilia,' her mother had answered and then
they had been alone with the night and the wind and the sky
outside their window that was never quite black enough for
stars, but always stained red from the belching foundry fires
of Johnstown.

It was full morning by the time Magda reached the top, and
her eyes stung with her own sweat and when she licked her
lips she tasted her own salt; not blood but something close.
Her dress clung wetly to her back, clammy damp armpits, and
she'd ripped her skirt and stockings in blackberry briars and
creeper vines. Twice she'd slipped on the loose stones and
there was a small gash on her left palm, purpling bruise below
her thumb. Now she stood a moment on the narrow road that
stretched across the breast of the dam, listening to her heart,
fleshpump beneath cotton and skin, muscle and bone. Watching the mist, milky wisps curling up from the green-grey
water, burning away in the sun.

Up here, the morning smelled clean, pine and the silent
lake, no hint of the valley's pall of coal dust or factory smoke.
There were clouds drifting slowly in from the southwest,
scowling, steelbellied thunderheads, and so the breeze smelled
faintly of rain and ozone as well.

Magda stepped across the road, over deep buggy ruts,
pressing her own shallow prints into the clay. The pockets of
her skirt bulged with the rocks she'd gathered as she climbed,
weather-smoothed shale and gritty sandstone cobbles the
colour of dried apricots. Four steps across, and on the other
side, the bank dropped away sharply, steep, but only a few
feet down to water, choked thick with cattails and weeds.

Quickest glance, then, back over her shoulder, not bother-
ing to turn full and play Lot's wife proper. The fire burned
inside her, scorching, righteous flame shining through her
eyes, incapable of cleansing, scarring and salting her brain.
And, careful, Magda went down to the cold water.

And when they have all finished with her, each in his turn,
when they have carved away at her insides and forced their fat
tongues past her teeth and so filled her with their hot seed that
it leaks like sea salt pus from between her bloodied thighs, they
slosh away through the mud and leave her; not for dead, not
for anything but discarded, done with. For a long time, she lies
still and watches the sky roiling above the alley, and the pain
seems very, very far away, and the red clouds seem so close that
if she raises her hand she might touch them, might break their
blister-thin skins and feel the oily black rain hiding inside.
Gazing up from the pit into the firelight her own Papa stokes
so that the demons can walk the streets of Johnstown.

But the demons have kept their promises, and her throat is
not sliced ear to ear, and she can still speak, knows this
because she hears the animal sounds from her mouth, distant
as the pain between her legs. She is not dead, even if she is no
longer alive.

'Tell us about the *Rusalky*, Mama,' her sister had said, and her
mother had frowned, looked down at hands folded on her lap
like broken wings.

'*Nem*, Emilia,' her mother had answered firmly, gently,
'*Rusalky* is not a good story for bedtime.'

And as her sister pleaded, Magda had sat straightbacked
on the edge of the bed, silent, watching the window, watching
the red and starless sky, and already, that had been two weeks
after the men with the buckboard and the white mare had
brought her home, two weeks after her mother had cried and
washed away the dirt and blood, the clinging semen. Two
weeks since her father had stormed down from Prospect Hill
with his deer rifle and had spent a night in jail, had been
reminded by the grave-jowled constable that they were, after

all, Hungarians, and what with all the talk of the Company taking on bohunkie contract workers, cheap labour depriving honest men with families of decent wages, well, it wouldn't do to look for more trouble, would it? And in the end, he'd said, it would have been the girl's word against anyone he might have brought in, anyway.

In that space of time, days stacked like broken dishes, not a word from Magda and no tears from her dark and empty eyes. When food was pressed to her lips, a spoonful of soup or *gulyás*, she'd eaten, and when the sun went down and the lamps were put out, she had lain with her eyes open, staring through the window at the seething sky.

'Please, Mama, *kérem*,' her sister had whined, whined and Magda turned then, had turned on them so furiously that a slat cracked gunshot-loud beneath the feather mattress. Emilia had cried out, reached for their startled mother. And Magda had pulled herself towards them, hands gone to claws, tetanus snarl and teeth bared like a starving dog. And all that furnace glow gathered, hoarded from the red nights, and spilling from her eyes.

'*Magda, stop this*,' and her mother had pulled Emilia to her, 'you're frightening your sister! You're frightening me!'

'No, Mama. She wants to hear a story about the *Rusalky*, then I will *tell* her about the *Rusalky*. I will *show* her about the *Rusalky*.'

But her mother had stumbled to her feet, too-big Emilia clutched awkwardly in her arms, and the wobbly chair tumbled over and kicked aside. Backing away from the sagging bed and Magda, burning Magda, Emilia's face hidden against her chest. Backing into the shadows crouched in the doorway.

'She wants to hear, Mama, she *wants* to hear my story.'

Her mother had stepped backwards into the hall gloom, had slammed the bedroom door shut behind her, and Magda had heard the key rattle in the lock, bone rattle, death rattle, and then she'd been alone. The oil lamp still bright on the wobbly table, and a train had wailed, passing down in the valley, and when the engineer's whistle and the rattle and throb of boxcars had faded away, there had been only her mother's sobs from the other side of the door and the distant clamour of the mills.

Magda had let the lamp burn, stared a while into its tiny flame haloed safe behind blackened chimney glass, and then she'd turned back to the window, the world outside framed safe within, and she'd held fingers to her mouth and between them whispered her story to the sympathetic night.

All the lost and pretty suicides, all the girls in deep lakes and swirling rivers, still ponds, drowned or murdered and their bodies secreted in fish-silvered palaces. Souls committed to water instead of consecrated earth, and see her on Holy Thursday, on the flat rocks combing out her long hair, grown green and tangled with algae and eels? See her sitting in the low branches of this willow, bare legs hanging like pale fruit, toes drawing ripples in the stream, and be kind enough this sixth week past Easter to leave a scrap of linen, a patch or rag. Come back, stepping quiet through the tall grass, to find it washed clean and laid to dry beneath the bright May sky.

And there is more, after that, garlands for husbands and the sound of clapping hands from the fields, voices like ice melting, songs like the moment before a dropped stone strikes unseen well water.

Carry wormwood in your pockets, young man, and bathe with a cross around your neck.

Leave her wine and red eggs.

And when she dances under the summer moon, when the hay is tall and her sisters join hands, pray you keep yourself behind locked doors, or walk quickly past the waving wheat; stay on the road, watch your feet.

Or you'll wind up like poor Józef; remember Józef, Old Viktor's son? His lips were blue, grain woven in his hair, and how do you think his clothes got wet, so muddy, so far from the river?

And see her there, on the bank beneath the trees, her comb of stickly fish bones? Watch her, as she pulls the sharp teeth through her green hair, and watch the water rise.

*

This is what it's like to drown, Magda thought, *like stirring salt into water*, as she drifted, dissolving, just below the lake, sinking slowly into twilight the colour of dead moss, the stones in her pockets only a little help. Her hair floated, wreathed her face and the last silver bubbles rose from her open mouth, hurrying towards the surface. Just the faintest, dull pressure in her chest, behind her eyes, and a fleeting second's panic, and then there was a quiet more perfect than anything she had ever imagined. Peace folding itself thick around her, driving back the numbing cold and the useless sun filtering down from above, smothering doubt and fear and the crushing regret that had almost made her turn around, scramble back up the slippery bank when the water had closed like molasses around her ankles.

Magda flowed into the water, even as the water flowed into her, and by the time she reached the bottom, there was hardly any difference any more.

*

Thursday, wet dregs of Memorial Day, and Mr Tom Givens slipped quietly away from the talk and cigar smoke of the clubhouse front rooms. Talk of the parade down in Johnstown and the Grand Army Veterans and the Sons of Veterans, the amputees on their crutches and in faded Union blues; twenty-four years past Appomattox, and Grant was dead, and Lee was dead, and those old men, marching clear from Main to Bedford Street despite the drizzling sky. He'd sat apart from the others, staring out across the darkening lake, the docks and the clubfleet, the canoes and sailboats and Mr Clarke's electric catamaran moored safe against the threat of a stormy night.

And then someone, maybe Mr D.W.C. Bidwell, had brought up the girl, and faces, smoke-shrouded, brandy-flushed, had turned towards him, curious, and

Oh, yes, didn't you know? Why, Tom here saw her, saw the whole damnable thing,

and so politely he'd excused himself. Had left them mumbling before the crackle and glow of the big sandstone fireplace, and by the time he'd reached the landing and the lush path of burgundy carpet that would carry him back to his room, the conversation had turned inevitably to iron and coke, the new Navy ironclads for which Carnegie, Phipps and Co. had been contracted to produce the steel plating. Another triumph for Pittsburgh, another blow to the Chicago competition.

Now he shut the door behind him and the only light was dim grey through the windows; for a moment he stood in the dark before reaching for the chain. Above the lake, the clouds were breaking apart, hints of stars and moonshine in the rifts, and the lake almost glimmered, out in the middle seemed to ripple and swirl.

It's only wind on the water, Tom Givens told himself as he pulled the lamp chain hard and warm yellow drenched the room, drove the black outside and he could see nothing in the windows except the room mirrored and himself, tall and very much needing a shave. By the clock on his dresser, it was just past nine, and *At least*, he thought, *maybe there'll be no storms tonight*. But the wind still battered itself against the clubhouse, and he sat down in a chair, back to the lake, and poured amber whiskey. He drank it quickly and quickly refilled the glass, tried not to hear the gusting wind, the shutter rattle, the brush of pine boughs like old women wringing their bony hands.

By ten the bottle was empty and Tom Givens was asleep in the chair, stocking feet propped on the bed.

An hour later, the rain began.

The storm was as alive as anything else, as alive as the ancient shale and sandstone mountains and the wind; as alive as the scorch and burn of the huge Bessemer converters and the slag-scabbed molten iron that rolled like God's blood across the slippery steel floors of the Cambria mills. And as perfectly mindless, as passionately indifferent. It had been born somewhere over Nebraska two days before, had swept across the plains and in Kansas spawned twister children who danced along the winding Cottonwood River and wiped away roads and farms. It had seduced Arctic air spilling off the Great Lakes and sired blizzards across Michigan and Indiana, had

spoken its throaty poetry of gale and thunder throughout the
Ohio River Valley, and finally, with its violent arms, would
embrace the entire Mid-Atlantic seaboard.

As Tom Givens had listened distractedly to the pomp and
chatter of the gentlemen of the club, the storm had already
claimed western Pennsylvania, had snubbed the sprawling scar
of Pittsburgh for greener lovers further east. And as he'd
slept, it had stroked bare ridges and stream-threaded valleys,
rain-shrouding Blairsville and Bolivar, New Florence and
Ninevah, had followed the snaky railroad through Conemaugh Gap into the deep and weathered folds of Sang
Hollow.

And then, Johnstown, patchwork cluster of boroughs
crowded into the dark hole carved in the confluence of two
rivers. The seething Cambria yards and the tall office buildings, the fine and handsome homes along Main Street. The
storm drummed tin and slate shingled roofs, played for the
handful of mill workers and miners drinking late inside
California Tom's, for the whores in Lizzie Thompson's
sporting house on Frankstown Hill. George and Mathilde
Heiser, closing up for the night, paused in the mercantile
clutter of their store to watch the downpour, and inside St
Joseph's parsonage, Reverend Chapman, who'd been having
bad dreams lately, was awakened by his wife, Agnes, and they
lay together and listened to the rain pounding Franklin Street.

Unsatisfied, insatiable, the storm had continued east, engulf-
ing the narrow valley, Mineral Point and the high arch of the
Pennsylvania Railroad viaduct, and, finally, sleeping South
Fork.

As alive as anything it touched.

The girl on the dam doesn't know he's watching, of that much
he's certain. He sits by open windows and the early morning
air smells like the lake, like fish and mud, and something
sharper. He's been drunk more than he's been sober since the
night down in Johnstown, the night he sat in the balcony of
the Washington Street Opera House, *Zozo the Magic Queen*

on stage and some other fellows from the club with him, talking among themselves.

The girl from the dam is walking on the water.

He leans forwards, head and shoulders out the window because he can't hear, Irwin braying like a goddamned mule from the seat behind and he can't hear the words, the players' lines, can only hear Irwin repeating the idiot joke over and over again. Beneath the window of his room, the audience is seated, and he stares down at men's heads and ladies' feathered hats, row after row on the front lawn of the South Fork Hunting and Fishing Club.

Somewhere, far away still but rushing like locomotive wheels, thunder, like applause and laughter and the footlights like lightning frozen on her face.

'Ask Tom,' the usher says, 'Tom saw the whole damnable thing,' and Irwin howls.

And then she's gone, if she was ever really there, and the crowd is on its feet, flesh smacking flesh in frenzied approval; if she was ever there. Lake Conemaugh is as smooth as varnished wood, and he knows it's all done with trapdoors and mirrors and that in a moment she'll rise straight up from the stage planks to take her bows. But the roses fall on the flat water and lie there and now the curtains are sweeping closed, velvet the colour of rain rippling across the sky.

'. . . saw the *whole* thing,' Irwin echoes, so funny he wants to say it over and over, and they're all laughing, every one, when he gets up to go, when it's obvious that the show's over and everyone else is leaving their seats, the theatre emptying into the front porch of the clubhouse.

Sidewalk boards creak loud beneath his shoes, thunk and mould-rotten creak; after the evening showers the air smells cleaner at least, coal dust and factory soot washed from the angry industrial sky into the black gutters, but the low clouds hold in the blast furnace glow from Cambria City and the sky is bloodier than ever.

Spring buggies and lacquered wagon wheels, satin skirts and petticoats held above the muddy street. The pungent musk of wet horse hair.

And he knows that he's only stepped out of his room, that he stands in the hall, second floor, and that if he walks straight on he'll pass three rooms, three numbered doors, and come to the stairs, the oak banister, winding down. But it's dark, the sputtering white arc streetlights not reaching this narrow slit, inverted alley spine between Washington and Union, and the carpet feels more like muck and gravel, and he turns, starts to turn when thunder rumbles like animal whispers and cloth tearing and

Why, Tom here saw her, saw the whole damnable thing

the shadow things hunched, claws and grunts and breath exhaled from snot wet nostrils, and she turns her head, hair mired in the filth and standing water, face minstrel smudged, but eyes bright and she sees him, and he knows she's begging him to help, to stop this, to pull the shadows off her before there's nothing left to save.

But a shaggy head rises ox-slow from the space between her breasts and these eyes are nothing but the red sky, molten pools of stupid hunger, and Tom turns away, lost for a moment, feeling his way along the silken-papered walls, until his fumbling hands find the brass cool doorknob and the thunder splits apart that world. Splits the alley girl like an overripe peach, and he steps across the threshold, his bare feet sinking through the floor into the icy lake, and she's waiting, dead hand shackle-tight around his ankle to pull him down into the fishslime and silting night.

Mr Tom Givens woke up, sweat-soaked, eyes wide, still seeing white-knuckled hands clasped, sucking air in shuddering gulps, air that seemed as thick, as unbreathable, as dark lake water. The crystal-cut whiskey glass tumbled from his hands, rolled away beneath the bed. And still the pain, fire twisting his legs, and outside the thunder rumbled across the Allegheny night like artillery fire and Old Testament judgment.

Both legs were still propped up on the four-poster and, as he shifted, the Charley horse began slowly, jealously, to relax its grip, and he realized there was no feeling at all in his left leg. Outside, furious rain pounded the windows, slammed the shutters against the clubhouse wall. Tom Givens cursed his stupidity, nodding off in the chair like a lousy drunkard, and carefully, he lowered his tortured legs on to the floor. Fresh pain in bright and nauseating waves as the blood rushed back into droughty capillaries; the room swam, lost its precious substance for a moment and the dream still so close, lingering like crows around the grey borders.

Lightning then, blinding sizzle that eclipsed the electric lamp, and the thunder clamoured eager on its heels.

He sat in the chair, waited for the last of the pins and needles stab to fade, listened to the storm. A wild night on the mountain, and that went a long way towards explaining the nightmare, that and the bourbon, that and the things he'd seen since he'd arrived at the lake two weeks before. He'd come out early, before the June crowds, hoping for rest and a little time to recover from the smoky bustle of Pittsburgh.

The loose shutters banged and rattled like the wind knocking to come inside, and he got up, cautious, legs still uncertain, but only two steps, three, to the window. And even as he reached for the latch, thumbed it back, even as he pushed against the driving rain, knowing that he'd be soaked before it was done, he heard the roar, not thunder, but something else, something almost alive. Immediate and stinging cold and the sashes were ripped from his hands, slammed back and panes shattered against the palsied shutters.

And through the darkness and the downpour he saw the white and whirling thing, impossibly vast, moving past the docks, dragging itself across the lake. Silvered clockwise, and the deafening roar and boom, and Tom Givens forgot the broken windows, the frantic drapery flutter, the shutters, ignored the rain blowing in, soaking him through, drenching the room. He watched as the waterspout passed by, and the girl, the girl standing there, her long dark hair whipped in the gale, her body an alabaster slash in the black night. She raised her bare arms, worshipping, welcoming, granting passage, and turning, her white gown a whirling echo of the thing, and her arms were opened to him now, and he knew the face.

The face that had turned to him, helpless, pleading, in the Johnstown alleyway, but changed, eyes swollen with bottomless fury and something that might be triumph, if triumph could be regret. And he knew as well that this was also the girl that he'd watched drown herself off South Fork Dam barely a week back.

Her lips moved but the wind snatched the words away.

And then lightning splashed the docks in noonday brilliance, and she was gone, nothing but bobbing canoes and the waves, and the trees bending down almost to the ground.

He passed the night downstairs, hours sobering into headache and listening to the storm from the huge main living room. He sat on pebble-grained calfskin and paced the Arabian carpeted floors, thumbed nervously through the new Mark Twain novel someone had left, finished or merely forgotten, on an end table. Occasionally, he glanced at the windows, towards the docks and the lake. And already the sensible, nineteenth century part of his mind had begun to convince itself that he'd only been dreaming, or near enough; drunk and dreaming.

Finally, others awake and moving, pot and pan noise and cooking smells from the kitchen, and the warm scents of coffee and bacon were enough to stall the argument, rational breakfast, perfect syllogism against the fading night. He smoothed his hair, straightened his rumpled shirt and vest with hands that had almost stopped shaking and rose to take his morning meal with the others.

Then young Mr Parke, resident engineer, shaved and dressed as smartly as ever, came quickly down the stairs, walked quickly to the porch door and let in the dawn, light like bad milk and the sky out there hardly a shade lighter than the night had been. And something roaring in the foggy distance.

John Parke stepped outside and Tom Givens followed him, knowing that he was certainly better off heading straight for the dining room, finding himself shivering on the long porch anyway. Before them, the lawn was littered with branches and broken limbs, with unrecognizable debris, and the lake was rough and brown.

'It's up a ways, isn't it?' and Tom's voice seemed magnified in the soppy air.

John Parke nodded slowly, contemplative, spoke without looking away from the water. 'I'd say it's up at least two feet since yesterday evening.'

'And that awful noise, what is that?'

Parke pointed southeast, towards the head of the lake, squinted as if by doing so he might actually see through the fog and drizzle.

'That awful noise, Mr Givens, is most likely Muddy Run coming down to the lake from the mountains.' Pause, and, 'It must be a blessed torrent after so much rain.'

'Doesn't sound very good, does it? Do you think that the dam is, ah, I mean, do you . . .'

'Let's see to our breakfasts, Mr Givens,' John Parke said, weak smile, pale attempt at reassurance, 'and then I'll see to the lake.'

The door clanged shut and he was alone on the porch, rubbing his hands together against the gnawing damp and chill. After breakfast, he would go upstairs and pack his bags, find a carriage into South Fork; from there, he could take the 9.15 back to Pittsburgh. More likely than not, there would be others leaving, and it would be enough to say he was sick of the weather, sick of this dismal excuse for a holiday.

Whatever else, that much certainly was true.

Tom Givens turned his back on the lake, on the mess the night had made of the club grounds, and as he reached for the door he heard what might have been laughter or glass breaking or just the wind whistling across the water. Behind him, one loud and sudden splash, something heavy off the docks, but he kept his eyes on the walnut dark woodgrain, gripped the brass handle and pulled himself inside.

A week drowned, and what was left of her, of her body, bloated flesh sponge like strawberry bruise and whitest cheese, pocked by nibbling, hungry black bass mouths, this much lay

knitted into the pine log tangle and underbrush jamming the
big iron fish screens. The screens that strained the water, that
kept the lake's expensive stock inside (one dollar apiece, the
fathers and grandfathers of these fish, all the way from Lake
Erie by special railroad car) and now sieved the cream-and-
coffee brown soup before it surged, six feet deep, through the
spillway; and the caretaker and his Italians, sewer diggers with
their shovels and pickaxes, watched as the lake rose, ate away
the mounds of dirt heaped all morning along the breast of the
dam.

Blackened holes that were her eyes, grub-clogged sockets
haloed in naked bone and meaty tatter, cribs for the blind and
newborn maggots of water beetles and dragonflies.

Some minutes past grey noon, the lake spread itself into a
wide and glassy sheet and spilled over the top, began its slice
and carve, bit by bit, sand and clay and stone washed free and
tumbled down the other side. And now the morning's load of
cautious suggestions, desperate considerations and shaken
heads, gambles passed on, the things that might have been
done, didn't matter any more; and the workmen and the
bystanders huddled, the dutiful and the merely curious, all
rain-drenched, on either hillside, bookends for a deluge.

Tom Givens sat alone, safe and almost drunk again within the
shelter of the South Fork depot, sipping Scotch whisky from
his silver flask and trying not to watch the nervous faces, not
to overhear the hushed exchanges between the ticket agent
and the yardmaster. During the night, almost a quarter mile
of track washed out between South Fork and Johnstown, and
so there had been no train to Pittsburgh or anywhere else that
morning, and by afternoon the tracks were backed up; the
Chicago Limited stretched across Lamb's Bridge like a rusty fat
copperhead and a big freight from Derry, too common for
names, steamed rainslick and sullen just outside the station.

He'd come from the club in Bidwell's springboard, but had
lost track of him around noon, shortly after John Parke had
ridden down from the dam. Soaked through to the skin, quite
a sorry sight, really, drowned rat of a man galloping in on a

borrowed chestnut filly; Parke had gathered a small crowd outside Stineman's supply store, had warned that there was water flowing across the dam, that, in fact, there was real danger of its giving way at any time.

Bidwell had snorted, practised piggy snort of authority and money, had busied himself immediately, contradicting the dripping engineer, assuring everyone who'd listen (and everyone listens to the undespairing cut of those clothes, the calm voice that holds itself in such high esteem) that there was nothing for them to get excited about. Mr Parke had shrugged, duty done, had known better than to argue. He'd sent two men across the street to wire Johnstown from the depot's telegraph tower, had climbed back on to the mud-spattered horse, and then he'd gone, clopping up the slippery road towards the lake.

Tom Givens' ass ached from the hardwood bench, torturous church pew excuse for comfort, and the rain was coming down hard again, hammering at the tin roof. He closed his eyes and thought briefly about dozing off, opened them again and checked his watch instead; twenty minutes past three, nearly three hours sitting, waiting. Tom Givens snapped the watch shut, slipped it back into his vest pocket. And he knew that the sensible thing to do was return to the club, return to its amenities and cloister, and he knew he'd sooner spend the night sleeping on this bench.

When he stood, his knees popped loud as firecrackers and the yardmaster was yelling to someone out on the platform; the ticket agent looked up from his paper and offered a strained and weary smile. Tom Givens nodded and walked slowly across the room, paused to warm his hands at the squat, pot-bellied stove before turning to stare out rainstreaky windows. Across the tracks, Railroad Street, its tidy row of storefronts, the planing mill and the station's coal tipple; further along, the Little Conemaugh and South Fork Creek had twined in a yellow-brown ribbon swallowing the flats below the depot, had claimed the ground floors of several houses out there. Along the banks, oyster-barked aspens writhed and whipped in the wind and current.

There were people in the street, men and women standing about like simple idiots in the downpour, shouting, some running, but not back indoors.

And he heard it too, then, the rumbling thunder growl past thunder, past even the terrible whirl and roar from his nightmare, and the trembling earth beneath his feet, the floorboards and walls and window panes of the depot, resonating with sympathetic tremor.

Run, Thomas, run away.

One, two quickened heartbeats and it rolled into view, very close, fifty feet high and filling in the valley from side to side, an advancing mountain of foam and churning rubbish. Every stump and living tree and fence post between the town and the dam, ripped free, oak and birch and pinewood teeth set in soil-frothy mad dog gums, chewing up the world as it came.

Run, Thomas, run fast. She's coming.

But there was no looking away, even as he heard footsteps and someone grabbed, tugged roughly at his shoulder, even as he pissed himself and felt the warm spread at his crotch. He caught a fleeting glimpse of a barn roof thrown high on the crest before it toppled over and was crushed to splinters underneath.

She's here, Tom, she's here.

And then Lake Conemaugh and everything it had gathered in its rush down to South Fork slammed into the town and in the last moment before the waters reached Railroad Street and the depot, Tom Givens shut his eyes.

Beneath the red sky, he has no precise memory of the long walk down to this particular hell, slippery cantos blurred with shock and wet, does not even remember walking out on to the bridge.

Dimmest recollection of lying on the depot floor, face down as it pitched and yawed, moored by telegraph cable stitchings; window shards and the live coals spilling from the fallen stove, steam and sizzle in the dirty water, grey-black soot shower from the dangling pendulum stove pipe; dimmer, the pell-mell stumble through the pitchy dark, leaf-dripping, hemlock slap and claw of needled branches and his left arm has stopped hurting, finally, and hangs useless numb at his side; falling again and falling again, and unseen dogs howling like paid mourners, the Negro boy, then, sobbing and naked and painted with blood the sticky-slick colour of molasses, staring down together at the scrubbed raw gash where Mineral Point should have been,

Where is it? Tell me where it's gone.

Mister, the water just came and washed it off.

and his eyes follow the boy's finger and howling dogs like mourners and

Mister, your arm is broke, ain't it?

There is nothing else, simply nothing more, and above him the sky is furnace red and he sits alone on the bridge. Sandstone and mortar arches clogged with the shattered bones of the newly dead, South Fork and Mineral Point, Woodvale and Franklin, Johnstown proper, the flood's jumbled vomit, piled higher than the bridge itself. Boxcars and trees, hundreds of houses swept neatly off foundations and jammed together here, telegraph poles and furniture. Impossible miles of glinting barbed wire from the demolished Gautier wireworks, vicious garland strung with the corpses of cows and horses and human beings.

And the cries of the living trapped inside.

And everything burns.

Tar black roil, oily exhalation from the flames, breathed crackling into the sky, choking breath that reeks of wood smoke and frying flesh. Embers spiral up, scalding orange and yellow-white, into the dark and vanish overhead, spreading the fire like sparkling demon seeds.

Around him, men and women move, bodies bend and strain to wrestle the dead and dying and the barely bruised from the wreckage. And if anyone notices that he makes no move to help, no one stops to ask why.

From somewhere deep inside the pyre, hoarse groan of steel, lumber creak, wood and metal folded into a single shearing animal cry, rising ululation, and the wreckage shudders, shivers in its fevered dreams; and for *this* they stop, for this they spare fearful seconds, stare into the fuming night, afraid of what they'll see, that there might still be something worse left, held back for drama, for emphasis. But the stifling wind carries it away, muffles any chance of echo, and once again there are only the pain sounds and the burning sounds.

And he is the only one who sees her, the only one still watching, as she walks between the jutting timbers, steps across flaming pools of kerosene-scummed water. One moment, lost inside the smoke and then she steps clear again. Her hair dances in the shimmering heat and her white gown is scorched and torn, hangs in linen tatters. And the stain blooming at her crotch, rust-brown carnation unfolding itself, blood rich petals, blood shiny on the palms of the hands she holds out to him.

Dead eyes flecked with fire and dead lips that move, shape soundless words, and *Oh, yes, didn't you know? Why, Tom here saw her*, and what isn't there for him to hear is plain enough to see; she spreads her arms and in another moment there is only the blazing rubbish.

. . . saw the whole damnable thing.

He fights the clutching grip of their hands, hands pulling him roughly back from the edge, hands grown as hard as the iron and coke they've turned for five or ten or fifteen years, forcing him down on to the smooth and corpse-cold stones, pinning him, helpless, to the bridge.

Above him, the sky is red and filled with cinders that sail and twinkle and finally fall like stars.

> 'If there were such a thing as ghosts, the night was
> full of them.'
> David McCullough, *The Johnstown Flood*

for Melanie Tem

Caitlín R. Kiernan began writing full time in 1992, after working as a vertebrate palaeontologist. Her short stories have been published in several anthologies, including *Love in Vein 2*, *Sandman: Book of Dreams*, *Wild Justice*, *Darkside: Horror for the Next Millennium*, *High Fantastic* and *Sons of Darkness*. Her début novel, *The Five of Cups*, will be released in 1997 as a limited edition from Canada's Transylvania Press, and she has recently completed a second book, *Silk*. The author explains that her stories occur by a gradual, mostly unconscious, accumulation of images: 'I wrote "To This Water (Johnstown, Pennsylvania 1889)" during June and July of 1994, and it seemed like it rained the entire time I was working on the piece; there were floods all across southern Georgia. I'd just seen a particular painting for the first time, Constantin Makovski's *The Roussalkas*, and Sarah McLachlan's song "Possession" was getting a lot of radio play. The ending of the story came to me first, or, rather, the image of the fire in the flood came to me, while I was hearing that song and then, a little later, other images coalesced into what would eventually become this story.'

Out of the Woods

RAMSEY CAMPBELL

The glass of Scotch gnashed its ice cubes as Thirsk set it down on his desk. 'I don't care where it comes from, I just want the best price. Are you certain you won't have a drink?'

The visitor shook his head once while the rest of him stayed unmoved. 'Not unless you have natural water.'

'Been treated, I'm afraid. One of the many prices of civilization. You won't object if I have another, will you? I don't work or see people this late as a rule.'

When the other shook his head again, agitating his hair, which climbed the back of his neck and was entangled like a bristling brownish nest above his skull, Thirsk crossed to the mahogany cabinet to pour himself what he hoped might prove to be some peace of mind. While he served himself he peered at his visitor, little of whom was to be seen outside the heavy brown ankle-length overcoat except a wrinkled knotted face and gnarled hands, which ornamented the ends of the arms of the chair. Thirsk could think of no reason why any of this should bother him, but – together with the smell of the office, which was no longer quite or only that of new books – it did, so that he fed himself a harsh gulp of Scotch before marching around his desk to plant himself in his extravagant leather chair. It wasn't too late for him to declare that he didn't see salesmen without an appointment, but instead he heard himself demanding, 'So tell me why we should do business.'

'For you to say, Mr Thirsk.'

'No reason unless you're offering me a better deal than the bunch who printed all these books.'

That was intended to make the other at least glance at the shelves which occupied most of the wall space, but his gaze didn't waver; he seemed not to have blinked since Thirsk had opened the door to his knock. 'Do you know where they get their paper?' he said, more softly than ever.

'I already told you that's immaterial. All I know is it's better and cheaper than that recycled stuff.'

'Perhaps your readers would care if they knew.'

'I doubt it. They're children.' The insinuating softness of the other's speech, together with the dark wistful depths of his eyes, seemed to represent an insubstantial adversary with which Thirsk had to struggle, and he raised his voice. 'They won't care unless they're put up to it. If you ask me there's a movement not to let children be children any more, but plenty of them still want fairy tales or they wouldn't buy the books I publish.'

The ice scraped the glass as he drained his Scotch and stood up, steadying himself with one hand on the desk. 'Anyway, I'm not arguing with you. If you want to send me samples of your work and a breakdown of the costs then maybe we can talk.'

His tone was meant to make it clear that would never happen, but the other remained seated, pointing at his own torso with one stiff hand. 'This is for you to consider.'

He wasn't pointing at himself but rather at a book which was propped like a rectangular stone in his lap. He must have been carrying it all the time, its binding camouflaged against his overcoat. He reared up from the chair as if the coat had stiffened and was raising him, and Thirsk couldn't help recoiling from the small gargoyle face immobile as a growth on a tree, the blackened slit of a mouth like a fissure in old bark. When the hands lowered the volume towards him he accepted it, but as soon as he felt the weight he said, 'You're joking.'

'We seldom do that, Mr Thirsk.'

'I couldn't afford this kind of production even if I wanted

to. I publish fairy tales, I don't live in them. The public don't care if books fall to bits so long as they're cheap, and that goes double for children.'

'Perhaps you should help them to care.'

'Here, take your book back.'

The other held up his hands, displaying knobbly palms. 'It is our gift to you,' he said in a voice which, soft as it was, seemed to penetrate every corner of the room.

'Then don't look so glum about it.' As Thirsk planted the book on his desk he glimpsed a word embossed on the heavy wooden binding. '*Tapioca*, is that some kind of pudding cookbook?'

Whatever filled his visitor's eyes grew deeper. They struck Thirsk as being altogether too large and dark, and for a moment he had the impression of gazing into the gloomy depths of something quite unlike a face. He strode to the door, more quickly than steadily, and threw it open.

The avenue of pines interspersed with rhododendrons stretched a hundred yards to the deserted road into town. For once the sight didn't appeal to him as peaceful. Surely it would when he'd rid himself of his visitor, who he was beginning to suspect was mad; a leaf and maybe other vegetation was tangled in his hair, and wasn't there a mossy tinge to his cracked cheeks? Thirsk stood aside as the other stalked out of the door, overcoat creaking. Too much to drink or not enough, he thought, because as the figure passed along the avenue, beneath clouds which were helping the twilight gather, it appeared to grow taller. A sound behind him – paper rustling – made him glance around the room. The next second he turned back to the avenue, which was as deserted as the road.

Had his visitor dodged into the bushes? They and the trees were as still as fossils. 'Get off my property,' Thirsk warned, and cleared his throat so as to shout, 'or I'll call the police.'

By now it was apparent to him that the man hadn't been a printer. He was tempted to hurl the book after him, except that might bring him back. As he stared at the avenue until the trees seemed to inch in unison towards him, he found he was unwilling to search the grounds when it was growing so rapidly dark. 'Go back where you came from,' he yelled, and slammed the door so hard the floorboards shook.

A chill had accompanied his visitor into the office, and now it felt even colder. Had one of Thirsk's assistants left a window open in the warehouse? Thirsk hurried to the stout door in the back wall of the room. The door opened with an unexpected creak which lingered in his ears as he reached a hand into the dark. The fluorescent tubes stuttered into life, except for one which left the far end of the central aisle unlit. Though all the windows crammed into the space above the shelves were closed tight, the fifty-yard-long room was certainly colder than usual, and there was more of a smell of old paper than he remembered. In the morning he would have to fix the lights: not now, when at least two of the tubes were growing fitful, so that the flickering contents of the shelves kept resembling supine logs multicoloured with lichen, the spines of the dust jackets. He thumbed the light-switch, a block of plastic so cold it felt moist, and as the dark lurched forward, shut it in. For the first time ever he was wishing he could go home from work.

He was already home. The third door of the office led to the rest of his bungalow. When he opened the door, the cold was waiting for him. The heating hadn't failed; he had to snatch his hand away as soon as he touched the nearest radiator. He poured himself an even larger Scotch, and once he'd fired up his throat and his stomach, dumped himself in the chair behind the desk. The unwelcome visit had left him so on edge that all he could do was work.

The late afternoon mail had brought him an armful of packages which he hadn't had time to open. The topmost padded envelope proved to contain the typescript of a children's book by Huntley Dunkley, who sounded familiar. In his present mood, just the title – *The Smog Goblin and the Last Forest* – was enough to put him off. 'Send your bloody propaganda somewhere it's wanted,' he snarled, grabbing a copy of the Hamelin Books rejection letter. 'Fit only for recycling,' he pronounced, and scrawled that as a postscript.

Usually one of his assistants would see to the outgoing mail, but he couldn't stand the sight of the typescript a moment longer. Having clipped the letter to it, he stuffed it into a padded envelope and slung it on the desk next to his, and glared at the discarded packing as it tried to climb out of the waste-bin. Presumably the silence of the room emphasized its movements, though he could have imagined it wasn't alone in making a slow deliberate papery sound, an impression sufficiently persuasive that he glanced out of the window.

The light from the office lay on the strip of grass outside but fell short of the trees, which were embedded in a darkness that had sneaked up on him. He knuckled the switch for the security light. The fierce illumination caught hold of the trees and bushes, and he felt an irrational desire to see them shrink back from the blaze which he could summon at the touch of a finger. Instead they stepped almost imperceptibly forward as though urged by their shadows, a mass of secret blackness interrupted by the drive. Just now the bright bare gravel looked as though it was inviting someone or something to emerge on to it, and he turned away so furiously that he almost tripped over an object on the floor.

It was the discarded envelope, writhing slowly on the carpet and extending a torn brown strip of itself like the remains of a finger towards him. He closed one fist on it, squeezing its pulpy innards, and punched it into the bin before grinding it down with his heel. 'That's enough,' he shouted, not knowing what he was addressing until his gaze fell on the book his visitor had brought him. 'Let's see what you are,' he said through his teeth, and flung the book open, wood striking wood. Then he let out a gasp that would have been a word if he'd known how he was feeling.

The thick untrimmed pages weren't composed of paper; each was a single almost rectangular dead leaf. For a moment he thought words were printed on the uppermost, and then he saw the marks were scattered twigs, formed into patterns which he could imagine someone more susceptible than himself assuming to be words in a forgotten language. 'If this is a joke,' he yelled, ignoring how small his voice sounded in the empty room, 'you can take it back,' and hoisting the book off the desk, ran to the door.

As the cover banged shut like a coffin lid, the tilting of the book rearranged the twigs into a different pattern – into words he was able to read. He fumbled the door open and raised the volume in both hands. By the glare of the security light he saw the title wasn't *Tapioca* but *Tapiola*. What difference did one letter make? 'Come and get it,' he roared, hurling the book from him.

It struck the grass with a thud which seemed to crush his shout. The cover raised itself an inch and fell shut, and then the book was as still as the trees and their shadows. Beyond the unlit road, and around his property, the forest stretched for miles. The words he'd glimpsed were growing clearer, embedding themselves in his mind. YOU TURNED AWAY ONE MESSENGER. The night sky seemed to lean towards the patch of light which contained him and the book, as though the sky was the forehead of the blackness behind the mass of trees, in which he heard a sudden gust of wind. Its chill found him while he waited to see the trees move, and he was continuing to wait when it subsided. It might have been a huge icy breath.

'Not likely,' he said in a voice which the darkness shrank almost to nothing. He backed away and closed the door. The breath of the night had smelled of decaying vegetation, and now the room did. He thought he saw a trace of his own breath in the air. Hugging himself and rubbing his upper arms, he went to his desk for a mouthful of Scotch. As the ice cubes clashed against his teeth, he almost bit through the glass. Beyond the window the lawn was bare. The book had gone, and there wasn't so much as a hint of a footmark on the grass.

'I bet you think that's clever. Let me introduce you to someone who's cleverer.' He was speaking aloud so that his voice would keep him company, he realized, but he wouldn't have to feel alone for long. Without glancing away from the window he groped for the phone on his desk, detached the receiver from its housing and jabbed the talk button. He was already keying the number for the police as he brought the receiver to his face.

A sound came to find him. Though the earpiece was emitting it, it wasn't the dialling tone. It could have been a gale passing through a forest, but it seemed close to articulate. He clawed at the button to clear the line and listened to the welcome silence; then he poked the talk button again, and again. The phone was dead.

And there was movement among the trees. High on the trunks, branches sprang up and waved at him, a series of them rapidly approaching the house. A branch of a tree at the edge of the grass drooped before gesturing triumphantly at him, and then a severed length of the telephone cable which they had all been supporting plummeted on to the grass.

'Having fun, are you?' Thirsk demanded, though his throat was so constricted he barely heard himself. 'Time I joined in.' He dropped the useless receiver on top of a pile of typescripts and dashed kitchenwards, switching on lights as he went. His bedroom lit up, the bathroom and toilet next to it, the large room in which he dined and watched television and listened to music, and finally the kitchen, where he lifted the largest and sharpest knife from the rack on the wall. Outside the window he saw an image of himself almost erased by the forest – an image which grew fainter, then was wiped out entirely as his breath appeared in front of him and condensed on the window.

He saw himself being engulfed by fog in the reflection of a room which had been invaded by trees. The glint of the knife looked feeble as a lantern lost in a forest. 'I'm still here,' he snarled. Driven by a defiance which he felt more than understood, he stormed back into his office.

He was still there, and for a while, since he couldn't call a taxi. He laid the knife within reach on the desk and drafted a letter to his printer. ... *looking forward to the Christmas consignment ... any way you keep costs down is fine ...* His words seemed insufficiently defiant until he scribbled *It's only paper, only pulp.* Of course he would never send such a letter, and he was about to tear off the page and bin it when he realized how like taking back a challenge that would seem. He drove the knife through the pad, pinning the letter to the desk like a declaration nailed to a door.

At first there was no apparent response. The only visible movement in the room was of his breath. It took him some minutes to be certain that the smell of decaying vegetation had intensified – that the source was in the room with him. Did the colours on the jackets of the new books resemble stains more than they should? His chair trundled backwards and collided with the wall as he reached the shelves, where he dug a finger into the top of the spine of the nearest book.

It came off the shelf at once – the spine did. The cheap glue had failed, exposing bunches of pages which looked aged or worse. His hand swung wildly, hooking another spine at random. That fell away, bearing a patch of its rotten jacket, and his finger poked deep into the pages, which were a solid lump of pulp. He dragged his finger out of it, dislodging both adjacent spines. Their undersides were crawling with insects. He staggered backwards just as sounds began in the warehouse: a ponderous creaking followed by a crash that shook the office.

'Leave my property alone,' Thirsk screamed. He ripped the knife out of the pad and, pounding across the office, hauled open the door to the warehouse. The bookcases that weren't attached to the walls had fallen together, forming an arched passage, in the darkness of which piles of books were strewn like jagged chunks of chopped timber. Not only books were in that darkness, and his hand clutched at the light-switch before he knew he didn't want to see.

As soon as his hand found the switch, the block came away like a rotten fungus from the wall. The surviving fluorescents lit for an instant before failing in unison with a loud sharp glassy ping, and he glimpsed a shape stalking up the passage of the bookcases towards him. It resembled a totem, carved or rather shaped out of a tree, walking stiffly as a puppet, though it was considerably taller than any puppet had a right to be. It grew as it advanced on him, as if whatever feet it had were picking up or absorbing the books on which they trod. Its

disproportionately large head was featureless and unstable as
a mass of foliage, and its arms, which were reaching for him,
were at least half the length of the warehouse. So much he
distinguished before he threw the door in its face. Twisting
the key, he wrenched it out of the lock and shied it across the
room.

There was silence then, a silence like the quiet at the secret
heart of a forest. He heard his pulse and his harsh unsteady
breaths. Gripping the knife two-handed, he glared about. Half
a dozen spines sagged away from books, spilling grubs, as the
telephone let out a hollow exhalation and began to speak in
the voice of the wind.

Thirsk shouted louder, drowning out its words. 'In here
too, are you? Not for long. This is my house, and one of us is
leaving.' But he wasn't sure why he was rushing to the front
door – to eject an intruder, or to confront the source of all
the intrusions?

The trees were out there, and the darkness behind them.
Neither appeared to have moved. 'I know it's you,' he yelled.
'I know you're out there.' He saw his shadow jerking towards
the trees before he was aware of heading for them. As he
reached the nearest, he slashed at the trunk, slicing off bark.
'You're my property and I can do what I like with you,' he
ranted. 'If you don't like it try and stop me, you and your big
friend.'

He felt his feet leave the gravel for the plushy floor of fallen
leaves and pine needles. He was well into the woods, hacking
at every tree within reach, when all the lights of the house
were extinguished. He whirled around, then discovered he
was able to see by the faint glow of the sky, which no longer
felt like a presence looming over him. 'Is that the best you can
do?' he cried, reeling deeper into the woods, no longer
knowing or caring where he was. 'That's for you, and so's
that.' When the trees around him began to creak he chopped
more savagely at them, daring them to move towards him;
when the mounded earth seemed to quiver underfoot he
trampled on it, ignoring how the forest had begun to smell as
if the earth was being dug up. He might have been miles into

the lightless forest when the hand whose enormous fingers he'd just slashed raised itself with an explosive creak, soil and undergrowth and decaying vegetation spilling from its palm, and closed around him.

Ramsey Campbell has been awarded the Bram Stoker Award, the World Fantasy Award (three times), the British Fantasy Award (seven times) and the Liverpool Daily Post & Echo Award for continuing literary excellence, all of which recognize the fact that he is one of the finest living writers in the genre. His fifteen novels include *The Count of Eleven*, *The Long Lost*, *The One Safe Place* and, most recently, *The House on Nazareth Hill*. He is currently working on a new crime novel, *The Last Voice They Hear*. Campbell's shorter work runs into hundreds of published stories, some of which can be found in the collections, *Alone with the Horrors* (which won both the World Fantasy Award and the Bram Stoker Award in 1994), *Waking Nightmares* and *Strange Things and Stranger Places*. He has also edited several fine anthologies, including *New Tales of the Cthulhu Mythos*, *Superhorror*, *New Terrors*, *The Gruesome Book* and (with Stephen Jones) the first five volumes of the annual *Best New Horror* series. As the author explains, '"Out of the Woods" was written to order, a task which I find every so often to be a useful discipline. A Belgian editor asked me to produce a story about wood, or paper, or a Finnish legend, but I decided it would be about all three once he had persuaded me to find space in my schedule to write it. This he did by telling me that the backers of the magazine involved had authorized him to offer me £1,000. His use of English was either shaky, if much firmer than my French, or minutely precise, because once the tale was delivered the money proved to be far less than forthcoming. At least I had a new story to read along with three old favourites ("Calling Card", "The Companion" and "The Guide") on *Twilight Tales from Merseyside*, a cassette available from BBC Radio Merseyside and, in America, Necronomicon Press. This is its first appearance in print. Admirers of Sibelius may see where it's bound sooner than other readers will. I recommend the latter to seek out the tone poem from which the book in my story takes its name. My anthologist friend Hugh Lamb regards it as the most terrifying music he has ever heard.'

The Rains

STEVE RASNIC TEM

Every time it rained, faces of water and steam formed in the windows of his house: dark ovals with smeared damp for eyes, but no mouths. He never could determine how they'd been made. He'd checked for drafts, imperfect insulation, leaks along the edges of the glass, crumbling putty. He finally gave up trying to figure it out, just watched for the faces. They usually appeared after dark, and with all the rain this fall they'd become virtually permanent decorations. Against the dark glass they looked like negative images, as if the house had taken photographs.

Brett had never felt comfortable with pathetic fallacies so he tried to ignore the rains. They angered him. They turned Nancy's death into a cliché. Sometimes he thought things would have been a lot easier if she'd died in the middle of the summer, when the air was a furnace and the ground was like cement and it might well have taken a jackhammer to get through it, to get her coffin in. His own tendency towards exaggeration made him wince. However hard he tried, saying things exactly the way they were was the hardest thing of all. *Nancy died in September, a year ago, of cancer. And the world has paid no attention.*

Again he wondered if he should have had her cremated as he'd originally planned. But he'd wanted to pretend he could actually visit her, that there was a form beneath her marker, although he dared not imagine what that form would look like after a year. He hadn't even visited the gravesite since the funeral.

Today his skin felt dry, despite the continuous rain. The air seemed to cling to his skin, leaving its dust behind in a thin, grey crust. He thought of her ashes coating him head to toe, forming a layer that the moisture could not penetrate. He felt too dry to live. He felt far too solid. Again he made his way down the long narrow staircase to shower.

The basement bathroom was lined with cool stones to keep the moisture in. Wanting to think of it as a life chamber, a place of survival, he ignored the faint hint of rot in the close air. He put his hand out to touch the stone, and his fingertips came away milky and smelling of salt. He'd gone as far as asking the funeral director what the cremation would have been like, how much the ashes would have weighed, what exactly would have been left behind. He didn't ask him what a year underground would do to the body, two years, five. He wiped his hand on the stone wall again, conscious of the salty lubrication there, imagining a little more of his flesh melting on to the stones with each swipe of his hand.

When the water first hit him he could not feel its dampness. It was a force against his skin, trying unsuccessfully to push itself inside him. He'd been showering at least six times a day since Nancy died.

His skin seemed to swell beneath the force of the warm needle-spray, as if trying to maintain its border against wet erosion. But gradually he sensed the outline of his body growing less distinct. After hours, his skin began to shrink, warp, break down.

He'd read somewhere that during every minute of a casual walk the human body loses tens of thousands of flakes of dead skin. Fewer if you stand still. He wondered how much skin sloughed off during the average shower. Food for the armies of dust mites (ordinarily invisible, but monstrous if you magnified them enough – he'd seen the pictures). He imagined breathing in that dead skin, consuming so much dead flesh during the year that there could hardly be room for any other form of nourishment.

We feed on each other. Nancy always said that. We couldn't

survive otherwise. Nancy had sometimes been a little too
honest. Thinking that now, he felt guilty.

The hospital bed had been hard, white, and tightly-made.
It looked too small for the room. Lots of curtains, and bi-fold
doors ready to close everything off. There had been a number
of nurses and aides in long uniform gowns, like androgynous
monks or nuns. With her hair gone, Nancy had grown to
resemble them.

'You let me go, as soon as you can, you hear?' Her whisper
was harsh and frayed in the emptiness. 'I don't want you
hanging on to me for ever. You have to have a life.' Nancy
never lied. He bent over to hug her, but held her at a distance.
Already he was beginning to pull away from the reality of her,
pretending she was gone, barely looking at her. She'd never
know, her eyes were almost blind. But he still felt he was
acting out a lie, not climbing into bed with her, not holding
on to her for all he was worth.

After two weeks he'd gone back to work. The columns of
figures ran together, then melted off the page. He wondered
how long it would be before anyone noticed. Some days he
would call in, telling them he was going to work at home that
day, two days, that week. His excuse was the rain.

Some mornings he would get up and take the quickest
shower possible. The spray would fill his muscles with an
electrical charge, and although lulled by the sweet song of the
water rushing out of the pipe, he'd force himself to cut it
short, to get out of the shower before the new energy
dissipated. Then he'd get dressed, grab his briefcase and rush
out into the rain.

But other days he'd spend long hours under the shower at
low pressure, the nozzle adjusted until the stream was a soft
probe that wore its way into his skin, spreading through his
flesh until it became the thinnest of membranes, rubbing his
skin away so softly that eventually he lost all sense of the
border between his skin and the water. It took increased
exposure to the water with each shower in order to achieve
that effect. He wondered if he was developing an immunity.

The water on his head was a constant, gentle persistence.

Softening his skull, pushing aside hair and scalp and bone to massage his brain directly, catching up anxiety and pain in its waves, washing them away. He wondered sometimes if what he felt when under the grace of the water was what Nancy, now, felt all the time. But he'd never *believed*. He continued to wonder, but without belief.

Dressing had become a slow, painful process. A friend at the gym had watched him one day, the slow way he slipped into pants and shirt, the fumbling with buttons, zips, laces, and had given Brett the name and address of a psychiatrist who specialized in depression. But it wasn't depression. It was just that his skin had become so raw and sensitive, so worn down by showers and rain, that even the softest materials hurt on first contact. The dark, wet faces stared from his bedroom windows as he struggled into his clothes.

This would be his fifth dinner date with Ann from his grief group. He hadn't wanted to join at first – he'd always thought there were just too many groups for everything – but both his brother and his boss had pushed him, and it seemed to make them feel better to know he was in the expected setting, dealing with the expected problems in the expected way. Making progress. Getting his life back together. He made a point of letting both of them know that he was 'dating' again. And it hadn't been all that bad. Ann was pleasant and a good listener. But he didn't always like the words the others in the group tossed around so easily. Words like 'mutual' and 'support'. He'd discovered that he no longer believed in either concept.

The ground surrounding his house was like a soup, dead leaves and stems floating to the top, using the push of the underlying liquid to press past stones and roots. A few days ago the ground had reached its saturation point. The air itself looked full, heavy with cloud. Late afternoons, the ground turned to steam. As the clay soil drank more and more of the heavy shower, the air pockets shrank and the ground swelled. Vague earth forms shaped like heads, limbs, torsos pushed hazily out of the ground. Brett worried distractedly about the condition of the house's concrete foundations. He was careful

where he stepped as he left his house for the street. The car
fish-tailed as he turned on to the highway leading downtown.

Autumn rains were not common in this part of the country,
and rain for a solid week or more was almost unheard of. Out
on the sidewalks people walked quickly by, without looking
up. The restaurant where Ann was waiting was somewhere in
the thick of the downpour, near the centre of the business
district. Great gushes of water fell out of the sky, plunging
past the tall buildings with tremendous speed. The pounding
on concrete and metal was constant and numbing.

'I didn't go out of the house for months after John died.'
Ann was on her third margarita. It occurred to Brett that the
longer he knew her the more she drank. She also talked quite
a bit more about her deceased husband. 'Things looked too
strange to bear, you know? People ... I don't know, something looked different about them. I was too aware of the way
they smelled, the sweat on their upper lips, the stains on their
clothes, that sort of thing. All so dirty ...'

'Like they were dying,' Brett said.

'That's right!' She laid her hand over his. Her skin was wet
and vaguely greasy, slightly repulsive to him. But he didn't
pull his hand away. She did, finally, in order to take another
sip. But he could still feel the hand-shaped outline of damp
on his skin, like a handprint of rain. He imagined he could
feel everything she was in that handprint.

She finished her drink and smiled. 'Well, it's the little girls'
room for me. I do hope you can stay out a little later tonight
than usual.' She gave a slightly crooked smile and left. Once
she'd disappeared he thought about her eyes, how distant and
unfocused they'd looked, even before she'd started drinking.
Maybe she wasn't seeing him at all; maybe she couldn't see
past her own sense of the strangeness. Maybe in her eyes he
was dying.

She'd left smudges of makeup on her napkin. White and
grey cigarette ash powdered her plate, spread across a terrain
of potato hills, gravied rivers. The stark white table cloth was
damp and fragrant with an earlier spilled drink.

Nancy's hospital bed had been white, hard and tight, but

under the fluorescent lights the sheets looked streaked with grey, like bone ash, skin ash, his memories of her. He knew the hospital room was clean, but it didn't look clean. You could scrub and scrub and it would never look clean to him. Two million dust mites in the average bed. Eating us one dead flake at a time.

Ann took him to her house after dinner. Somehow he couldn't stand the idea of the damp faces staring from his bedroom windows while he had sex with her. He wasn't attracted to her, but then he suspected she wasn't particularly attracted to him either. Her house was cool and damp; she said she hadn't bothered to turn the heat on yet this year, and she thought there might be a leak in the basement wall as well as several in the roof. But Brett came to view the damp smell as a kind of perfume, and didn't mind it so much.

The rain clouds outside kept her bedroom dark. He couldn't see her. Her body was unusually soft and buoyant. He rocked into her gently and almost immediately lost all sense of her borders or the borders of the bed as she melted away into the rhythm. When he came there was no sense of a change, just a continuation.

Sometimes everything is so grey under the rain. It's as if everything is melting, the houses, the people, everything. And I want to know where we're all running off to. The whispered voice didn't sound much like Ann's. He reached out his fingers in the darkness and could feel the damp oval of her face, slick and milky-feeling, as if she had been crying for a very long time. Then she turned away from him and for a frightening moment he could not feel her on the bed. The damp sheets stuck to his skin, and Brett could not feel the difference. *You let me go*, the moist whisper continued. *I don't want you hanging on to me for ever.*

Back in his own house early the next morning Brett stood under the shower for over four hours. Once again it had rained through the night and going from the outer damp and mist to the shower in his basement seemed like no transition at all. At first the shower made him feel better. He could imagine the microscopic layers of dirt and dried semen peeling off and flushing away. Then layer after layer of deadness, layer after layer of sadness and grief and desperation, so that he'd never have to feel those things again. After a time, after the constant exposure to water, he felt as if his body were absorbing it, becoming lighter, more spiritual. Life-giving rain. Rain everlasting. His body was slowly becoming as soft and pale as a cloud. When he touched himself with his warped fingertips, he could barely feel a thing.

But when he moved to step away from the shower he discovered that he could hardly walk. The basement hallway outside the bathroom was dark and close, and for a moment he wasn't sure in which direction the staircase lay. He stopped and tried to orient himself, breathing deeply of the musty air, rubbing his arms and chest briskly to heighten circulation. He had difficulty finding his fingers and toes. Finally he became aware of a dim square of light down at one end, and he slowly headed in that direction. The wet footprints he left on the tile behind him seemed to have independent life, misty bodies growing up out of their roots.

He almost never thought about dying any more. Or maybe he thought so much about it he'd gone right past it. It was like looking at a strange house and trying to imagine what the life inside was like. When he wasn't thinking about anything else, speculations about Nancy rushed in to fill the gap. He wondered what she might be feeling at that moment, what she might be thinking, seeing, tasting. And do the dead dream? He didn't believe, he'd never believed, and yet still he couldn't shake these persistent speculations. He wondered if the place where she was now was the same one she'd expected, if she had names for any of the landmarks or the celestial bodies floating overhead, if the mountains were still mountains, and if there were mirrors, what did she see in them? He did not believe but he still wondered about these things. He wondered if the weather there was constant, and if it were the same weather he was living in now.

He sat at the kitchen table drinking his morning juice. The citric acid burned the raw skin around his mouth, but he didn't mind. The metal table was damp and cool against his skin. He stood and walked to the window. Rain had leaked in and ran down the pane. He pushed closer to the glass and stared outside at the storm, which seemed ancient by now. Rainy mists collapsed all around him. The dark clouds were a river flowing over the city. He'd come to understand that shadows were different in the rain. So much grey and grey-green, streaked with silver. The shadows, swollen with rain-water, had been pushed out of their usual resting places in the yard. They stood out three-dimensionally now, weaving and growing in the rain, their faces dull and watching the house.

Everything is melting, the houses, the people, everything. And I want to know where we're all running off to. Our created world was just another lie.

The rain was the only thing in the city he could hear. It forced everything else to be quiet. Wind-driven branches clawed at the window, wanting to pull him to pieces. The rain poured from giant rips in the bellies of the clouds. And standing naked in his kitchen Brett could feel the outer layers of his skin beginning to dry. He went back down the basement stairs to take another shower.

There'd been a funeral for the sake of Nancy's parents. They did believe in eternal life, 'passing over', and all that. Nancy never had. 'You get used up, then unfortunately the people closest to you have to do something with the discard.' Brett wondered how she would have felt about there being a minister and everything. It was still another lie, of course, but then Nancy always said that sometimes you have to lie to your parents. 'That's what makes us civilized,' she'd say, and grin.

When they lowered the coffin Brett thought about elaborate magic tricks. He could not believe Nancy wasn't there so that he could share the insight. She would have scolded him for his irreverence, then laughed.

Burying day had been full of an uneasy mist. Maybe the sky was trying to tell him something, but he didn't believe in all that. In the distance he could hear some kids breaking up their ballgame because of the overhanging threat. As a kid he'd always have funerals – for birds and fish and once a dead hamster – during good weather because his parents wouldn't let him go out when the weather was bad. The body would wait in a cigar box on his shelf until the time was right.

At dinner that night Nancy's folks had stuffed themselves. Some of the neighbours and a few more distant relatives came over. Food had been arriving all day – about half-and-half covered dishes and plates bought from the grocery deli counter down the street. Far too many desserts. Nancy's mother had already made a list of what Brett would keep to sustain him for the next week ('After that you might want to try restaurants for a while,' she'd advised. 'You won't be able to cook at first.') and what the relatives would take home. Brett ate more than he'd expected, though the food seemed more bulk than taste. There was a need to be *solid* that night. He'd never before experienced a meal quite like that – that particular mix of foods and company, and everyone talking about the food and not much else – it was the kind of meal, he suspected, that's served only after a funeral. And they all ate a little shame with each bite, knowing that someone they had loved desperately had died, had slipped into mud, and yet they could still eat, in fact had to eat if they were to remain human. It was a need for weight and substance and everyday living. And it was a terrible thing.

The vision of that meal disappeared as he raised his face into the full force of the shower; he thought the water was going to rip his eyelids away. He wondered what things he might see if he could never close his eyes. But if he stayed under the shower too long, the water dripping down his back felt like a line of spiders suddenly breaking rank and spreading across his skin.

'I haven't seen you in days.' Ann's voice on the telephone was soft and moist, but accusing. Brett thought he detected a throaty quality, as if she'd been crying. He pictured her naked, her hair wringing wet. 'I called your work but they said you never come in any more.' He stared at the handset. Tiny drops of cloudy water were oozing from the speaker holes. *Already he was beginning to pull away from the reality of her, pretending she was gone, barely looking at her. She'd never know.*

He stared at his face mirrored in the fogged window. Damp smears for eyes, but no mouth.

'If you need me I'll come,' he told her. But there was so much rain on the line he couldn't hear her reply. He hung up the dripping phone and went to get dressed. The clothes rubbed his raw skin and he gasped. He had to spread Vaseline over his body before he could put most of them on. He expected a lot of blood, but there was just the redness, and occasional trails of salty, milky water issuing from invisible rents in his flesh.

With each stride towards his car parked at the kerb the rain made him heavier. His feet became part mud. The rain shook its long hair and twirled its dresses, repeating the same hard endearments over and over. It swept over him and pushed him into the ground. Finally he gave up and just lay there while the rain soaked into his clothes and the mud oozed into his open cuffs. Eventually he felt as if his clothes were dissolving, and he struggled to stand up but found that he could not. The rain was a collection of individual currents picking at his clothes, his skin, his bones. After an hour of this his bones felt like rocks, his muscle and skin waves breaking against them.

A neighbour finally dragged him inside. The man was massive, an ex-steelworker, and yet he still obviously had trouble carrying Brett. Brett had become too soft and pliable, too insubstantial to hold on to. The neighbour's hands kept slipping off.

The neighbour insisted that Brett take a long hot bath. 'You won't find anything left of me if I do,' he told the man. The neighbour helped Brett into the tub, even though Brett continued to complain that the individual fibres of his flesh were beginning to unravel.

The rain crashed against the glass of the bathroom window in waves. There was a definite rhythm to it. Brett rocked back and forth in the tub, humming along. Finally losing consciousness, he dreamed of climbing the buildings to get above the raining clouds.

Ann came once to visit him. She sat at the edge of his bed,

leaning over, watching his face. Her skin looked pale and colourless, shrivelled. Brett wondered if he looked the same way. She talked a great deal about her dead husband, but if he heard any of these things specifically he could not remember them. Rain clouded the windows. Faces pushed against the glass. After a time he looked up and Ann wasn't there any more. He leaned over the side of the bed and examined the floor for damp. The windows still shook with water. Invisible fingers streaked the panes.

Brett took an umbrella with him to the cemetery but didn't use it. He wasn't sure why he'd brought it, unless it was to give his cab driver a reassuring picture of normality.

He'd never really looked at the place during the funeral. It was much like any suburb or development, careful plantings and wide, straight walks. Only the houses were squat and disturbingly solid. He felt at home here, particularly with the ongoing presence of the rain. The rain was thick silver threads hanging from a sky that couldn't be seen any more. The ground here was the same soup he had at home, only with different ingredients: aches and fears, cold hands and discarded moments. Glistening flesh, thunderous hair, and damp-chilled nipples he used to love to touch. But the rain swept all these up and took them beyond desire. The wet marble looked oddly comfortable. If he stretched out on it, he might sink in.

Brett began stripping off his clothes, far beyond modesty in the face of such a cloudburst. His shirt, pants, and underwear seemed to dissolve in the raining grey as quickly as he was able to remove them.

The shadows moved forward with their dark oval faces. He tried to look between the falling lines of rain as the too solid stones became less substantial and the balance between liquid and solid began to tip. The shower poured into his face and the mists closed in.

As he felt on the verge of liquefying he thought about how once someone so close to you dies, you will always wonder what it's like, even when you don't believe. As much as it terrifies you, you will always seek the rains.

At one time, he knew, a close member of the family would have bathed the body of the dead. He would have done that if she'd asked him; he could have forced himself.

When her shadow stepped into the shower with him he began to bathe her, although he could not touch her. The eyes, the shoulders, the breasts and thighs. He told her about the rains, even though she already knew. She brought her wetness closer, and burning damp reached under the edges of his skin.

I want you to let me go, she'd said. *You have to have a life*, she'd promised. As her terrible rain began removing his flesh, he knew that she had lied.

Steve Rasnic Tem has been nominated for the Bram Stoker Award and the World Fantasy Award for his short fiction, and he won the British Fantasy Award in 1988 for his story 'Leaks'. A prolific author, his stories have recently appeared in *The Best New Horror, The Year's Best Fantasy and Horror, The Year's Best Horror Stories, The Anthology of Fantasy & the Supernatural, Forbidden Acts, 100 Wicked Little Witches, Flesh Fantastic, It Came from the Drive-In* and *Sisters of the Night*. His own books include the novel *Excavation* and the collections *Fairytales and Beautiful Strangers* (with his wife, Melanie Tem), *Absences: Charlie Goode's Ghosts, Celestial Inventory, Decoded Mirrors: 3 Tales After Lovecraft* and the French *Ombres sur la Route*. Tem has also edited *The Umbral Anthology of Science Fiction Poetry*, which was a finalist for the Philip K. Dick Award, and *High Fantastic*, an illustrated collection of Colorado's fantasy, dark fantasy and science fiction. 'As for "The Rains",' he explains, 'a few years back I decided I wanted to write four stories revolving around the four elements of the ancients (earth, wind, fire and water). The first of these, the earth story "Underground", appeared in Dennis Etchison's *MetaHorror*. "The Rains", my water story, is the second. The stories are meant to be in part obsessive meditations on these elements, and I'm approaching them as I approach all my works whose themes collect about one central image, substance, person etc. I first assume that this "thing" or "person" also exists within me person-ally, and I must discover and explore the thing within myself before I can write the story. So where was the water in me? There were three touchstones in particular: my first poetry writing instructor in college, who during various sanatorium stays over the years had submitted to the "cold water" treatment for depression; driving through Loveland,

Colorado, the day after the Big Thompson flood, and thinking of all those people who had drowned; and a recollection of the weeks following the death of my youngest son back in 1988, when I'd felt compelled to take shower after shower.'

Underbed

GRAHAM MASTERTON

As soon as his mother had closed the bedroom door, Martin burrowed down under the blankets. For him, this was one of the best times of the day. In that long, warm hour between waking and sleep, his imagination would take him almost anywhere.

Sometimes he would lie on his back with the blankets drawn up to his nose and his pillow on top of his forehead so that only his eyes looked out. This was his spaceman game, and the pillow was his helmet. He travelled through sparkling light-years, passing Jupiter so close that he could see the storms raging on its surface, then swung on to Neptune, chilly and green, and Pluto, beyond. On some nights he would travel so far that he was unable to return to Earth, and he would drift further and further into the outer reaches of space until he became nothing but a tiny speck winking in the darkness and he fell asleep.

At other times, he was captain of a U-boat trapped thousands of feet below the surface. He would have to squeeze along cramped and darkened passageways to open up stopcocks, with water flooding in on all sides, and elbow his way along a torpedo tube in order to escape. He would come up to the surface into the chilly air of the bedroom, gasping for breath.

Then he would crawl right down to the very end of the bed, where the sheets and the blankets were tucked in really tight. He was a coalminer, making his way through the narrowest of fissures, with millions of tons of carboniferous rock on top of him.

He never took a flashlight to bed with him. This would have revealed that the inside of his space-helmet didn't have any dials or knobs or breathing tubes; and that the submarine wasn't greasy and metallic and crowded with complicated valves; and that the grim black coal-face at which he so desperately hewed was nothing but a clean white sheet.

Earlier this evening he had been watching a programme on pot-holing on television and he was keen to try it. He was going to be the leader of an underground rescue team, trying to find a boy who had wedged himself in a crevice. It would mean crawling through one interconnected passage after another, then down through a water-filled sump, until he reached the tiny cavern where the boy was trapped.

His mother sat on the end of the bed and kept him talking. He was going back to school in two days' time and she kept on telling him how much she was going to miss him. He was going to miss her, too, and Tiggy, their golden retriever, and everything here at Home Hill. More than anything, he was going to miss his adventures under the blankets. You couldn't go burrowing under the bedclothes when you were at school. Everybody would rag you too much.

He had always thought his mother was beautiful and tonight was no exception, although he wished that she would go away and let him start his pot-holing. What made her beauty all the more impressive was the fact that she would be thirty-three next April, which Martin considered to be prehistoric. His best friend's mother was only thirty-three and she looked like an old lady by comparison. Martin's mother had bobbed brunette hair and a wide, generous face without a single wrinkle; and dark brown eyes that were always filled with love. It was always painful, going back to school. He didn't realize how much it hurt her, too: how many times she sat on his empty bed when he was away, her hand pressed against her mouth and her eyes filled with tears.

'Daddy will be back on Thursday,' she said. 'He wants to

take us all out before you go back to school. Is there anywhere special you'd like to go?'

'Can we go to that Chinese place? The one where they give you those cracker things?'

'Pang's? Yes, I'm sure we can. Daddy was worried you were going to say McDonald's.'

She stood up and kissed him. For a moment they were very close, face-to-face. He didn't realize how much he looked like her – that they were both staring into a kind of a mirror. He could see what he would have looked like, if he had been a woman; and she could see what she would have looked like, if she had been a boy. They were two different manifestations of the same person, and it gave them a secret intimacy that nobody else could understand.

'Good night,' she said. 'Sweet dreams.' And for a moment she laid a hand on top of his head as if she could sense that something momentous was going to happen to him. Something that could take him out of her reach for ever.

'Good night, Mummy,' he said, and kissed her cheek, which was softer than anything else he had ever touched. She closed the door.

He lay on his back for a while, waiting, staring at the ceiling. His room wasn't completely dark: a thin slice of light came in from the top of the door, illuminating the white paper lantern that hung above his bed so that it looked like a huge, pale planet (which it often was). He stayed where he was until he heard his mother close the living-room door, and then he wriggled down beneath the blankets.

He cupped his hand over his mouth like a microphone and said, 'Underground Rescue Squad Three, reporting for duty.'

'Hello, Underground Rescue Squad Three. Are we glad you're here! There's a boy trapped in Legg's Elbow, 225 metres down, past Devil's Corner. He's seventeen years old, and he's badly injured.'

'Okay, headquarters. We'll send somebody down there straight away.'

'It'll have to be your very best man . . . it's really dangerous down there. It's started to rain and all the caves are flooding. You've probably got an hour at the most.'

'Don't worry. We'll manage it. Roger and out.'

Martin put on his equipment. His thermal underwear, his boots, his backpack and his goggles. Anybody who was watching would have seen nothing more than a boy-shaped lump under the blankets, wriggling and jerking and bouncing up and down. But by the time he was finished he was fully dressed for crawling his way down to Devil's Corner.

His last radio message was, 'Headquarters? I'm going in.'

'Be careful, Underground Rescue Squad Three. The rain's getting heavier.'

Martin lifted his head and inhaled a lungful of chilly bedroom air. Then he plunged downwards into the first crevice that would take him down into the caves. The rock ceiling was dangerously low, and he had to crawl his way in like a commando, on his elbows. He tore the sleeve of his waterproof jacket on a protruding rock and he gashed his cheek, but he was so heroic that he simply wiped away the blood with the back of his hand and carried on crawling forward.

It wasn't long before he reached a tight, awkward corner, which was actually the end of the bed. He had to negotiate it by lying on his side, reaching into the nearest crevice for a handhold, and heaving himself forward inch by inch. He had only just squeezed himself around this corner when he came to another, and had to struggle his way around it in the same way.

The air in the caves was growing more and more stifling, and Martin was already uncomfortably hot. But he knew he had to go on. The boy in Legg's Elbow was counting on him, just like the rest of Underground Rescue Squad Three, and the whole world above ground, which was waiting anxiously for him to emerge.

He wriggled onwards, his fingers bleeding, until he reached the sump. This was a 10-metre section of tunnel which was completely flooded with black, chill water. Five pot-holers had drowned in it since the caves were first discovered, two of them experts. Not only was the sump flooded, it had a tight bend right in the middle of it, with rocky protrusions that could easily snag a pot-holer's belt or his backpack. Martin hesitated for a moment, but then he took a deep breath of stale air and plunged beneath the surface.

The water was stunningly cold, but Martin swam along the tunnel with powerful, even strokes until he reached the bend. Still holding his breath, he angled himself sideways and started to tug himself between the jagged, uncompromising rocks. He was almost through when one of the straps on his backpack was caught and he found himself entangled. He twisted around, trying to reach behind his back so that he could pull the strap free from the rock, but he succeeded only in winding it even more tightly. He tried twisting around the other way, but now the strap tightened itself into a knot.

He had been holding his breath for so long now that his lungs were hurting. Desperately, he reached into his pocket and took out his clasp knife. He managed to unfold the blade, bend his arm behind his back and slash at the tightened strap. He missed it with his first two strokes, but his third stroke managed to cut it halfway through. His eyes were bulging and he was bursting for air, but he didn't allow himself to give in. One more cut and the strap abruptly gave way.

Martin kicked both legs and swam forward as fast as he could. He reached the end of the sump and broke the surface, taking in huge grateful breaths of frigid subterranean air.

He had beaten the sump, but there were more hazards ahead of him. The rainwater from the surface was already beginning to penetrate the lower reaches of the cave system. He could hear water rushing through crevices and clattering through galleries. In less than half an hour, every pot-hole would be flooded, and there would be no way of getting back out again.

Martin pressed on, sliding on his belly through a fissure that was rarely more than 30 centimetres high. He was bruised and exhausted, but he had almost reached Devil's Corner. From there, it was only a few metres to Legg's Elbow.

Rainwater trickled from the low limestone ceiling and

coursed down the side of the fissure, but Martin didn't care. He was already soaked and he was crawling at last into Devil's Corner. He slid across to the narrow vertical crevice called Legg's Elbow and peered down it, trying to see the trapped boy.

'Hallo!' he called. 'Is anybody there? Hallo, can you hear me? I've come to get you out!'

Martin listened but there was no answer. There wasn't even an *imaginary* answer. He forced his head further down, so that he could see deeper into the crevice, but there was nobody there. Nobody crying; nobody calling out. No pale distressed face looking back up at him.

He had actually reached the bottom of the bed, and was looking over the edge of the mattress, into the tightly-tucked dead-end of blankets and sheets.

He had a choice, but there was very little time. Either he could climb down Legg's Elbow to see if he could find where the boy was trapped, or else he could give up his rescue mission and turn back. In less than twenty minutes, the caves would be completely flooded, and anybody down here would be drowned.

He decided to risk it. It would take him only seven or eight minutes to climb all the way down Legg's Elbow, and another five to crawl back as far as the sump. Once he was back through the sump, the caves rose quite steeply towards the surface, so that he would have a fair chance of escaping before they filled up with water.

He pushed his way over the edge of Legg's Elbow, and began to inch down the crevice. He could slip at any moment, and his arms and legs were shaking with effort. He could feel the limestone walls starting to move – a long slow seismic slide that made him feel as if the whole world were collapsing all around him. If Legg's Elbow fell in, he would be trapped, unable to climb back out, while more and more rainwater gushed into the underground caverns.

Panting with effort, he tried to cling on to the sides of the crevice. There was one moment when he thought he was going to be able to heave himself back. But then everything slid – sheets, blankets, limestone rocks, and he ended up right at the bottom of Legg's Elbow, buried alive.

For a moment, he panicked. He could hardly breathe. But then he started to pull at the fallen rockslide, tearing a way out of the crevice stone by stone. There had to be a way out. If there was a deeper, lower cavern, perhaps he could climb down to the foot of the hill and crawl out of a fox's earth or any other fissure he could locate. After all, if the rainwater could find an escape-route through the limestone, he was sure that *he* could.

He managed to heave all of the rocks aside. Now all he had to do was burrow through the sludge. He took great handfuls of it and dragged it behind him, until at last he felt the flow of fresh air into the crevice: fresh air, and wind. He crawled out of Legg's Elbow on his hands and knees, and found himself lying on a flat, sandy beach. The day was pearly-grey, but the sun was high in the sky and the ocean peacefully glittered in the distance. He turned around and saw that, behind him, there was nothing but miles and miles of grey tussocky grass. Somehow he had emerged from these tussocks like somebody emerging from underneath a heavy blanket.

He stood up and brushed himself down. He was still wearing his waterproof jacket and his pot-holing boots. He was glad of them, because the breeze was thin and chilly. Up above him, white gulls circled and circled, not mewing or crying, their eyes as expressionless as sharks' eyes. In the sand at his feet tiny iridescent shells were embedded.

For a moment, he was unable to decide what he ought to do next, and where he ought to go. Perhaps he should try to crawl back into the pot-hole, and retrace his route to the surface. But he was out in the open air here, and there didn't seem to be any point in it. Besides, the pot-hole was heavily covered in grass, and it was difficult to see exactly where it was. He thought he ought to walk inland a short way, to see if he could find a road or a house or any indication of where he might be.

But then, very far away, where the sea met the sky, he saw

a small fishing-boat drawing in to the shore, and a man
climbing out of it. The fishing-boat had a russet-coloured
triangular sail, like a fishing-boat in an old-fashioned watercolour. He started to walk towards it; and then, when he
realized how far it was, he started to run. His waterproof
jacket made a chuffing noise and his boots left deep
impressions in the sand. The seagulls kept pace with him,
circling and circling.

Running and walking, it took him almost twenty minutes
to reach the fishing-boat. A white-bearded man in olive-
coloured oilskins was kneeling down beside it, stringing fat
triangular fish on to a line. The fish were brilliant, and they
shone with every colour of the rainbow. Some of them were
still alive, thrashing their tails and blowing their gills.

Martin stopped a few yards away and watched and said
nothing. Eventually the man stopped stringing fish and looked
up at him. He was handsome, in an old-fashioned way –
chiselled, like Charlton Heston. But his eyes were completely
blank: the colour of sky on an overcast day. He reminded
Martin of somebody familiar, but he couldn't think who he
was.

Not far away, sitting cross-legged on a coil of rope, was a
thin young boy in a hooded coat. He was playing a thin,
plaintive tune on a flute. His wrists were so thin and the tune
was so sad that Martin almost felt like crying.

'Well, you came at last,' said the man with eyes the colour
of sky. 'We've been waiting for you.'

'Waiting for me? Why?'

'You're a tunneller, aren't you? You do your best work
underground.'

'I was looking for a boy. He was supposed to be stuck in
Legg's Elbow, but – I don't know. The whole cave system
was flooded, and it seemed to collapse.'

'And you thought that you escaped?'

'I did escape.'

The man stood up, his waterproofs creaking. He smelled
strongly of fresh-caught fish, all that slime on their scales.
'That was only a way of bringing you here. We need you to

help us, an experienced tunneller like you. What do you think of these fish?'

'I never saw fish like that before.'

'They're not fish. Not in the strictest sense of the word. They're more like ideas.'

He picked one up, so that it twisted and shimmered; and Martin could see that it *was* an idea, rather than a fish. It was an idea about being angry with people you loved; and how you could explain that you loved them, and calm them down. Then the man held up another fish; and this was a different fish altogether, a different idea. This was a glittering idea about numbers: how the metre was measured by the speed of light. If light could be compressed, then distance could, too – and the implications of that were quite startling.

Martin couldn't really understand how the fish managed to be ideas as well as fish; but they were; and some of the ideas were so beautiful and strange that he stood staring at them and feeling as if his whole life was turning under his feet.

The sun began to descend towards the horizon. The small boy put away his flute and helped the fisherman to gather the last of his lines and his nets. The fisherman gave Martin a large woven basket to carry, full of blue glass fishing-floats and complicated reels. 'We'll have to put our best foot forward, if we want to get home before dark.'

They walked for a while in silence. The breeze blew the sand in sizzling snakes, and behind them the sea softly applauded, like a faraway audience. After four or five minutes, though, Martin said, 'Why do you need a tunneller?'

The fisherman gave him a quick, sideways glance. 'You may not believe it, but there's another world, apart from this one. A place that exists right next to us, like the world that you can see when you look in a mirror ... essentially the same, but different.'

'What does that have to do with tunnelling?'

'Everything, because there's only one way through to this world, and that's by crawling into your bed and through to the other side.'

Martin stopped in his tracks. 'What the hell are you talking about, *bed*? I tunnel into caves and pot-holes, not beds.'

'There's no difference,' said the fisherman. 'Caves, beds, they're just the same . . . a way through to somewhere else.'

Martin started walking again. 'You'd better explain yourself.' The sun had almost reached the horizon now, and their shadows were giants with stilt-like legs and distant, pin-size heads.

'There isn't much to explain. There's another world, beneath the blankets. Some people can find it, some can't. I suppose it depends on their imagination. My daughter Leonora always had the imagination. She used to hide under the blankets and pretend that she was a cave-dweller in prehistoric times; or a Red Indian woman, in a tent. But about a month ago she said that she had found this other world, right at the very bottom of the bed. She could see it, but she couldn't wriggle her way into it.'

'Did she describe it?'

The fisherman nodded. 'She said that it was dark, very dark, with tangled thorn-bushes and branchy trees. She said that she could see shadows moving around in it – shadows that could have been animals, like wolves; or hunched-up men wearing black fur cloaks.'

'It doesn't sound like the kind of world that anybody would *want* to visit.'

'We never had the chance to find out whether Leonora went because she wanted to. Two days ago my wife went into her bedroom to discover that her bed was empty. We thought at first that she might have run away. But we'd had no family arguments, and she really had no cause to. Then we stripped back her blankets and found that the lower parts of her sheets were torn, as if some kind of animal had been clawing at it.' He paused, and then he said, with some difficulty, 'We found blood, too. Not very much. Maybe she scratched herself on one of the thorns. Maybe one of the animals clawed her.'

By now they had reached the grassy dunes and started to climb up them. Not far away there were three small cottages, two painted white and one painted pink, with lights in the windows, and fishing nets hung up all around them for repair.

'Didn't you try going after her yourself?' asked Martin.

'Yes. But it was no use. I don't have enough imagination. All I could see was sheets and blankets. I fish for rational ideas – for astronomy and physics and human logic. I couldn't imagine Underbed so I couldn't visit it.'

'Underbed?'

The fisherman gave him a small, grim smile. 'That's what Leonora called it.'

They reached the cottage and laid down all of their baskets and tackle. The kitchen door opened and a woman came out, wiping her hands on a flowery apron. Her blonde hair was braided on top of her head and she was quite beautiful in an odd, expressionless way, as if she were a competent oil-painting rather than a real woman.

'You're back, then?' she said. 'And this is the tunneller?'

The fisherman laid his hand on Martin's shoulder. 'That's right. He came, just like he was supposed to. He can start to look for her tonight.'

Martin was about to protest, but the woman came up and took hold of both of his hands. 'I know you'll do everything you can,' she told him. 'And God bless you for coming here and trying.'

They had supper that evening around the kitchen table – a rich fish pie with a crispy potato crust, and glasses of cold cider. The fisherman and his wife said very little, but scarcely took their eyes away from Martin once. It was almost as if they were frightened that he was going to vanish into thin air.

On the mantelpiece, a plain wooden clock loudly ticked out the time, and on the wall next to it hung a watercolour of a house that for some reason Martin recognized. There was a woman standing in the garden, with her back to him. He felt that if she were able to turn around he would know at once who she was.

There were other artefacts in the room that he recognized: a big green earthenware jug and a pastille-burner in the shape of a little cottage. There was a china cat, too, which stared at him with a knowing smile. He had never been here before, so he couldn't imagine why all these things looked so familiar. Perhaps he was tired, and suffering from *déjà vu*.

After supper they sat around the range for a while and the fisherman explained how he went out trawling every day for idea-fish. In the deeper waters, around the sound, there were much bigger fish, entire theoretical concepts, swimming in shoals.

'This is the land of ideas,' he said, in a matter-of-fact way. 'Even the swallows and thrushes in the sky are little whimsical thoughts. You can catch a swallow and think of something you once forgot; or have a small, sweet notion that you never would have had before.

'You – you come from the land of action, where things are *done*, not just discussed.'

'And Underbed? What kind of a land is that?'

'I don't know. The land of fear, I suppose. The land of darkness, where everything always threatens to go wrong.'

'And that's where you want me to go looking for your daughter?'

The fisherman's wife got up from her chair, lifted a photograph from the mantelpiece and passed it across to Martin without a word. It showed a young blonde girl standing on the seashore in a thin summer dress. She was pale-eyed and captivatingly pretty. Her bare toes were buried in the sand. In the distance, a flock of birds were scattering, and Martin thought of 'small, sweet notions that you never would have had before'.

Martin studied the photograph for a moment and then gave it back. 'Very well, then,' he said. 'I'll have a try.' After all, it was his duty to rescue people. He hadn't been able to find the boy trapped in Legg's Elbow: perhaps he could redeem himself by finding Leonora.

Just after eleven o'clock they showed him across to her room. It was small and plain, except for a pine dressing-table crowded with dolls and soft toys. The plain pine bed stood right in the middle of the longer wall, with an engraving of a park hanging over it. Martin frowned at the engraving more closely. He was sure that the park was familiar. Perhaps he had visited it when he was a child. But here, in the land of ideas?

The fisherman's wife closed the red gingham curtains and folded down the blankets on the bed.

'Do you still have the sheets from the time she disappeared?' Martin asked her.

She nodded, and opened a small pine linen-chest at the foot of the bed. She lifted out a folded white sheet and spread it out on top of the bed. One end was ripped and snagged, as if it had been caught in machinery, or clawed by something at least as big as a tiger.

'She wouldn't have done this herself,' said the fisherman. 'She *couldn't* have done.'

'Still,' said Martin. 'If she didn't do it, what did?'

By midnight Martin was in bed, wearing a long white borrowed nightshirt, and the cottage was immersed in darkness. The breeze persistently rattled the window-sash like somebody trying to get in; and beyond the dunes Martin could hear the sea. He always thought that there was nothing more lonely than the sea at night.

He didn't know whether he believed in Underbed or not. He didn't even know whether he believed in the land of ideas or not. He felt as if he were caught in a dream – yet how could he be? The bed felt real and the pillows felt real and he could just make out his pot-holing clothes hanging over the back of the chair.

He lay on his back for almost fifteen minutes without moving. Then he decided that he'd better take a look down at the end of the bed. After all, if Underbed didn't exist, the worst that could happen to him was that he would end up half-stifled and hot. He lifted the blankets, twisted himself around, and plunged down beneath them.

Immediately, he found himself crawling in a low, peaty crevice that was thickly tangled with tree-roots. His nostrils were filled with the rank odour of wet leaves and mould. He must have wriggled into a gap beneath the floor of a wood or forest. It was impenetrably dark, and the roots snared his hair and scratched his face. He was sure that he could feel black-beetles crawling across his hands and down the back of his collar. He wasn't wearing nightclothes any longer. Instead, he was ruggedly dressed in a thick checkered shirt and heavy-duty jeans.

After 40 or 50 metres, he had to crawl right beneath the bole of a huge tree. Part of it was badly rotted, and as he inched his way through the clinging taproots, he was unnervingly aware that the tree probably weighed several tons and if he disturbed it, it could collapse into this subterranean crevice and crush him completely. He had to dig through heaps of peat and soil, and at one point his fingers clawed into something both crackly and slimy. It was the decomposed body of a badger that must have become trapped underground. He stopped for a moment, suffocated and sickened, but then he heard the huge tree creaking and showers of damp peat fell into his hair, and he knew that if he didn't get out of there quickly he was going to be buried alive.

He squirmed out from under the tree, pulling aside a thick curtain of hairy roots, and discovered that he was out in the open air. It was still night-time, and very cold, and his breath smoked in the way that he and his friends had pretended to smoke on winter mornings when they waited for the bus for school – which was, when? Yesterday? Or months ago? Or even years ago?

He stood in the forest and there was no moon, yet the forest was faintly lit by an eerie phosphorescence. He imagined that aliens might have landed behind the trees. A vast spaceship filled with narrow, complicated chambers where a space-mechanic might get lost for months, squeezing his pelvis through angular bulkheads and impossibly-constricted service-tunnels.

The forest was silent. No insects chirruped. No wind disturbed the trees. The only sound was that of Martin's footsteps, as he made his way cautiously through the brambles, not sure in which direction he should be heading. Yet he felt that he was going the right way. He felt drawn: *magnetized*, almost, like a quivering compass-needle. He was plunging deeper and deeper into the land of Underbed: a land of airlessness and claustrophobia, a land in which most people couldn't even breathe. But to him, it was a land of closeness and complete security.

Up above him, the branches of the trees were so thickly entwined together that it was impossible to see the sky. It could have been daytime up above, but here in the forest it was always night.

He stumbled onwards for over half an hour. Every now and then he stopped and listened, but the forest remained silent. As he walked on he became aware of something pale, flickering behind the trees, right in the very corner of his eye. He stopped again, and turned around, but it disappeared, whatever it was.

'Is anybody there?' he called out, his voice muffled by the encroaching trees. There was no answer, but now Martin was certain that he could hear dry leaves being shuffled, and twigs being softly snapped. He was certain that he could hear somebody *breathing*.

He walked further, and he was conscious of the pale shape following him like a paper lantern on a stick, bobbing from tree to tree, just out of sight. But although it remained invisible, it became noisier and noisier, its breath coming in short, harsh gasps, its feet rustling faster and faster across the forest floor.

Suddenly, something clutched at his shirtsleeve – a hand, or a claw – and ripped the fabric. He twisted around and almost lost his balance. Standing close to him in the phosphorescent gloom was a girl of sixteen or seventeen, very slender and white-faced. Her hair was wild and strawlike, and backcombed into a huge birdsnest, decorated with thorns and holly and moss and shiny maroon berries. Her irises were charcoal-grey – night-eyes, with wide black pupils. Eyes that could see in the dark. Her face was starved-looking but mesmerically pretty. It was her white, white skin that had made Martin believe that he was being followed by a paper lantern.

Her costume was extraordinary and erotic. She wore a short blouse made of hundreds of bunched-up ruffles of grubby, tattered lace. Every ruffle seemed to be decorated with a bead or a medal or a rabbit's-foot, or a bird fashioned out of cooking-foil. But her blouse reached only as far as her navel, and it was all she wore. Her feet were filthy and her thighs were streaked with mud.

'What are you searching for?' she asked him, in a thin, lisping voice.

Martin was so confused and embarrassed by her half-nakedness that he turned away. 'I'm looking for someone, that's all.'

'Nobody looks for *anybody* here. This is Underbed.'

'Well, *I'm* looking for someone. A girl called Leonora.'

'A girl who came out from under the woods?'

'I suppose so, yes.'

'We saw her passing by. She was searching for whatever it is that makes her frightened. But she won't find it here.'

'I thought this was the land of fear.'

'Oh, it is. But there's a difference between fear, isn't there, and what actually makes you frightened?'

'I don't understand.'

'It's easy. Fear of the dark is only a fear. It isn't anything real. But what about things that really do hide in the dark? What about the coat on the back of your chair that isn't a coat at all? What about your dead friend standing in the corner, next to your wardrobe, waiting for you to wake?'

'So what is Leonora looking for?'

'It depends what's been frightening her, doesn't it? But the way she went, she was heading for Under-Underbed; and that's where the darkest things live.'

'Can you show me the way?'

The girl emphatically shook her head so that her beads rattled and her ribbons shook. 'You don't know what the darkest things are, do you?' She covered her face with her hands, her fingers slightly parted so that only her eyes looked out. '*The darkest things are the very darkest things; and once you go to visit them in Under-Underbed, they'll know which way you came, they'll be able to smell you, and they'll follow you back there.*'

Martin said, 'I still have to find Leonora. I promised.'

The girl stared at him for a long, long time, saying nothing, as if she were sure that she would never see him again and wanted to remember what he looked like. Then she turned away and beckoned him to follow.

They walked through the forest for at least another twenty minutes. The branches grew sharper and denser, and Martin's cheeks and ears were badly scratched. All the same, with his arms raised to protect his eyes, he followed the girl's thin, pale back as she guided him deeper and deeper into the trees. As she walked, she sang a high-pitched song.

> *The day's in disguise*
> *It's wearing a face I don't recognize*
> *It has rings on its fingers and silken roads in its eyes*

Eventually they reached a small clearing. On one side the ground had humped up, and was thickly covered with sodden green moss. Without hesitation the girl crouched down and lifted up one side of the moss, like a blanket, revealing a dark, root-wriggling interior.

'Down there?' asked Martin, in alarm.

The girl nodded. 'But remember what I said. Once you find them, they'll follow you back. That's what happens when you go looking for the darkest things.'

'All the same, I promised.'

'Yes. But just think *who* you promised, and why. And just think who Leonora might be; and who I am; and what it is you're doing here.'

'I don't know,' he admitted; and he didn't. But while the girl held the moss-blanket as high as she could manage, he climbed on to his side and worked his way underneath it, feet-first, as if he were climbing into bed. The roots embraced him, they took him into their arms like thin-fingered women, and soon he was buried in the mossy hump up to his neck. The girl knelt beside him and her face was calm and regretful.

For some reason her nakedness didn't embarrass him any more. It was almost as if he knew her too well. But without saying anything more, she lowered the blanket of moss over his face and his world went completely dark.

He took a deep, damp-tasting breath, and then he began to insinuate his way under the ground. At first, he was crawling quite level, but he soon reached a place where the soil dropped sharply away into absolute blackness. He thought he could feel a faint draft blowing, and the dull sound of hammering and knocking. This must be it: the end of Underbed, where Under-Underbed began. This was where the darkest things lived. Not just the fear, but the reality.

For the first time since he had set out on his rescue mission he was tempted to turn back. If he crawled back out of the moss-blanket now, and went back through the forest, then the darkest things would never know that he had been here. But he knew that he had to continue. Once you plunged into bed, and Underbed, and Under-Underbed, you had committed yourself.

He swung his legs over the edge of the precipice, clinging with both hands on to the roots that sprouted out of the soil like hairs on a giant's head. Little by little, he lowered himself down the face of the precipice, his shoes sliding in the peat and bringing down noisy cascades of earth and pebbles. The most frightening part about his descent was that he couldn't see anything at all. He couldn't even see how far down he had to climb. For all he knew, the precipice went down and down for ever.

Every time he clutched at a root, he couldn't help himself from dragging off its fibrous outer covering, and his hands soon became impossibly slippery with sap.

Below him, however, the hammering had grown much louder, and he could hear echoes too, and double-echoes.

He grasped at a large taproot, and immediately his hand slipped. He tried to snatch a handful of smaller roots, but they all tore away, with a sound like rotten curtains tearing. He clawed at the soil itself, but there was nothing that he could do to stop himself from falling. He thought, for an instant: *I'm going to die.*

He fell heavily through a damp, lath-and-plaster ceiling. With an ungainly wallop he landed on a sodden mattress, and tumbled off it on to a wet-carpeted floor. He lay on his side for a moment, winded, but then he managed to twist himself around and climb up on to his knees. He was in a bedroom – a bedroom which he recognized, although the wallpaper was mildewed and peeling, and the closet door was tilting off its hinges to reveal a row of empty wire hangers.

He stood up, and went across to the window. At first he thought it was night-time, but then he realized that the window was completely filled in with peat. The bedroom was buried deep below the ground.

He began to feel the first tight little flutters of panic. What if he couldn't climb his way out of here? What if he had to spend the rest of his life buried deep beneath the surface, under layers and layers of soil and moss and suffocating blankets? He tried to think what he ought to do next, but the hammering was now so loud that it made the floor tremble and the hangers in the closet jingle together.

He had to take control of himself. He was an expert, after all: a fully-trained pot-holer, with thirty years' experience. His first priority was to find Leonora, and see how difficult it was going to be to get her back up the precipice. Perhaps there was another way out of Under-Underbed which didn't involve 20 or 30 metres of dangerous climbing?

He opened the bedroom door and found himself confronted by a long corridor with a shiny linoleum floor. The walls were lined with doors and painted, with a tan dado, like a school or a hospital. A single naked light hung at the very far end of the corridor, and under this light stood a girl in a long white nightgown. Her blonde hair was flying in an unfelt wind, and her face was so white that it could have been sculpted out of chalk.

The hem of her nightgown was ripped into tatters and spattered with blood. Her calves and her feet were savagely clawed, with the skin hanging down in ribbons, and blood running all over the floor.

'Leonora?' said Martin, too softly for the girl to be able to hear. Then, 'Leonora!'

She took one shuffling step towards him, and another, but then she stopped and leaned against the side of the corridor. It was the same Leonora whose photograph he had seen in the fisherman's cottage, but three or four years older, maybe more.

Martin started to walk towards her. As he passed each door along the corridor, it seemed to fly open by itself. The hammering was deafening now, but the rooms on either side were empty, even though he could see armchairs and sofas and coffee-tables and paintings on the walls. They were like tableaux from somebody's life, year by year, decade by decade.

'Leonora?' he said, and took her into his arms. She was very cold, and shivering. 'Come on, Leonora, I've come to take you home.'

'There's no way out,' she whispered, in a voice like blanched almonds. 'The darkest things are coming and there's no way out.'

'There's always a way out. Come on, I'll carry you.'

'*There's no way out!*' she screamed at him, right in his face. '*We're buried too deep and there's no way out!*'

'Don't panic!' he shouted back at her. 'If we go back to the bedroom we can find a way to climb back up to Underbed! Now, come on, let me carry you!'

He bent down a little, and then heaved her up on to his shoulder. She weighed hardly anything at all. Her feet were badly lacerated. Two of her left toes were dangling by nothing but skin, and blood dripped steadily on to Martin's jeans.

As they made their way back down the corridor, the doors slammed shut in the same way that they had flown open. But they were still 10 or 11 metres away from the bedroom door when Leonora clutched him so tightly round the throat that she almost strangled him, and screamed. '*They're here! The darkest things! They're following us!*'

Martin turned around, just as the lightbulb at the end of

the corridor was shattered. In a single instant of light, however, he had seen something terrible. It looked like a tall, thin man in a grey monkish hood. Its face was as beatifically perfect as the effigy of a saint. Perfect, that is, except for its mouth, which was drawn back in a lustful grin, revealing a jungle of irregular, pointed teeth. And below that mouth, in another lustful grin, a second mouth, with a thin tongue-tip that lashed from side to side as if it couldn't wait to start feeding.

Both its arms were raised, so that its sleeves had dropped back, exposing not hands but hooked black claws.

This was one of the darkest things. The darkest thing that Leonora had feared, and had to face.

In the sudden blackness, Martin was disoriented and thrown off balance. He half-dropped Leonora, but he managed to heft her up again and stumble in the direction of the bedroom. He found the door, groped it open and then slammed it shut behind them and turned the key.

'Hurry!' he said. 'You'll have to climb on to the bed-head, and up through the ceiling!'

They heard a thick, shuffling noise in the corridor outside, and an appalling screeching of claws against painted plaster walls. The bedroom door shook with a sudden collision and plaster showered down from the lintel. There was another blow, and then the claws scratched slowly down the door-panels. Martin turned around. In spite of her injured feet, Leonora had managed to balance herself on the brass bed-rail, and now she was painfully trying to pull herself through the hole in the damaged ceiling. He struggled up on to the mattress to help her, and as the door was shaken yet again, she managed to climb through. Martin followed, his hands torn by splintered laths. As he drew his legs up, the bedroom door racketed open and he glimpsed the hooded grey creature with its upraised claws. It raised its head and looked up at him and both its mouths opened in mockery and greed.

The climb up the precipice seemed to take months. Together, Martin and Leonora inched their way up through soft, collapsing peat, using even the frailest of roots for a handhold. Several times they slipped back. Again and again they were showered with soil and pebbles and leaf-mould. Martin had to spit it out of his mouth and rub it out of his eyes. And all the time they knew that the darkest thing was following them, hungry and triumphant, and that it would always follow them, wherever they went.

Unexpectedly, they reached the crest of the precipice. Leonora was weeping with pain and exhaustion, but Martin took hold of her arm and dragged her through the roots and the soft, giving soil until at last they came to the blanket of moss. He lifted it up with his arm, trembling with exhaustion, and Leonora climbed out from under it and into the clearing. Martin, gasping with effort, followed her.

There was no sign of the forest-girl anywhere, so Martin had to guess the way back. Both he and Leonora were too tired to speak, but they kept on pushing their way through the branches side by side, and there was no doubt of their companionship. They had escaped from Under-Underbed, and now they were making their way back through Underbed and up to the worlds of light and fresh air.

It took Martin far longer than he thought to find the underground cavity which would take them back to Leonora's world. But a strong sense of direction kept him going: a sense that they were making their way *upwards*. Just when he thought that they were lost for good, he felt his fingers grasping sheets instead of soil, and he and Leonora climbed out of her rumpled bed into her bedroom. Her father was sitting beside the bed, and when they emerged he embraced them both and skipped an odd little fisherman's dance.

'You're a brave boy, you're a brave boy, bringing my Leonora back to me.'

Martin smeared his face with his hands. 'She's going to need treatment on her feet. Is there a doctor close by?'

'No, but there's lady's smock and marigolds; and myrtle, for dismissing bad dreams '

'Her toes are almost severed. She needs stitches. She needs a doctor.'

'An idea will do just as well as a doctor.'

'There's something else,' said Martin. 'The thing that hurt her . . . I think it's probably following us.'

The fisherman laid his hand on Martin's shoulder and nodded. 'We'll take care of that, my young fellow.'

So they stood by the shore in the mauvish light of an early summer's evening and they set fire to Leonora's bed, blankets and sheets and all, and they pushed it out to sea like an Arthurian funeral barge. The flames lapped into the sky like dragons' tongues, and fragments of burned blanket whirled into the air.

Leonora with her bandaged feet stood close to Martin and held his arm; and when it was time for him to go she kissed him and her eyes were filled with tears. The fisherman gratefully clasped his hand. 'Always remember,' he said. 'What might have been is just as important as what actually was.'

Martin nodded; and then he started walking back along the shoreline, to the tussocky grass that would lead him back to Legg's Elbow and the caves. He turned around only once, but by then it was too dark to see anything but the fire burning from Leonora's bed, 300 metres out to sea.

His mother frantically stripped back his sheets and blankets in the morning and found him at the bottom of the bed in his red-and-white striped pyjamas, his skin cold and his limbs stiff with rigor mortis. There was no saving him: the doctor said that he had probably suffocated some time after midnight, and by the time his mother found him he had been dead for seven-and-a-half hours.

When he was cremated, his mother wept and said that it was just as if Martin's was a life that had never happened.

But who could say such a thing? Not the fisherman and his family, who went back to their imaginary cottage and said a prayer for the tunneller who rescued their daughter. Not a wild, half-naked girl who walked through a forest that never was, thinking of a man who dared to face the darkest things. And not the darkest thing which heaved itself out from under the moss and emerged at last in the world of ideas from a smoking, half-sunken bed; a hooded grey shape in the darkness.

And, in the end, not Martin's mother, when she went back into his bedroom after the funeral to strip the bed.

She pulled back the blankets one by one; then she tugged off the sheets. But it was just when she was dragging out the sheets from the very end of the bed that she saw six curved black shapes over the end of the mattress. She frowned, and walked around the bed to see what they were.

It was only when she looked really close that she realized they were claws.

Cautiously, she dragged down the sheet a little further. The claws were attached to hands and the hands seemed to disappear into the crack between sheet and mattress.

This was a joke, she thought. Some really sick joke. Martin had been dead for less than a week and someone was playing some childish, hurtful prank. She wrenched back the sheet even further and seized hold of one of the claws, so that she could pull it free.

To her horror, it lashed out at her, and tore the flesh on the back of her hand. It lashed again and again, ripping the mattress and shredding the sheets. She screamed, and tried to scramble away, her blood spotting the sheets. But something rose out of the end of the bed in a tumult of torn foam and ripped-apart padding – something tall and grey with a face like a saint and two parallel mouths crammed with shark's-teeth. It rose up and up, until it was towering above her and it was cold as the Arctic. It was so cold that even *her* breath fumed.

'There are some places you should never go,' it whispered at her, with both mouths speaking in unison. 'There are some things you should never think about. There are some people whose curiosity will always bring calamity, especially to themselves, and to the people they love. You don't need to go looking for your fears. Your fears will always follow you, and find you out.'

With that, and without hesitation, the darkest thing

brought down its right-hand claw like a cat swatting a thrush and ripped her face apart.

Before she could fall to the carpet, it ripped her again, and then again, until the whole bedroom was decorated with blood.

It bent down then, almost as if it were kneeling in reverence to its own cruelty and its own greed, and it firmly seized her flesh with both of its mouths. Gradually, it disappeared back into the crevice at the end of the bed, dragging her with it, inch by inch, one lolling leg, one flopping arm.

The last to go was her left hand, with her wedding-ring on it.

Then there was nothing but a torn, bloodstained bed in an empty room, and a faint sound that could have been water, trickling down through underground caves, or the sea, whispering in the distance, or the rustling of branches in a deep, dark forest.

Graham Masterton is the author of nearly seventy novels, from *The Manitou*, published in 1975, to his latest, *The House that Jack Built*. A former editor of *Mayfair* and *Penthouse*, the author's thrillers, historical and horror novels include *Burial*, *The Sleepless*, *Spirit*, and *Flesh and Blood* which interweaves all three genres. One of his most recent books, *The Chosen Child*, is set in Warsaw and the city is also the setting for a new literary television programme he's creating on Polish Channel 1 with his wife, Wiescka. He has published over fifty short stories, some of which are collected in *Fortnight of Fear* and *Flights of Fear*, the latter having topped the bestseller list in Poland. Masterton's story 'The Hungry Moon' appeared in the first *Dark Terrors*, and about this new story he reveals: '"Underbed" was born one night in 1954, when I discovered a tear in my top sheet. I decided to explore the next layer in my bed and became hopelessly disorientated, confused and claustrophobic.' He explains that the theme is part of his continuing exploration into the concept that there are worlds within worlds (as in his three novels, *Mirror*, *Walkers* and *The House that Jack Built*). 'Neutrinos make up ninety per cent of the mass of the universe,' he continues, 'and yet millions will have passed through you and this book in the time it took you to read these contributor's notes.'

Animal Life

Clive Barker

Ralph was dreaming of Kathleen again. She was standing on the edge of the pool he was building for Jerry Meuse on Coldwater Canyon, looking into the water saying:

'It's milk, Ralph!'

As he realized that yes, indeed, the pool was filled with milk, the ground began to shake. Somewhere far off, he heard Duffy barking frantically.

I'm not dreaming, he thought, and opened his eyes. The walls were creaking, the doors flying open, the bed pitching around. This was no minor temblor. This was big, and getting bigger. He felt a patter of dust on his face and threw himself out of bed. A heartbeat later, the ceiling came down, burying the place where he'd been sleeping seconds before.

The drapes were open a few inches (he'd not been able to sleep in total darkness since Kathleen's departure), and there was moonlight enough to get him across the pitching floor to the door. 'Duffy?' he yelled as he raced down the stairs. 'Where are you, boy?'

He ducked into the kitchen, where Duffy usually spent the night (he'd protect his food before us, Kathleen had pointed out), but there was no response. The shaking had given way to brutal jolts now, as though some titanic foot were kicking the house. Every jar, plate, fork and glass was either on the floor in pieces or on its way.

'Duffy?' he yelled again, fearing the worst.

Then, from the study, a fretful whine. He raced across the

hall. The dog was under the desk, which was a more sensible place to be than—

Behind him, the sound of plaster cracking and splintering. He turned in time to see one of the huge book-cases, six of its shelves weighed down with files on recent projects, the seventh with his secret stash of skin magazines, toppling towards him. He started to retreat, but a hail of pools and *Penthouses* felled him.

Ralph's partner, Vincent, surveyed the chaos in the study.

'This is not a safe place to be right now,' he said. 'Come and stay with Lauren and me till you get a structural engineer in here.'

Ralph was at his desk, which had become a life raft in this sea of destruction. Preserved upon it: pictures of Kathleen, an antique clock, his first editions of Chandler. 'Thanks, but no, thanks. I've already lost enough. First Kathleen—'

'She'll be back, Ralphie.'

'—then Duffy running off. I'm damned if I'm going to leave this house. It's practically all I've got left.' He put his hand to his bandaged brow. 'Besides a permanent headache.'

The bedroom was uninhabitable, so the next night he made up a bed for himself on the sofa. The aftershocks had continued through the day – the seismologists up at Cal Tech were predicting they'd go on for several weeks after a quake of such magnitude – but in the brightness and warmth of the day the tremors hadn't bothered him. Once darkness fell, however, he began to feel jittery. Sleep did not come easily. Twice he woke from a light doze thinking he felt plaster dust on his face.

The third time, it was a sound that stirred him, that of somebody eating. He rose, picking up the heavy-duty flash-light he'd left on the floor, and followed the noise through to the kitchen. He could just make out a diminutive figure in the darkness, sitting at the table. It wasn't a child. A sliver of light caught the whiskers around its chin.

'Ralphie?' The interloper's voice was deep and warm.

Ralph snapped on the light.

'Too bright,' said Duffy, squinting. He was sitting up at the table with a tub of peach ice cream in front of him. There was a spoon and a bowl beside it, but he'd apparently decided they weren't worth the bother, and just plunged his snout into the tub. 'Boy,' he said, 'you look like hell.'

Ralph put his hands to his throbbing head. His concussion was plainly worse than he'd thought.

'I know, I shouldn't be eating ice cream,' Duffy was saying. 'Our digestive system wasn't designed for sugar. But I thought, what the hell? Why not celebrate? It's not every day a dog gets to talk with his master.'

'This isn't happening,' Ralph said flatly.

'Now that, Ralphie, is a terrible cliché. Come and have some ice cream, and I'll explain.' Ralph didn't move. 'Come on,' Duffy coaxed him. 'I'm not going to bite.'

'I'm hallucinating this,' Ralph told him, and went to sit down opposite his illusion, so as to find some flaw in its solidity.

'Kathleen was right, you know,' Duffy said. 'We'd be a lot safer in Wisconsin. But then we'd have her damn mother living around the corner. Are you sure you won't have some ice cream?' Ralph shook his head. 'You're probably wondering how I got to talk an' all, right? Well, after I ran off – sorry about that, by the way, but I guess it was instinct – I was wandering up in the hills off Mulholland, an' I saw this pack of coyotes, so I followed them in case there was something worth scavenging.'

'And was there?'

'I'm gettin' to that. They disappeared among these trees, and there were animals arriving from all directions. Deer and raccoons and snakes and birds and lizards. There were a few pets, too. Runaways who'd found their way up there by some fluke.' He broke off, and smiled at his astonished master. 'It gets weirder,' he said. 'See, there was this crack in the ground, with smoke coming out of it, and all the animals were takin' a breath of this smoke. So I did the same. And you know what? I could talk. We could all talk. You never heard such bedlam.'

He laughed, much entertained by the memory. 'And then—'
He leaned across the table, his voice dropping to a whisper,
'—out of the earth comes this woman. And she says to us all:
"You know me . . ."'

'And did you?'

'Vaguely. She was huge, maybe three hundred pounds, and
beautiful. Every kind of blood in her, every kind of feeling in
her face, all at once. Rage and love and rapture . . .' He was
entranced, even now. 'Unbelievable,' he said.

And who was she?'

'Some earth spirit. A goddess. My mother. I don't know.
The point is, she said to us: "I need to know whether I should
shake this city to pieces."'

'Oh, my God.'

'So then everybody starts talking at once, saying how cruel
you people are, and how stupid and destructive.'

'And what did you say?'

'I shut up. I mean, we've had some fine times, you and me,
but it put me in a spin, hearing all these terrible stories. I
didn't know what to think.'

'So, was there a vote of some kind?'

'Oh, yes.'

Ralph studied Duffy's brown eyes, looking for a clue as to
the result. 'And?' he said, his voice a whisper.

'I'm not allowed—' He stopped, ears pricked. 'Uh-oh,' he
murmured.

'What's wrong?'

'Don't you feel it?' He was up from the table now and
heading for the door.

A moment later, the aftershock came rolling through the
house. The lights went out. The windows rattled. The walls
creaked.

This time, Ralph was fast. Arms over his head to keep his
skull from a further beating, he raced across the shuddering
ground and out the front door, not looking back until he
made the safety of the street. From there, he had all too fine
a view of his house collapsing, the already wounded walls

folding in upon themselves, and the roof coming down in the
rubble, burying in one moment all he'd called his own.

He called Kathleen from Vince's place, to tell her the news.
She said she was sorry, but, then, they'd said that to each
other countless times and not really meant it. Before the
conversation ended, he asked if she was planning to come
back out to California any time soon. She told him no.

'You can rebuild,' Vince said the next day when they went
to sort through the rubble. 'The government's already promised interest-free loans, and you've got the insurance.'

It was true. Of course he could rebuild. Stronger foundations next time. More steel, more concrete. But right now,
the thought sickened him.

He kept thinking of his hallucination. Of Duffy devouring
ice cream and talking about the cruelty of men. The headaches
were diminishing, so he assumed he wouldn't be bothered
further by such deliriums, but the conversation stayed with
him.

'Rebuild?' he wanted to say to Vince. 'Why?'

He kept his doubts to himself, however. Put a brave face on
things, even managed a smile or two. But when Vince headed
off to get some beer, he immediately ceased digging and sat
with his back to the rubble, staring down the canyon.

Where had Duffy gone this time? he wondered. Back where
he'd gone before, up on to Mulholland?

Without really thinking about what he was doing, he got
up and started to walk. The thought of searching for Duffy
was only a vague notion at the back of his head, but the
further he got from the house the more focused that ambition
became. If he could just find his dog, it would be a sign that
his life was not beyond reclamation. He would rebuild it, with
stronger foundations.

There were scenes of devastation everywhere – houses he
had yearned to own obliterated, swimming pools upended,
cars crushed – but once he got on to the ridge the air was
clear and the view finer than he remembered it. He walked on
for maybe a quarter-mile, until he reached a spot where the

bushes at the side of the road had been trampled. Curious, he turned off the asphalt and on to the dirt, following the muddied ground towards a spot concealed from human sight by a wall of trees.

Even before he reached the grove itself, an absurd suspicion began to make the hairs on his neck prickle. The ground had not been churned up by human feet. Animals had been here, in considerable numbers. Nor had they come from a single direction. Paths had been beaten to this place from every compass point.

He wanted to turn and run, but curiosity overruled his fear. With his heart thumping in his temples, he slipped between the trees.

The grove was deserted. But there was everywhere evidence that an extraordinary congregation had gathered here. Hoof marks and paw marks in the churned dirt, feathers and fur flitting about, splashes and pellets and mounds of excrement spread all around.

And in the middle of the grove, a crack in the earth. Tentatively, he approached it. There was no smoke. The ground was still and cold. Whatever miracle had been here – if any – it had passed.

Or had it? He caught a motion from the corner of his eye, and glancing round saw Duffy appear from between the trees.

'So . . .' he said to the dog. 'It was all true.'

At the sound of his master's voice, Duffy came pounding over, jumped up at Ralph's face to lick him.

'Duffy,' Ralph said. 'Are you listening to me? I said I believe you.'

Duffy just barked and ran in circles.

'Speak to me, damn you!' Ralph hollered.

The dog barked again, his tail wagging furiously. Then he was away, out of the cool of the grove, glancing back over his shoulder to see if his master was following.

Ralph took one last look at the crack below him, then followed the dog out into the sun, stepping in a dozen kinds of excrement on his way. Duffy was still cavorting and barking, and did not let up all the way back to the house. Ralph kept listening, hoping to hear a recognizable phrase (even a word) somewhere in the din. But all he heard was the dog's bliss at being alive and back with the creature that fed him. That didn't answer any of his questions, of course. But Duffy's joyful mood was contagious. By the time they came in sight of the rubble, Ralph was already planning the house that would one day replace it.

He would not, however, waste his heart loving it, he decided, in case the vote had gone badly and the animal running ahead of him was pretending simple doghood to keep his master from despair.

Clive Barker has been busy recently with the publication of *Incarnations: Three Plays*; a major new novel, *Sacrament*, and two non-fiction projects: *Clive Barker's A–Z of Horror* (with Stephen Jones), based on the BBC-TV series, and *Clive Barker A–Z* by Fred Burke. He also wrote and directed *Lord of Illusions* (inspired by his story 'The Last Illusion'), and executive-produced the sequels *Candyman: Farewell to the Flesh* and *Hellraiser: Bloodline*. Since his highly successful six-volume *Books of Blood* collections appeared in the mid-1980s, he has published a string of bestselling novels, including *The Damnation Game*, *Weaveworld*, *Cabal*, *The Great and Secret Show*, *Imajica*, *The Thief of Always* (currently being developed as an animated musical) and *Everville*. In 1987 he scripted and directed *Hellraiser*, loosely based on his novella 'The Hell Bound Heart'. The film was a surprise low-budget hit, and created a horror icon in the character of the demonic Pinhead (played by Doug Bradley). It has spawned three sequels to date, each scripted by Peter Atkins who also appears alongside Barker in the recent video release of the latter's early experimental shorts *Salome/The Forbidden*. 'Animal Life' was inspired by the January 1994 earthquake in Los Angeles (where Barker now lives) and deals with one of the author's favourite themes, the intersection of the real and the mystical. 'There are two ways to read this story,' he suggests.

Lily's Whisper

JAY RUSSELL

Sometimes, at the edge of consciousness, on that unsteady divide between my waking and dreaming life, I'll hear her wonderful little song. The spectral voice of memory, I suppose. All in my head. But then, isn't everything?

An orderly asked if anything was wrong. *A lot*, I thought, but I told him I was fine and forced myself to walk on in. I'd been standing, frozen with dread, outside the door to my grandmother's hospital room. I stared at the small white paper with her name in blurry type: **Bernstein, Sally**. No middle initial. When I was little I used to ask her why it was that she had no middle name. She always answered with the same joke: 'We were too poor to afford one.' It drove me crazy because it didn't make any sense, but now I smiled thinking about it. *Okay, Grandma*, I thought, *let's get this over with*.

My Aunt Lily died when I was a kid. She was actually my great-aunt. My mother's aunt. Grandma Sally's sister.

Although she didn't live far away from the house where I grew up, I never knew Lily very well. Once or twice a year someone would bring her along to a family gathering – she couldn't drive – where she always showered the children with fruit candies and cheap but wonderful presents. Unlike my mother's other seemingly born-ancient aunts and uncles, Lily seemed not just to like children, but to understand them. To think like them. Even though she was the only one without kids of her own.

I never much cared for those other relatives, who were somehow sort of scary to me in their sere way, but I was always happy to see Lily. It wasn't just that she treated us differently or better (though she did), she somehow seemed utterly apart from her siblings. Her face betrayed the same harsh, Eastern European stock, but there was a gentle quality to her that none of the others possessed. A humour in her eyes and playfulness to her touch which made the cloying affections of her shrewish kin all the more glaring.

I suppose I realized that there was something unusual about Lily – something secret – from the way the others talked about her. They always lowered their voices when Lily's name came up, as if she was something to hide or to be ashamed of. If not for the fact of our Jewishness, I think they would have crossed themselves at the mention of her name. Even when Lily was in the room the others spoke about her as if she wasn't there. Or as if she was dead. Perhaps the reason the children identified with her so closely was because, among the other adults, she was treated as if she, too, was of no real consequence.

Hospital rooms are like shopping malls in their dislocated uniformity. Stepping into one, whether in Los Angeles or West Palm Beach, removes you from the normal fabric of local time and space and into the antiseptic, spiritually liminal realm of the sick and dying.

The bed nearest the door had been stripped of linens and I had the sudden ominous sense that the last person to occupy it had not walked out on their own. A tall plastic curtain had been drawn around the far bed, the elongated shadows of the guard rails silhouetted like prison bars on the laminated barrier. As I got closer I could hear raspy breathing. The curtain hadn't been pulled all the way around, and as I reached the foot of the bed I saw my grandmother for the first time in almost ten years.

Sally had always been a short, plump woman, but age and

illness had shrunk her down so that, lost under her covers, she looked like an old ventriloquist's dummy. She stirred in uneasy sleep and I saw that she was little more than a bag of withered flesh. The sight of her reminded me of a balloon you'd find behind the couch two weeks after a party, limp and wrinkled and only vaguely suggestive of its original shape. Her skin had stretched and sagged beyond the capacity of her diminutive frame. As a child I had always marvelled at my grandmother's upper arms; they were fatty and thick and dangled like jowls, jiggling wildly with every gesture she made. Now I saw that the folds of skin remained, but the meat beneath them had dissolved and the flesh hung limp as a ghost ship's sails.

Her stained dentures swam in a plastic cup on the formica night table and her hollow mouth drooped open. A glistening thread of saliva trailed down her chin and tufts of thin, colourless hair dotted her mottled scalp. In fact, the sight of her made me feel a little queasy and I started to walk back out when her eyes opened, nailing me to the floor.

She stared at me, but I wasn't certain she could see me or if she could, that she recognized who I was. The last time I'd seen her had been at my mother's funeral almost a decade before. Despite her numerous illnesses and various surgeries, I had spoken with Sally only once since then, when she had called on my birthday. It was a hellish call in which she quizzed me accusatorially about my lack of contact with her.

Like all good New York Jews, she and my grandfather had retired to Florida when I was a kid. As a result I had never been particularly close to her – from an adult's point of view, I never knew her at all – though I still carried a certain latent guilt over having ignored her so in her declining years.

Especially after first her husband, then my mother died.

It was primarily that lurking guilt (along with my father springing for the cost of the air fare) which had served to bring me all the way from my home in Los Angeles to her Florida hospital for this reunion. A reunion for which Sally had hysterically and inexplicably begged.

The silence was broken only by my grandmother's fractured

breathing. She scanned me up and down, but her only movement was the slight rise and fall of her chest. I shifted nervously and cleared my throat. I was about to identify myself when, with a low moan, she pulled herself up against the pillow and slowly lifted an arthritic hand.

'Brucie,' she said.

I came around the side of the bed and took her hand. It felt as light as a Styrofoam coffee cup, the skin hard and cool to the touch.

'Hi, Grandma,' I croaked.

She left her hand in mine for a moment then drew it back beneath the covers. Her eyes never left mine.

'You're so thin,' she said and coughed. Then she farted wetly. I felt slightly embarrassed, but she didn't seem bothered. 'And a beard, yet.'

'Yeah,' I said, scratching my chin. 'That's right.'

She didn't reply. The tension could have been cut with oh, say a small sword: six-foot blade.

'So,' I said, posing the stupidest question of all time: 'How are you?'

Here is everything that I knew about Lily's life:

She was the youngest sibling of the large Petrowski family, something like eight or nine children in all. They were dirt poor and lived like sharecroppers in seriously anti-Semitic Poland at the turn of the century. Neither my great-grandparents nor any of their children were educated and they all worked at maintaining the subsistence-level farm.

Most of the family emigrated to America in the early years of the century with the great human tide that fled the miseries of the Old World. A couple of the older siblings stayed behind, but the rest, including Lily, settled in Brooklyn.

While the various children who became my mother's aunts and uncles started families of their own in America, Lily never married. She lived out her drab life and died, alone, in the basement flat of a Brooklyn tenement. In the end, no one even knew exactly when she died. Her body was found by a stranger because of the stench rising from her corpse.

I only really remember three things about Lily. Once, when she came to visit, she brought along a new puppy. It was a mad, brown ball of energy. In what even at the time I recognized as pure Lily style, she had named it Wolfie. My cousins and I spent a wondrous day chasing the dog around the small yard of my parents' suburban New York house while Lily watched and clapped along in delight. She seemed, I remember, not to handle the dog very well, as if she didn't understand that it was a living thing and not a toy, but her pleasure in its company was clear. A couple of weeks later I overheard my mother tell my father that Wolfie had been run over by a car.

I also remember a simple little song Lily used to sing to us. My mother knew it too – had probably learned it from Lily – and often sang it to me as a lullaby. Lily would sing in Polish mostly, but sometimes in English. My mother only knew the English version. It went:

> *Meet me at midnight, my sweet one.*
> *By the tree in the garden,*
> *Where the white roses grow.*
> *Meet me at midnight, my darling.*
> *But don't let anyone know.*
> *Never let anyone know.*

The song had a tender, happy/sad melody and to this day it summons, however fleetingly, that childhood feeling of utter safeness and security that simply doesn't exist in maturity.

The third thing I remember is not so much about Lily as about myself. It concerns her death and I recall it, even after all these years, with some shame.

I was maybe eight or nine years old and my best friend and I were playing in the house one day when the phone rang. My mother picked it up in the kitchen while I eavesdropped (as usual) from the hall. Sally was on the line and I heard my mother start to cry. I understood that it was because Lily had died. I knew Lily was my mother's favourite aunt. I stood there listening to her cry when my friend came down the hall to see what was up. As soon as he looked at me I began to laugh. He kept asking what was so funny, but each time I tried to tell him the laughter grew more hysterical. I couldn't stop myself. We retreated to the safety of my room and I told him what had happened. I don't think I'll ever forget the look on his face.

In the years since I've tried to rationalize my behaviour without real success. I've told myself that the laughter was a child's nervous response to the mystery of death or a cathartic emotional release. Hell, maybe it's even true. For a time I thought that I'd blown the incident out of proportion, but years later, that same friend and I were talking and he asked me about that day and my laughter. It had stuck with him, too. I managed to change the topic of conversation, but I've never forgotten the shame.

I leaned against the hall's cool tiles waiting for a nurse to finish helping Sally with the bedpan. I heard the gulping flush of a toilet and a moment later the nurse came out and nodded at me.

The room stank of shit and piss, but I pretended not to notice. I pulled a chair over next to the bed and as I sat down I saw that Sally had put her teeth in. Her eyes looked a little clearer, too. Her wasted body still suggested the proximity of the scythe, but she seemed more alert and, I hoped, able to explain her desperate need to see me.

'I know you don't care so much for me,' she began, and seeing my burgeoning protest held up a finger. 'No, no, you don't have to say. It's all right.'

I sat back in the chair and exhaled a deep breath. I felt desperately trapped, like being stuck in bumper-to-bumper traffic at the entrance to a long tunnel.

'I know also you're only here because your father insisted, but this I don't care either.'

That was true as well. Not only had my father paid for my ticket, he had seriously guilted me into making the haul from California at all.

'I have something to ask you, but first I have a story to tell.

It's to do with your Aunt Lily, I don't know if you even remember.'

I nodded, suddenly more interested. Though Sally didn't ask, I recited the outline of what I knew and remembered. I didn't mention how I laughed the day that Lily died.

'What you say is right. I don't remember a dog, but with Lily it could be. Always she did such things. But this is like the skin of the apple what you know. The fruit is underneath, but I'll tell you now and you should understand, it's not so sweet.

'Lily we always hated,' Sally said. She stared past me, out the window as she spoke. 'When she was born she was too small, like to die, and Mama was very sick. They have what to call it today.'

'Premature,' I said.

'Yes, I think. Always weak Lily was and so tiny. For a long time she didn't walk or talk. A terrible burden she was on us. We lived all of us then in a little house, like you don't know. Always Lily had to have special and we all had to make do with less she could get. Terrible jealous it made us.

'My father came first to America and sent back money for the children to go one by one, but Mama died soon after we all arrived. But this you probably know. Lily was then a big girl already, but still she was . . . not right. Slow, she was and difficult. But with Mama gone Lily wasn't special any more and terrible mean we could be to her, like how we always wanted.'

My grandmother laid back against the pillows and closed her eyes. Her breathing became shallow and even and I thought perhaps she had dozed off, but then she opened her eyes again and stared up at the ceiling.

'When Bella died. . .'

'Whoa! Wait a minute. Who's Bella?'

Sally shook her head. 'I forget, Brucie. These people, some you never met. But to me it's all like yesterday. Bella was the oldest sister. She married and stayed yet in Poland.'

'You know, I don't think I've ever even heard her name.'

Sally only nodded, but somehow communicated to me: *such is the sad nature of time and memory*. She went on:

'Bella died from the typhus, left alone a husband and a little boy. Such could not be in those days and something had be done. We saw then a chance to get rid of Lily. Lily had no husband and who would ever marry such a thing? Bella's husband we knew from before. A hard man. Like only in Poland you find. We knew it was a bad thing to send Lily to him, but jealousy is—' Sally shook her head '—she went, you know, it was not so long before the war. We didn't know then from Hitler, but even if we did, I can't say sure that we would have done different.'

'Christ,' I muttered. I'd never heard *any* of this before.

'What happened, who would have thought? Lily married to Bella's husband and took the little boy to her heart. And she was happy. The life there wasn't easy, but Lily made for herself a place. The baby she thought of like her own and Bella's husband she even maybe could love. Who can say?'

Sally laid back again and I could see she was exhausted. She could barely keep her eyes open.

'Maybe you should take a little nap, Grandma,' I said, though I was intrigued by her story and puzzled as to where it was leading.

She nodded and offered me a little smile. She was asleep before I could get out of the chair.

I waited around the hospital for a while, ogling the student nurses and drinking bitter coffee from a machine. I saw a nurse go in and out of my grandmother's room and ran after her. She told me that Sally would probably sleep for a few hours at least.

'Can you tell me . . .' I started. I felt a little silly asking, actually.

'What?' the nurse asked.

'What, exactly, is wrong with her?' I knew from my father that Sally had undergone some treatments for cancer a while back, and that at least one hip had been replaced fairly recently, but I didn't actually know why she was hospitalized now.

'Some heart trouble. Bad circulatory problems. Mostly, she's old,' the nurse said. 'Just plain worn out.' She must have seen I wasn't too thrilled with the answer and sort of shrugged. 'You're Brucie, aren't you?'

'Bruce,' I said, clearing my throat.

'She's been going on and on about you.'

'Really?' I asked. 'Do you have any idea why?'

'No, she wouldn't say,' she said. She started to walk away then half turned around again. 'Though maybe if you called her once in a while, you'd know.'

I scraped my lower jaw – and my pride – off the floor and walked out of the hospital.

West Palm Beach ain't exactly the thrill capital of the world. That is to say, if you aren't up for a rollicking round of Bingo or a day at the jai alai fronton, there's not one heck of a lot to do. There *is* the beach, I reckon, but living in Los Angeles pretty well spoils you for such things.

So I went to visit my cousin.

Beth owned a condo in one of those godawful, prefab developments which litter the Florida landscape like broken shells on the beach. She worked for a bank and wasn't married, which is the extent of what I knew about her life. I had to call my dad to get her address.

I don't even know how long it had been since I'd seen Beth. We'd been close as children – we were born just two months apart – but that was ancient history. She was my mother's sister's only child and had somehow come to serve as kind of caretaker to Sally after my aunt passed away. Neither of us had even bothered to attend the funeral of the other's mom. I didn't even think I'd be able to recognize Beth, but when she opened the door I was pleasantly surprised to find the face of the little girl I remembered etched inside the older-than-her-years lines of the woman I didn't even vaguely know.

I hadn't bothered to call or write, but she wasn't surprised to see me. 'Grandma said you'd be coming,' she told me. 'I didn't believe it though.'

'I'm not entirely sure why I'm here,' I told her.

We tried the small-talk thing for a while, but it didn't go too well. I found her life in banking as dull as she found mine as a teacher. Neither of us was too keen to talk over good old days which didn't exist, so all that was left was Sally. Beth told me about the old woman's physical decline in rather clinical, unemotional terms. I got the strong feeling that Sally's glacially slow deterioration had worn Beth out. She basically told me what the nurse had said about Sally's health.

'A tumour, some angina there. Old age everywhere,' Beth shrugged between chain-smoked cigarettes.

'And you don't know why she's been so adamant about wanting to see me?' I asked.

'Not a fucking clue,' Beth said.

I could hear the resentment in her voice, got the feeling that my seeing Sally was somehow treading on territory Beth thought of as her own. I couldn't blame her, really. *I* wasn't the one who'd been changing the old bag's diapers these past years.

'Apparently it has something to do with Lily,' I told her.

Beth coughed out a cloud of smoke. '*Aunt* Lily?' she choked.

'Yeah. She started telling me all about her before she dozed off. I haven't a clue as to why, though.'

'Unbelievable,' Beth whispered, shaking her head.

'What?' I asked.

'I've been trying to get her to talk about Lily for years. I've asked her time after time and she'd never tell me a goddamn thing.'

'Why did you want to know about Lily?' I asked. But somewhere a memory stirred in the back of my head.

'My mom used to talk about her a lot. She always thought there was something important about Lily. I wanted to make a film about her. Once.'

I remembered. I remembered from years before that in our very practical and deeply unimaginative family, Beth had been an 'artsy' kid with dreams of being a filmmaker. I never quite got it straight how she ended up working for a bank. Looking now at her tired face and nicotine-stained fingertips, I didn't want to ask. A hint of a smile formed at the edge of her lips.

'She was in the camps, you know,' Beth said.

'Excuse me?'

'You don't know, do you?' Beth shook her head. 'Lily was in a concentration camp for a while during the Second World War.'

'No,' I said weakly. This was quite the day for family tales. 'I didn't know. How did . . . how could she have been in the camps? Who told you this?'

'My mom. But she didn't know much more than that, either. It was something no one ever talked about, apparently.'

'I'm not surprised,' I said. But I was trying to picture the sweet old lady with candy who I remembered superimposed into one of those archive-issue black and white images of Dachau or Treblinka that we all have stowed in our heads. I couldn't suppress a shudder. 'What happened?' I asked. 'Do you know?'

Beth got up and rooted around for another pack of cigarettes. She let me dangle while she fiddled with the wrapper, searched for some matches and oh-so-deliberately lit up the smoke.

'You'll tell me what this is all about? Why Grandma wants to see you? What she says about Lily?'

'Of course,' I said. 'Why wouldn't I?'

Beth shrugged and I realized it was information *she* would hoard.

'Come on,' I said. 'Please?'

'I don't know that much, really. But I guess it's more than *you*.' I realized all of a sudden that there was some deep resentment happening here, but I didn't have a clue what it was all about.

'You know that Lily was in Poland right before the war? She went back to like nursemaid her brother-in-law or something.'

'Grandma was just telling me about it. She said that Lily married a dead sister's husband. And there was a kid, too.'

'Yeah,' she said and hesitated again. I summarized what

Sally had told me in the hospital. Beth listened and nodded, seemed to think about it for a little while.

'I don't know the details,' she finally said. 'I don't think any of the family really did. But Lily got rounded up by the Nazis at some point. Just for being Jewish, far as I know. They all got herded into the cattle cars. Lily was separated from the husband and the kid, but apparently she still had American papers or something. Anyway, she was in a camp for a while. I don't know which one. Not a death camp, obviously. But they let her go.'

'I didn't think they ever let anyone go.'

Beth shrugged again. 'Who knows? A US citizen, a woman. They probably just didn't give a shit. Or she was just fucking lucky.'

'What about the brother-in-law – the husband, I mean – and the little boy?'

'Soap. Lamp shades. Ash. Whatever.'

I winced at the harshness, the casual tone of my cousin's response. 'Jesus,' I said.

'I don't think old JC was involved,' Beth said, sucking in the last of the smoke. 'But you never know.'

'Do you know anything else?'

'Apparently she waited out the war in Europe. Don't ask me where or how. She waited for the others. She never found them, of course.'

'How did you find all this out?' I asked again.

'My mom. She told me the whole story once when she was stoned.' I must have looked at Beth oddly, because she laughed and quickly explained. 'You never saw her during her post-menopausal hippy phase did you?'

'Uh, no,' I admitted.

'Far out. Literally. I'd get home from work and we'd share a joint. Man, you ain't lived till you've had it out with your mom for bogarting a roach.'

'I can only imagine,' I said. But remembering my aunt as a suburban housewife, I really couldn't. Beth lit up another cigarette and neither of us said a word for a while.

'What must have it been like?' I finally said. Beth raised an eyebrow. 'For Lily, I mean. Growing up hated by her brothers and sisters. Treated like a piece of shit. Finally finding a family only to lose it to the . . . you know. What would that do to you?'

Beth didn't have any answer, but for the first time since I arrived, some of the hard edges fell out of her face.

'It's too bad you never got to make your film,' I said.

She turned away, ostensibly to reach for another cigarette, but through the swirl of smoke I'm sure I saw a tear in the corner of one bloodshot eye.

I got back to the hospital just after six that evening and walked smack dab into chaos. Sally had become hysterical wanting to know where I was. It seemed they could only dope her up with the mildest of sedatives and she fought it tooth and nail. She had just dozed off again when I arrived, much to the relief of the third-floor staff. I chatted with a couple of nurses who told me Sally had been driving them nuts for weeks. They all seemed to know who I was; Sally had been ranting to them about me and about Lily, though the connection was unclear.

I went back to Sally's room to wait until she stirred. I stared out the window as a thunder squall broke apart the still hot Florida evening. I listened to the sizzle of the warm rain on concrete and to Sally's graveyard hack. I looked over at her as she began moaning lowly in her sleep, her drawn face contorting.

Suddenly, her eyes shot open and her face took on a frenzied expression. She started to yell, then saw me sitting by the window. The wildness went out of her eyes and she settled back against the rumpled sheets. I asked her if she was all right and she nodded.

'I went to see Beth,' I told her.

'A good girl,' Sally said, nodding. But her face suggested she didn't entirely believe her own words.

'We talked about what you were telling me. She said that Lily was once in a concentration camp. That she lost her family there.'

My grandmother looked up sharply, but wouldn't meet my
eye. She nodded again, but looked down into the sheets as she
spoke.

'This is true,' she said. 'Terrible. Terrible.' She seemed to
want to say more, but I don't think she could.

'So what happened?' I prompted.

'Lily we brought back to New York after the war. . .'

'Wait,' I said. 'What happened to. . .'

Sally just closed her eyes and started to shake her head.
Like a little kid throwing a tantrum. I half-expected her to
stick her fingers in her ears and yell 'blah-blah-blah' to drown
me out. I got the message.

'Lily came back,' she continued, 'and she was like a child
again. We all thought she would be different maybe, but she
barely could take care of herself. So a tiny apartment we found
for her, cheap but close to where we lived. We took turns
bringing her food when we could and your mother. . .' she
paused here, choking on the words. I felt a coldness roll
through my bowel.

'Your mother liked to go over to Lily and play. She kept
Lily company and Lily would sing to her.'

I thought I saw Sally's eyes moisten and felt a pang myself.
I imagined it was the Polish lullaby that Lily sang to my
mother.

'It was later yet that the troubles started. We hadn't been
to see Lily for a while and your mother wanted to visit. I
made a kugel to take her.

'We knocked on her door, but she wouldn't open. Inside
we could hear Lily, talking and laughing, but to us there was
no answer. I knocked and knocked and your mother called
out to her. We heard her voice, but still the door was shut.

'I began to think something is terrible wrong, so I went to
get the super and I made him to open the door.'

Sally paused for a moment, her eyes open wide. She seemed
to be someplace else, looking at a picture from the past.

'Inside Lily sat at her table, all set with the best china and a
beautiful dinner. Two other chairs also she had there and she
was serving food and laughing.'

Sally looked right at me, now, streaks of moisture cutting across the deep crags in her old face.

'Who was she talking to, Grandma?'

Sally shook her head. 'Dolls. Two dolls, like made from *shmates*, she sat up in those chairs. She talked to them like they were people. She never looked at us, never saw. The super, he didn't say a word, just ran away fast as he could.

'I tried to talk to her, but Lily had not to hear. She just kept serving the food and talking to the dolls. One I heard her call Joseph and the other Avram. Such a coldness I felt, you shouldn't know. My heart still doesn't beat like it should when I think about it.'

'Were those the names of the husband and the boy? The ones who'd died?' I asked. Sally nodded, painfully.

'For days, only to the dolls Lily would talk, and never to leave the house. We all went, but she didn't see through her eyes. We left her food and cleaned a little, not that she noticed. Finally, one day your grandpa and me went over and the dolls were gone. We tried to ask her about it, but she made like she didn't know. Like a stone she was. Like a golem.

'Long after she would go funny like this. Everything fine, then suddenly she went away to that other place. To be with the dolls.'

There was a long silence. I thought about the horrors of Lily's life, of the terrible loss and the place her mind must have fled to escape from her memories. I thought again of my laughter that day so many years before and felt a rush of self-loathing. The nurse came in then and asked me to step out while she changed Sally's IV. I went into the men's room to piss and wash my face, but I couldn't look in the mirror as I stood at the sink.

I settled back into the chair, saw the nurse had smoothed the sheets and fluffed the pillow. Sally still looked uncomfortable, but a fresh glass of orange juice with a flex-straw sat on the tray by the bed.

'Why are you telling me all this now, Grandma? Why did you want me to come here after so many years?'

'It's Lily,' she said. 'Lily needs you.'

I exhaled slowly and deeply. I had no idea how to deal with this, wished more than anything that I was back home in Los Angeles with only earthquakes and riots and semi-literate student essays to worry about.

'Lily's dead, Grandma,' I said as softly as I could.

'I see her, Brucie,' Sally said. Her eyes took on the most life I'd yet seen. 'Every night she comes to me. I see her. Every night she tells me what it is has to be done. It's Brucie, she says, he's the only one who can do it.'

I didn't know what else to do but humour her. 'Do what, Grandma?'

Sally looked away from me, turned her head towards the tall curtain. She spoke without once looking back my way.

'This what I tell you now no one knows. Your grandpa and the others are all gone. Only me now. Your mother I never told and I don't want you should say to anyone else. Especially not your father.'

I was puzzled, but told her okay. Still she wouldn't look at me.

'Before Lily went back to Poland, there was a man. She was a foolish girl, Lily, but not so bad looking. This man, he . . . took advantage. You understand what I mean?'

I swallowed and nodded. I may have blushed.

'There was a baby, but Lily we knew couldn't take care on her own. So we all decided that someone else had to look after the little girl, this child without a father and no kind of a mother.

'It was agreed your grandfather and me should be the ones to take care of her. Always like our own we treated her. Never we told her the truth. We sent Lily away not just for Bella's family in Poland, but for ours. For yours. For your mother.'

Senility, I thought. Or drug-induced fantasy brought on by a lifetime of guilt over the mistreatment of her sister. Surely, that explained Sally's belief that the long-dead Lily came to see her.

And this other grotesque fantasy.

I was tired and annoyed that this was what I had come all

this way for, inconvenienced my life about. Until Sally turned and faced me and I looked into her eyes.

And I knew, I just knew, that it was all true.

'Oh Jesus, Grandma,' I said. 'Jesus Christ.'

'A terrible thing this has been to keep inside so many years, but it was the only way. Before the war it was a thing that was done. And after. . .'

I was in shock. The thought that Lily was my real grandmother sent me into new paroxysms of guilt. I looked back out the window. The rain had stopped and a setting sun made its final appearance of the day.

'What does Lily want me to do?' I asked, mostly to fill the deadly silence, intending sarcasm.

Sally didn't seem to notice.

'Lily wants you should find her son,' Sally said.

I'd already seen the in-flight movie, but sought refuge in it again to avoid my troubled thoughts. After an hour I surrendered and stuffed the cheap plastic headphones back into the seat pocket and stared out at the clouds.

I thought of poor Lily – *Grandma*, for Christ's sake – and the nightmare of her life. I racked my brain till my head ached trying to remember something more about her: the details of how she looked and dressed, the inflections of her voice, the things she said.

Anything.

But it was no use.

It came down, every time, to that damn dog, my hellish laughter and her sweet sad song.

Back in the hospital, Sally had told me that every night it was the same. She'd wake with a start and though she could feel the hospital bed beneath her, hear the blips and bleeps of her various monitors, she could also see her old Brooklyn apartment. The door would open and a youthful Lily stood there, naked and pregnant with the daughter that Sally would claim as her own. Lily would drift in like a balloon and float around the room. Sally would reach out for her, but Lily always bobbed out of reach. As she wafted through the air she rubbed at her swollen belly and tears streamed off her troubled face.

Lily told Sally how her adopted son had survived the Nazi killing machine, had been adopted by a Christian family not very far from the Sobibor death camp which had claimed his father. The boy was a boy no longer, Lily said, but he was in terrible trouble. He lived now not in Europe but in Montreal, where his adoptive parents had emigrated. Her grandson – me – she told Sally, had to go to this place to save him from some terrible thing. What it was, or how it was to be done she would or could not say. But the son of the daughter she had been denied was the only one who could act. Only through the daughter that was stolen, could she redeem the son who had been lost.

As Sally told me the story and no doubt saw my dubious expression she grew increasingly frantic. I tried to convince her that it was just a recurring dream, but she'd have none of it. She insisted it was real and that her nights had become a kind of torture. She clutched at my arm and dug her nails into my flesh, pleading with me to honour Lily's wishes and make good the offences of her past. She gasped for breath like a runner at the end of a marathon and her voice became a shrill chalkboard scratch as she begged me to promise to fulfill Lily's plea.

'What do you expect me to do?' I yelled at her. 'What do you expect? Am I supposed to scour a foreign city to find some old Polish guy and tell him his dead mother sent me to be his guardian angel? This is crazy!'

'No,' she told me. 'His new name Lily told to me. Wajda. Stefan Wajda. And where he lives even. You have to promise me, Brucie, you have to!'

I tried to protest again, but she started to scream. I couldn't believe, frail as she was, that the old lady could muster such intensity. The IV was slipping our of her arm and spittle and mucus exploded from her lips and nose. I feared she was about to stroke out.

'Promise,' Sally shrieked, 'promise, promise!'

'I promise,' I finally said in desperation. 'I do, I promise.'

She calmed down as soon as the words passed my lips and collapsed back on to the bed.

Yeah, I thought in the merciful quiet, *I promise.*

And I love you and the cheque's in the mail and I won't. . .

I promise, I thought again, silently mouthing the words as the plane descended into the Christmas-tree fantasy of lights that is Los Angeles.

Shit.

I awoke to the starkest moment of terror in my life. I've always been jealous of people who can remember their dreams because I never do. At most I usually recall an image or a feeling that melts like a vampire in the morning sun. This dream, though, was as real and solid to me as my own name.

It was Lily, of course. In what had to be the horrid Brooklyn tenement where she spent her life after the war. I saw her sitting at a rickety table heaped with plates piled with bones and gristle and rotten fruit. She stood between two high-backed chairs, each with a midget-sized rag doll perched on it. Sawdust stuffing spilled out of gaping holes and button-eyes hung off torn faces by frayed, black threads. One doll had an arm of real flesh with a bluish-black number etched into the peeling skin. The other was slighter, but no less ragged. Lily forced sharpened spoonfuls of greyish meat between their tightly sewn lips. I tried to move towards the table but hung suspended, like an insect in amber, condemned to watch. I looked at Lily, and for a moment, saw my mother's face ripple across her countenance like a slight Florida wave lapping across a sandbar.

Lily looked up at me. Tears of blood flowed from her soft eyes and ran down her cheeks in jagged streaks. She opened her mouth and through blackened teeth the horrid sound that emerged was the world's sorrow.

I woke with a start and dashed into the bathroom to throw up. I ran cold water over my wrists and splashed my face, rinsed my mouth. I stumbled back to bed, but sleep was out of the question. I lay awake thinking and shivering, though the night air was quite warm.

As the first grey finger of dawn poked a hole in the darkness, I got up and went to the phone. I looked up the Montreal area code in the phone book and dialled the number for information. In a voice as dry as a perfect martini I asked if there was a listing for Stefan Wajda, apologized for not having an address. The line was quiet for two unendurable moments. 'Thank you,' a computer-generated voice said, 'the number is. . .'

Fresh doubts assailed me as the plane hit turbulence near Salt Lake. I thought again of the crazy phone call that sent me packing, considered the possibility, the likelihood, that the Stefan Wajda I was going to see was a mere namesake of Lily's lost son. Was Wajda the Polish equivalent of Smith or Jones? Still, I was so shaken by the reality of *someone* by that name in the city of which Sally spoke that in a less than rational moment, I booked the flight. I didn't have a clue what I was going to do when I got there.

I thought again about Sally and about Lily and my terrible dream. I kept coming back to that brief moment in the dream when my mother's face flashed across Lily's and knew that this was about her as much as anything else. My mother had died, rather horribly, of cancer while I was at college, drinking and screwing and having fun. I hadn't wanted to face the horrors of her condition. Just as, at a younger age, I found a way not to face Lily's death, and more recently had avoided dealing with Sally's decline.

The promise I'd made to Sally, I knew, meant nothing in and of itself. I could tell myself that it was the reason for this insane excursion, but in that deep mental pit where we live with our unspeakable truths, I knew that this was about my mother. It was about a kind of expiation, a purging. About the debts – and respect – we each owe to our past.

Ain't guilt grand?

I had called an old college friend named Dornan who lived in Montreal. He met me at the airport. He was a bit puzzled by the sudden visit, but had happily agreed to put me up for a few days. He seemed to sense that I had something on my mind, but didn't pry. We reminisced some about the good old days as we drove back to his apartment. He already had a date arranged for the evening, invited me – sincerely – to tag along, but I told him no, that I had something to do.

I was exhausted physically and mentally, but grew restive shortly after Dornan went out. I snooped among his many bookshelves. I found the city White Pages on the third shelf, wedged between copies of Max Weber's *Protestant Ethic and the Spirit of Capitalism* and Art Spiegelman's *Maus*. I briefly puzzled over his organizational scheme, but my head hurt too much already.

There was only one Wajda, S in the book. The address listed was for Rue Saint-Cuthbert. A quick look at a map showed it to be a street within walking distance of Dornan's place. I stuffed the map in my pocket and carefully shut the door behind me.

Wajda's street was yuppy-ritzy with lots of black Saabs and BMWs parked in front of restored brownstones. It was quiet, with only the omnipresent background rush of the city to break the silence. The house matching Wajda's number stood at the end of the block. A great maple tree by his gate whispered in the warm night breeze, and through a small square of leaded glass in the front door I saw the glow of a dim yellow bulb. The rest of the house looked dark and empty. I leaned on the gate to the entrance path and stared at the door, unsure of what to do. What the hell was I *supposed* to do? It was almost eleven o'clock at night. I could hardly go up and knock at this hour. What would I say? I must have looked pretty damn suspicious lurking out front, but there was no one else on the street and not a single car passed while I waited.

What the fuck am I doing here? I thought. I suddenly felt ridiculous and was prepared to turn around and head back to Dornan's place, discounting the whole trip as temporary insanity, when I noticed the sound of an idling automobile engine. I glanced around at the parked cars, but they were all dark and lifeless. Cautiously, I opened the gate at the front of the house and took a few steps up the path.

The low rumble grew slightly louder.

I found my way around the side of the building and saw that there was a garage in back that opened on to a narrow alley running the length of the block. I pressed an ear to the corrugated steel door and heard and felt a deep bass reverberation from within.

I stood there for a minute, listening to the steady throb of the idle. I tried peering under the garage door, but no trace of light filtered out from inside. I glanced down the dark alley, but like the street, there wasn't a sign of life. Just a long row of locked garages.

As I stood there, a sick feeling overcame me with the suddenness of a heart attack. A sheen of nervous sweat oozed from my pores and my tongue went thick and dry in my mouth. I started to knock, then pound on the garage door and called Wajda's name at the top of my voice. When there was no response but the engine's throaty hum I began to kick at the door with all my strength. I saw some lights go on in nearby windows, but I ignored them.

I tried to turn the handle, but the garage door was locked and wouldn't budge. I kicked it again, trying to force the mechanism. Someone next door leaned out the window and yelled at me in French, but I didn't stop to respond. Instead, I dashed back around the house and leapt up the steps to the front door. I tried the knob, but of course it too was locked. I pounded on the door and stabbed repeatedly at the bell without result.

I stopped and thought carefully about my choices.

If I was wrong Dornan would likely be bailing me out of a Montreal jail and I was going to have to make up one hell of a story.

But if it was what I feared. . .

I saw a small garden spade among the shrubs and used it to break the thin square of glass in the front door, knocking jagged shards into the hall. I snaked my arm through the window and opened the locks, cutting my elbow on a tiny piece of glass.

I dashed about the house looking for the way in to the garage. I ran madly from room to room until I realized that I was one floor *above* the level of the back alley. I tried every door I came to until I found a flight of steps leading down. I couldn't feel the light switch and crashed into a second door at the bottom.

I flung that door open and smashed it into the dark headlights of the idling car. I was nearly overcome by the noxious carbon monoxide fumes. A bare thirty-watt bulb suspended from the ceiling had come on when I opened the door, illuminating the narrow garage. I gagged and covered my mouth and nose, peering through the smoke towards the driver's side. Slumped over the wheel of a Mercedes I saw the wan outline of a figure, one hand dangling out of the open window.

Coughing and retching, I ran around to the driver's door, but I could only open it a few inches before it scraped against the garage wall. I tugged at the limp body but he was too heavy for me to pick up. I touched his hand. It felt warm, but I couldn't find a pulse. Not that I ever could.

I switched off the engine then squeezed past to the back of the car. At the base of the garage door I saw that sheets and towels had been firmly wedged into all the gaps. I kicked them aside and reached for the handle. The door opened readily from the inside. I heaved it open as far as I could and took a deep gulp of the fresh night air. I hurried back inside and released the car's emergency brake. Then I went around front and, bracing myself against the garage wall, pushed the car backwards with my legs.

It rolled slowly, but the garage floor was on a slight grade. With another shove the car picked up speed and scooted out of the garage and into the alley until it crashed loudly into a solid brick wall across the way. I ran out behind it gasping for a clean breath.

In the alley, several neighbours had come to investigate the ruckus. Through blurry eyes, I saw a thin man in a red bathrobe pull Wajda out of the car and start to administer CPR. I heard the sound of approaching sirens even as I dizzily fell forward, the Mercedes' hood ornament looming in my vision like a harvest moon.

I sat in the back of an ambulance while a uniformed policeman interviewed me and a paramedic dressed the cut on my arm and a small gash in my forehead. I gave them Dornan's address and told them Wajda was a friend of a friend who I didn't know but had been told to look up while I was in town. The cop asked me what led me to check the garage or even suspect that anything was wrong. I glanced away, shook my head and told him the truth.

'I don't know,' I said. 'Just a feeling.'

The cop didn't look happy, but he had one of those faces that probably never did.

The crowd started to disperse as the ambulance sped off. I made eye contact with the man in the red bathrobe and went over to talk to him. He nodded as I approached and cinched his belt. He had bony legs. We watched for a moment as the last of the police pulled out of the alley, then introduced ourselves.

'Hell of a thing this, eh?' he said.

'You have no idea,' I said.

'You're a friend of Steve's, then?'

'Relative,' I said with a half-smile.

'Is that right? So you must know what this was about then.' *A-bewt*, he said, like a good Canadian.

I shook my head nervously. '*Distant* relative. Several times removed, you might say. And then some.'

'The wife and kid, I figure,' my new friend nodded.

'How's that?' I asked, my gut starting to roil. 'What about his wife and kid?'

'Don't you know?' he asked in that special voice reserved for the perversely joyful presentation of lurid news. 'Killed. Just a couple of weeks ago. Car accident, don't you know. The boy was quite young. I mean, considering Steve's age.

Terrible thing. Just awful. I suppose it was all too much for him.'

I must have visibly blanched because the man asked if I was all right. I nodded and mumbled something about the effects of the evening. He clucked sympathetically and patted me on the shoulder as we said goodnight.

I walked for a while – a few hours, actually – until I didn't know where I was and eventually found a cab. I started to give the driver Dornan's address, but suddenly changed my mind. I told him to take me to the hospital. I wanted, needed, to know how Wajda was. To make sure he had made it okay.

I wanted to see him again.

I emptied my mind as we drove, too numb to think or try and understand what had happened, how I got here or what it meant that Sally had really known about what was going to happen. I pressed my bruised forehead against the cool glass of the air-conditioned cab and let the lights of Montreal dance and shimmer in my fuzzy vision.

At the front desk I was told that Wajda's condition was listed as 'guarded', but that I would have to wait until morning for more details. I got his room number and thanked the receptionist. Then for reasons I can't entirely explain, I snuck around to a deserted hospital entrance. I tried to appear officious as I walked the quiet halls, but no one even looked at me twice. I hesitated outside his room. With a quick glance around, I eased the door open.

Wajda's wrists were secured to the guard rails as a precaution and an IV dripped into his left arm. I looked carefully at his thin, ashen face in the faint fluorescent glow. It was crazy to expect him to look like Lily – he was, I reminded myself, her blood nephew, not her son – but I thought I detected a trace of the family genes in his sharp-ridged cheeks and deep-set eyes.

He seemed to be breathing well and I somehow felt sure that he was going to be fine. That my bizarre journey of redemption, a trip I could never hope to truly understand, was over.

I started to sneak back out when my cousin's eyes opened

and he looked up at me. I froze as I saw a mixture of puzzlement and fear cross his face. I was tempted to bolt, but he dragged his tongue across chapped lips. I really didn't know if he should have water, but there was a cup and pitcher beside the bed so I figured it would be okay. I poured out two fingers' worth and held the cup to his lips. He lifted his head slightly and dabbed at it gingerly with his tongue. I put the cup aside and he smiled at me and for ever so slight a moment I thought I saw my mother's face in his.

I don't know what made me do it, it certainly wasn't a conscious thing.

I started to sing Lily's song.

With the second note, his expression went as wide as a western sky. As I sang, I saw tears pool in his eyes, felt them fall down my own cheeks.

When I got to the last line he sang it, too, in a voice as slight as a rose petal:

Never let anyone know.

I fell asleep almost as soon as I got back home to LA. And I dreamed. At least, I think it was a dream.

It was strange, because I could sort of make out the familiar contours of my bedroom in the background.

I found myself staring at Lily's apartment again, but this time the light was bright and soft and the air rich with the oniony smell of good home cooking. The table had been set for one, the plate heaped with steaming potato *latkes* and sour cream and a big bowl of borscht. Lily stood in the kitchen fussing over the stove, sweetly humming her little tune. She looked up at me for a moment and passed a wisp of a smile. Then she turned back to her cooking.

The telephone woke me up. I mean if I was asleep. The smell of fresh *latkes* seemed to linger in the air and it made me wonder.

I stumbled over to the receiver and mumbled a hello. It was my father calling from New York. Where had I been, he demanded, he had been calling all night. I made up a story about visiting friends in Santa Barbara and staying over when

I hadn't planned to. What was the big deal, I asked. He yelled a little more then calmed himself down.

He was calling, he said, because he had some bad news: my grandmother had died in her hospital in Florida.

I didn't bother to correct him about her identity, but I asked what had happened.

Nothing, he said. She died during the night. Peacefully. In her sleep.

> The red rose cries, 'She is near, she is near;'
> And the white rose weeps, 'She is late;'
> The larkspur listens, 'I hear, I hear;'
> And the lily whispers, 'I wait.'
> Alfred, Lord Tennyson, *Maud*

Jay Russell's audacious Hollywood horror romp *Celestial Dogs* was published in 1996. He recently followed it up with a revisionist vampire saga, *Blood!*, and is currently at work on an even more outrageous sequel to his début novel. Russell's short stories have previously appeared in the anthologies *Splatterpunks*, *Still Dead: Book of the Dead 2* and *The King is Dead: Tales of Elvis Post-Mortem*. 'The most horrible bits of Lily's story, which is to say the non-supernatural bits, are true,' explains the author. 'Lily died about twenty years ago, having lived at least as sad and lonely a life as the story suggests. I can remember her only from a child's point of view – which is to say fondly, but unreliably – and it was only as an adult that I learned, rather sketchily, of her experiences during the War and of her life afterwards. Thinking about it still makes me shudder with a kind of horror that even the best fiction (and I make no such claim for my own work) cannot begin to approximate. Many bits of 'Lily's Whisper' have been made up, partly out of dramatic necessity, partly because the details of Lily's real story are for ever lost. But at least Lily is remembered. And as I get older, I realize ever more just how important such things become.'

Hell Hath Enlarged Herself

MICHAEL MARSHALL SMITH

I always assumed I was going to get old. That there would come a time when just getting dressed left me breathless, when I would count a day without a nap as a victory; when I would go into a barber's and some young girl would lift up the remaining grey stragglers on my pate and look dubious if I asked her for anything more than a trim. I would have been polite to her, and tried to be charming, and she would have thought to herself how game the old bird was, while cutting off rather less than I'd asked her to. I thought all that was going to come, some day, and in a perverse sort of way I had even looked forward to it. A quiet end, a slowing down, an ellipsis to some other place.

But now I know it will not happen, that I will remain unresolved, like some fugue which didn't work out. Or perhaps more like a voice in a symphony, because I won't be the only one. I regret that. I'm going to miss having been old.

I left the facility at 6.30 yesterday, on the dot, as had been my practice. I took care to do everything as I always had, carefully collating my notes, tidying my desk and making a list of things to do tomorrow. I hung my white coat on the back of my office door as always and said goodbye to Johnny on the gate with a wink. For six months we have been engaged in a game which involves making some comment on the weather every time I enter or leave the facility, without either of us recoursing to speech. Yesterday Johnny raised his eyebrows at the dark and heavy clouds overhead and rolled his eyes – a standard gambit. I turned one corner of my mouth down and shrugged with the other shoulder, a more adventurous riposte, in recognition of the fact that this was the last time the game would ever be played. For a moment I wanted to do more, to say something, reach out and shake his hand; but that would have been too obvious a goodbye. Perhaps no one would have stopped me anyway, as it has become abundantly clear that I am as powerless as everyone else – but I didn't want to take the risk.

Then I found my car amongst the diminishing number which still park there, and left the compound for good.

The worst part for me, is that I knew David Ely, and understand how it all started. I was sent to work at the facility because I am partly to blame for what has happened. The original work was done together, but I was the one who had always given creed to the paranormal. David had never paid much heed to such things, not until they became an obsession. There may have been some chance remark of mine which made him open to the idea. Just having known me for so long may have been enough. If it was, then I'm sorry. There's not a great deal more I can say.

David and I met each other at the age of six, both of our fathers having taken up new positions at the same college – the University of Florida, in Gainesville. My father was in the Geography Faculty, his in Sociology, but at that time – the late eighties – the departments were drawing closer together and the two men became friends. Our families mingled closely, in countless back-yard barbecues and summer clambakes on the coast, and David and I grew up more like brothers than friends. We read the same clever books and hacked the same stupid computers, and even ended up losing our virginity on the same evening. One spring when we were both sixteen I borrowed my mother's car and the two of us loaded it up with books, a modem and a laptop and headed off to Sarasota in search of sun and beer. We found both, in quantity, and also two young English girls on holiday. We spent a week in courting spirals of increasing tightness,

playing pool and talking fizzy nonsense over cheap and exotic
pizzas, and on the last night two couples walked up the beach
in different directions.

Her name was Karen, and for a while I thought I was in
love. I wrote a letter to her twice a week, and to this day she's
probably received more mail from me than anyone else put
together. Each morning I went running down to the mailbox,
and ten years later the sight of an English postage stamp
would still bring a faint rush of blood to my ears. But we were
too far apart, and too young. Maybe she had to wait a day too
long for a letter once, or perhaps it was me who, without
realizing it, came back empty-handed from the mailbox one
too many times. Either way the letters started to slacken in
pace after six months and then, without either of us ever
saying anything directly, they simply stopped altogether.

A little while later I was with David in a bar and, in between
shots, he looked up at me.

'You ever hear from Karen any more?' he asked.

I shook my head, only at that moment realizing that it had
finally died. 'Not in a while.'

He nodded, and then took his shot, and missed, and as I
lined up for the black I realized that he'd probably been
through a similar thing. For the first time in our lives we'd
lost something. It didn't break our hearts. It had only lasted a
week, after all, and we were old enough to begin to recognize
that the world was full of girls, and that if we didn't get a
move on we'd hardly have got through any of them before it
was time to get married.

But does anyone ever replace that first person? That first
smile, first kiss, first fierce hug hidden in the sand amidst
darkness, dunes and grass? Sometimes, I guess. I kept the
letters from Karen for twenty years. Never read them, just
kept them. Last week I threw them all away.

What I'm saying is this. I knew David for a long, long time,
and I understood what we were trying to do. He was just
trying salve his own pain, and I was trying to help him.

What happened wasn't our fault.

*

I spent the evening driving slowly down 75, letting the freeway take me towards the Gulf coast of the panhandle. There were a few patches of rain, but for the most part the clouds just scudded overhead, running to some other place. I didn't see many other cars. Either people have given up fleeing, or all those capable of it have already fled. I got off just after Jocca, and headed down minor roads, trying to cut round Tampa and St Petersburg. I managed it, but it wasn't easy, and I ended up getting lost more than a few times. I would have brought a map but I'd thought I could remember the back way. I couldn't. It had been too long.

We'd heard on the radio in the afternoon that things weren't going so hot around Tampa. It was the last thing we heard, just before the signal cut out. The six of us remaining in the facility just sat around for a while, as if we believed the radio would come back on again real soon now. When it didn't we got up one by one and drifted back to work.

As I passed the city I could see it burning in the distance, and I was glad I had taken the back way, no matter how long it took. If you've seen what it's like when a large number of people go together, you'll understand what I mean.

Eventually I found 301 and headed down it towards 41, towards the old Coast Road.

Summer of 2005. For David and me it was time to make a decision. There was no question but that we would go to college – our families were both book-bashers from way back. The money was already in place, some from our parents but most from holiday jobs we'd played at. The question was what we were going to study.

I thought long and hard, but in the end still couldn't come to a decision. I postponed for a year and decided to take off round the world. My parents shrugged, said, 'Okay, keep in touch, try not to get killed, and stop by at your Aunt Kate's in Sydney.' They were that kind of people. I remember my sister bringing a friend of hers back to the house one time; the girl called herself Yax and her hair had been carefully dyed and sculpted to resemble an orange explosion. My mother just asked her where she had it done, and kept looking at it in a thoughtful way. I guess my dad must have talked her out of it.

David went for computers. Full-on systems design. He got a place at Jacksonville's new Centre for Advanced Computing, which was a coup but no real surprise. David was always a hell of a bright guy. That was part of his problem.

It was strange saying goodbye to each other after so many years in each other's pockets, but I suppose we knew it was going to happen sooner or later. The plan was that he'd come out and hook up with me for a couple of months during the year. It didn't happen, for the reason that pacts between old friends usually get forgotten. Someone else entered the picture.

I did my grand tour. I saw Europe, started to head through the Middle East and then thought better of it and flew down to Australia instead. I stopped by and saw Aunt Kate, which earned me big brownie points back home and wasn't in any way arduous. She and her family were a lot of fun, and there was a long drunken evening when she seemed to be taking messages from beyond, which was kind of interesting. My mother's side of the family was always reputed to have a touch of the medium about them, and Aunt Kate certainly did. There was an even more entertaining evening when my cousin Jenny and I probably overstepped the bounds of conventional morality in the back seat of her jeep – but I plead the Fifth on that. After Australia I hacked up through the Far East for a while until time and money ran out, and then I went home.

I came back with a major tan, an empty wallet, and still no real idea of what I was going to do with my life. With a couple months to go before I had to make a decision, I decided to go visit David. I hopped on a bus and made my way up to Jacksonville on a day which was warm and full of promise. Anything could happen, I believed, and everything was there for the taking. Perhaps that was adolescent naïveté, but I was an adolescent. How was I supposed to know otherwise? I'd led a pretty charmed life up until then, and I didn't see any real reason why it shouldn't continue. I sat in the bus and stared out the window, watching the world go by and wishing it the very best. It was a good day, and I'm glad it was. Because though I didn't know it then, the new history of the world probably started at the end of it.

I got there late afternoon, and asked around for David. Eventually someone pointed me in the right direction, to a house just off campus. I found the building and tramped up the stairs, wondering whether I shouldn't maybe have called ahead.

Eventually I found his door. I knocked, and some man I didn't recognize opened it. It took me a couple of seconds to work out it was David. He'd grown a beard. I decided not to hold it against him just yet, and we hugged like, well, like what we were. Two best friends, seeing each other after what suddenly seemed like far too long.

'Wow, big bonding,' drawled a female voice. A head slipped into view from round the door, with wild brown hair and big green eyes. That was the first time I saw Rebecca.

Four hours later we were in a bar somewhere. I'd met Rebecca properly and realized she was special. In fact, it's probably a good thing that they'd met six months before, and that she was so evidently in love with David. Had we met her at the same time, she could have been the first thing we'd ever fallen out over. She was beautiful, in a strange and quirky way that always made me think of forests; and she was clever, in that particularly appealing fashion which meant she didn't always be having to prove it. She moved like a cat on a sleepy afternoon, but her eyes were always alive – even when they couldn't co-operate with each other enough to allow her to accurately judge the distance to her glass. She was my best friend's girl, she was a good one, and I was very happy for them.

Rebecca was at the School of Medical Science, designing little machines, little bigger than molecules, which could float round the body doing maintenance work. Nanotech was just coming off big around then, and it looked like she was going to catch the wave and go with it. In fact, when the two of them talked about their work, it made me wish I hadn't taken the year off. Things were happening for them. They had a direction. All I had was goodwill towards the world, and the belief that it loved me too. For the first time I had that terrible sensation that life is leaving you behind and you'll never catch up again.

Around 1.00 a.m. we were still going strong. David lurched in the general direction of the bar to get us some more beer, navigating the treacherously level floor like a man on stilts for the first time.

'Why don't you come here?' Rebecca said suddenly. I turned to her, and she shrugged. 'David misses you, I don't think you're too much of an asshole, and what else are you going to do?'

I looked down at the table for a moment, thinking it over. Immediately it sounded like a good idea. But on the other hand, what would I do? And could I handle being a third wheel, instead of half a bicycle? I asked the first question first.

'We've got plans,' Rebecca replied. 'Stuff we want to do. You could come in with us. I know David would want you to. He always says you're the cleverest guy he's ever met.'

I glanced across at David, who was conversing affably with the barman. We'd decided that to save energy we should start buying them two at a time, and David appeared to be explaining this plan. As I watched, the barman laughed. David was like that. He could get on with absolutely anyone.

'And you're sure I'm not too much of an asshole?'

Deadpan: 'Nothing that I won't be able to kick out of you.'

And that's how I ended up applying for, and getting, a place on Jacksonville's nanotech programme. When David got back to the table I wondered aloud whether I should come up to college, and his reaction was big enough to seal the decision there and then. It was he who suggested I go nanotech, and he who explained their plan.

For years people had been trying to crack the nanotech nut. Building tiny biological 'machines', some of them little bigger than large molecules, designed to be introduced into the human body to perform some function or other: promoting the secretion of certain hormones; eroding calcium build-ups in arteries; destroying cells which looked like they were going cancerous. In the way that these things have, it had taken a long time before the first proper results started coming through – but in the last three years it had really been gathering pace. When David had met Rebecca, a couple of weeks into the first semester, they'd talked about their two subjects, and David had immediately recognized that sooner or later there would be a second wave, and that they could be the first to realize it.

Lots of independent little machines was one thing. How about lots of little machines which worked together? All designed for particular functions, but co-ordinated by a neural relationship with each other, possessed of a power and intelligence that was greater than the sum of its parts. Imagine what *that* could do.

When I heard the idea I whistled. I tried to, anyway. My lips had gone all rubbery from too much beer and and instead the sound came out as a sort of parping noise. But they understood what I meant.

'And no one else is working on this?'

'Not yet,' David said, and I had to smile. We'd always both nurtured plans for world domination. 'With the three of us together, no one else stands a chance.'

And so it was decided, and ratified, and discussed, over just about all the beer the bar had left. At the end of the evening we crawled back to David and Rebecca's room on our hands and knees, and I passed out on the sofa. The next day, trembling under the weight of a hangover which passed all understanding, I found a place to stay in town and went to talk to someone in the faculty of Medical Science. By the end of the week it was confirmed.

On the day I was officially enrolled in the next year's intake the three of us went out to dinner. We went to a nice restaurant, and we ate and drank, and then at the end of the meal we placed our hands on top of each other's in the centre of the table. David's went down first, then Rebecca's, and then mine on top. With our other hands we raised our glasses.

'To us,' I said. It wasn't very original, I know, but it's what

I meant. We drank, and then the three of us clasped each other's hands until our knuckles were white.

Ten years later Rebecca was dead.

The Coast Road was deserted, as I had expected. The one thing nobody is doing these days is heading off down to the beach to hang out. I passed a few vehicles abandoned by the side of the road, but took care not to drive too close. Often people will hide inside or behind and then leap out at anyone who passes, regardless of whether that person is in a moving vehicle or not.

I kept my eyes on the sea for the most part, concentrating on what was the same, rather than what was different. The ocean looked exactly as it always had, though I suppose usually there would have been ships to see out on the horizon. There probably still are a few, floating aimlessly wherever the tide takes them, their decks echoing and empty or awash with blood. But I didn't see any.

When I reached Sarasota I slowed still further, until I pulled to a halt in the centre of the square. It's not a big town, Sarasota. Many, many years ago I suspect it had class, before the tide of its fashionability drew out. For the last forty or so it has only had the ocean, but that was enough. Though the stores around the square were more than full enough of the usual kind of junk the restaurants were good, and some of the old, small hotels were attractive, in a dated kind of way. Not as flashy as the deco strips on Old Miami Beach, but nice enough.

Last night the square was littered with burned-out cars, and the pizzeria where we used to eat was still smouldering, the embers glowing in the fading light.

We worked through our degrees and out into post-graduate years. At first I had a lot to catch up on. Sometimes Rebecca snuck me into class, but most of the time I just pored over their notes and books, and we talked long into the night. Catching up wasn't too hard, but keeping up with both of them was a struggle. I never understood the nanotech side as well as Rebecca, or the computing as deeply as David, but that was probably an advantage. I stood between the two of them, and it was in my mind where the two disciplines most equally met. Without me there, it's probable none of it would ever had come to fruition. So maybe if you come right down to it, and it's anyone's fault, it's mine.

David's goal was designing a system which would take the input and imperatives of a number of small component parts, and synthesize them into a greater whole – catering for the fact that the concerns of biological organisms are seldom clear-cut. The fuzzy logic wasn't difficult – God knows we were familiar enough with it, most noticeably in our ability to reason that we needed another beer when we couldn't even remember where the fridge was. More difficult was designing and implementing the means by which the different machines, or 'beckies', as we elected to call them, interfaced with each other.

Rebecca concentrated on the physical side of the problem, synthesizing beckies with intelligence coded into artificial DNA in a manner which enabled the 'brain' of each type to link up with and transfer information to the others. And remember, when I say 'machines' I'm not talking about large metal objects which sit in the corner of the room making unattractive noises and drinking a lot of oil. I'm talking about strings of molecules hardwired together, invisible to the naked eye.

I helped them both with their specific areas, and did most of the development work in the middle, designing the overall system. It was me who came up with the first product to aim for, 'ImmunityWorks'.

The problem of diagnosing malfunction in the human body has always been the number of variables, many of which are difficult to monitor effectively from the outside. If someone sneezes, they could just have a cold. On the other hand, they could have flu, or the bubonic plague – or even just some dust up their nose. Unless you can test all the relevant parameters, you're not going to know what the real problem is – or the best way of treating it. We were aiming for an integrated set of beckies which could test all the relevant conditions, share their findings, and determine the best way of tackling the problem – all at the molecular level, without human intervention of any kind. The system had to be robust – to withstand interaction with the body's own immune system – and intelligent. We weren't intending to just tackle things which made you sneeze, either: we were never knowingly under-ambitious. Even for ImmunityWorks 1.0 we were aiming for a system which could cope with a wide range of viruses, bacteria and general senescence: a first aid kit which lived in the body, anticipating problems and solving them before they even got started. A kind of guardian angel, which would co-exist with the human system and protect it from harm.

We were right on the edge of knowledge, and we knew it. The roots of disease in the human body weren't properly understood, never mind the best ways to deal with them. An individual trying to do what we were doing would have needed about three hundred years and a research grant bigger than God's. But we weren't just one person. We weren't even just three. Like the system we were trying to design, we were a perfect symbiosis, three minds whose joint product was incomparably greater than the sum of its parts. Also, we worked like maniacs. After we'd received our Doctorates we rented an old house together away from the campus and turned the top floor into a private lab. Obviously there were arguments for putting it in the basement, historical precedents for example, but the top floor had a better view and as that's where we spent most of our time, that kind of thing was an issue. We got up, we did enough to maintain our tenure at the University, and we worked on our own project in secret.

David and Rebecca had each other. I had an intermittent string of short liaisons, each of whom felt I was being unfaithful to something, or to someone. It wasn't Rebecca I was thinking of. God knows she was beautiful enough, and lovely enough, to pine after, but I didn't. Lusting after Rebecca would have felt like one of our beckies deciding to work with only some, not all, of the others in its system. The whole thing would have ground to a halt.

Unfaithful to us, I suppose is what I felt. To the three of us.

It took us four years to fully appreciate what we were getting into, and to establish just how much work was involved. The years after that were a process of slow, grinding progress. David and I modelled an artificial body on the computer, creating an environment in which we could test virtual versions of the beckies Rebecca and I were busy trying to synthesize. Occasionally we'd enlist the assistance of someone from the medical faculty, when we needed more of an insight into a particular disease; but this was always done covertly, and without letting on what we were doing. This was our project, and we weren't going to share it with anyone.

By July of 2016 the software side of ImmunityWorks was in beta, and holding up well. We'd created code equivalents of all the major viruses and bacteria, and built creeping failures into the code of the virtual body itself – to represent the random processes of physical malfunction. An initial set of 137 different virtual beckies was doing a sterling job of keeping an eye out for problems, then charging in and sorting them out whenever they occurred.

The physical side was proceeding a little more slowly. Creating miniature biomachines is a difficult process, and when they didn't do what they were supposed to you couldn't exactly lift up the hood and poke around inside. The key problem, and the one which took the most time to solve, was that of imparting a sufficient degree of consciousness to the system as a whole – the aptitude for the component parts to work together, exchanging information and determining the most profitable course of action in any given circumstance. We probably built in a lot more intelligence than was necessary in the end; in fact I know we did; but it was simpler than trying to hone down the necessary conditions right away. We could always streamline in ImmunityWorks 1.1, we felt, when the system had proved itself and we had patents nobody could crack. We also gave the beckies the ability to perform simple manipulations of the matter around them. It was an essential part of their role that they be able to take action on affected tissue once they'd determined what the problem was. Otherwise it would only have been a diagnostic tool, and we were aiming higher than that.

By October we were closing in, and were ready to run a test on a monkey which we'd infected with a copy of the Marburg strain of the Ebola virus. We'd pumped a whole lot of other shit into it as well, but it was the filovirus we were most interested in. If ImmunityWorks could handle that, we reckoned, we were really getting somewhere.

Yes, of course it was a stupid thing to do. We had a monkey jacked full of the most communicable virus known to man *in our house*. The lab was heavily secured by then, but it was still an insane risk. I think in retrospect that we were so caught up in what we were doing, in our own joint mind, that normal considerations had ceased to really register. We didn't even need to do the Ebola test. That's the really tragic thing. It was unnecessary. It was pure arrogance, and also fantastically illegal. We could have just tested ImmunityWorks on plain vanilla viruses, or artificially induced cancers. If it had worked we could have contacted the media and owned our own islands within two years.

But no. We had to go the whole way.

The monkey sat in its cage, looking really very ill, with any number of sensors and electrodes taped and wired on and into its skull and body. Drips connected to bioanalysers gave a second-by-second read-out of the muck that was floating around in the poor animal's bloodstream. About two hours before the animal was due to start throwing clots, David threw the switch which would inject a solution of ImmunityWorks 0.9b7 into its body.

The time was 16.23, October 14th, 2016, and for the next twenty-four hours we watched.

At first the monkey continued to get worse. Arteries started clotting and the heartbeat grew ragged and fitful. The artificial cancer which we'd induced in the animal's pancreas also appeared to be holding strong. We sat, and smoked, and drank coffee, our hearts sinking. Maybe, we began to think, we weren't so damned clever after all.

Then ... that moment. Even now, as I sit here in this abandoned hotel and listen for sounds of movement outside, I can remember the moment when the read-outs started to turn around.

The clots started to break up. The cancerous cells started to lose vitality. The breed of simian flu which we'd acquired illicitly from the University's labs went into remission.

The monkey started getting better.

And we felt like Gods, and stayed that way even when the monkey suddenly died of shock a day later. We knew by then that there was more work to do in buffering the effects the beckies had on the body. That wasn't important. It was just a detail. We had screeds of data from the experiment, and David's AI systems were already integrating it into the next version of the ImmunityWorks software. Rebecca and I made the tweaks to the beckies, stamping the revised software into the biomachines and refining the way they interfaced with the body's own immune system.

We only really came down to earth the next day, when we realized that Rebecca had contracted Marburg.

Eventually the sight of Sarasota's dying heart palled and I started the car up again. I drove a little further along the coast to the Lido Beach Inn, which stands just where the town starts to settle into a line of beach motels. I turned into the driveway and cruised slowly up to the entrance arch, peering into the lobby. There was nobody inside, or if there was, they were crouching in darkness. I let the car roll down the slope until I was inside the hotel court proper, and then pulled into a space.

I climbed out, pulled my bag from the passenger seat and locked the car up. Then I went to the trunk and took out the bag of groceries which I'd carefully culled from the stock back at the facility. I stood by the car for a moment, hearing nothing but the sound of waves over the wall at the end, and looked around. I saw no one, and no signs of violence, and so I headed for the stairs to go up to the second floor, and towards room 211. I had an old copy of the key, 'accidentally' not returned many years ago, which was just as well. The lobby was a pool of utter blackness in an evening which was already dark, and I had no intention of going anywhere near it.

For a moment, as I stood outside the door to the room, I thought I heard a girl's laughter, quiet and far away. I stood still for a moment, mouth slightly open to aid hearing, and heard nothing else.

Probably it was nothing more than a memory.

Rebecca died two days later in an isolation chamber. She bled and crashed out in the small hours of the morning, as David and I watched through glass. My head hurt so much from crying that I thought it was going to split, and David's throat was so hoarse he could barely speak. David wanted to be in there with her, but I dissuaded him. To be frank, I punched him out until he was too groggy to fight any more. There was nothing he could do, and Rebecca didn't want him to die. She told me so through the intercom, and as that was her last comprehensible wish, I decided it would be so.

We knew enough about Marburg that we could almost feel her body cavities filling up with blood, smell the blackness as it coagulated in her. When she started bleeding from her eyes I turned away, but David watched every moment. We talked to her until there was nothing left to speak to, and then watched powerless as she drifted away retreating into some upper and hidden hall while her body collapsed around her.

Of course we tried ImmunityWorks. Again, it nearly worked. Nearly but not quite. When Rebecca's vital signs finally stopped, her body was as clean as a whistle. But it was still dead.

David and I stayed in the lab for three days, waiting. Neither of us contracted the disease. Lucky old us.

We dressed in biohazard suits and sprayed the entire house with a solution of ImmunityWorks, top to bottom. Then we put the remains of Rebecca's body into a sealed casket, drove upstate and buried it in a forest she would have liked. Her parents were dead, and she had no family to miss her, except us.

David left the day after the burial. We had barely spoken in the intervening period. I was sitting numbly in the kitchen on that morning and he walked in with an overnight bag. He looked at me, nodded, and left. I didn't see him again for two years.

I stayed in the house and once I'd determined that the lab was clean, I carried on. What else was there to do?

Working on the project by myself was like trying to play chess with two thirds of my mind burned out: the intuitive leaps which had been commonplace when the three of us were together simply didn't come, and were replaced by hours of painstaking, agonizingly slow experiment. On the other hand, I didn't kill anyone. I worked. I ate. I drove most weekends to the forest where Rebecca lay, and became familiar with the paths and light beneath the trees which sheltered her.

I refined the beckies, eventually understanding the precise nature of the shock reaction which had killed our two subjects. I pumped more and more intelligence into the system, amping the ability of the component parts to interact with each other and make their own decisions. In a year I had the system to a point where it was faultless on common viruses, like flu. Little did the world know it, but while they were out there sniffing and coughing I had stuff sitting in ampoules which could have sorted them out for ever. But that wasn't the point. Immunity-Works had to work on everything. That had always been our goal, and if I was going to carry on, I was going to do it our way. I was doing it for us, or for the memory of how we'd been. The two best friends I'd ever had were gone, and if the only way I could hang on to some memory of them was through working on the project, that was what I would do.

Then one day one of them reappeared.

I was in the lab, tinkering with the subset of the beckies whose job it was to synthesize new materials out of damaged body cells. The newest strain of biomachines was capable of far, far more than the originals had been. Not only could they fight the organisms and processes which caused disease in the first place, but they could then directly repair essential cells and organs within the body to ensure that it made a healthy recovery.

'Can you do anything about colds yet?' asked a voice, and I turned to see David, standing in the doorway to the lab. He'd lost about two stone in weight, and looked exhausted beyond words. There were lines around his eyes, and he looked older in other ways too. As I stared at him he coughed raggedly.

'Yes,' I said, struggling to keep my voice calm. David held his arm out and pulled his sleeve up. I found an ampoule of my most recent brew and spiked it with a hypo. 'Where did you pick it up?'

'England.'

'Is that where you've been?' I asked, as I slipped the needle into his arm and sent the beckies scurrying into his system.

'Some of the time.'

'Why?'

'Why not?' he shrugged, and rolled his sleeve back up.

I waited in the kitchen while he showered and changed, sipping a beer and feeling obscurely nervous. Eventually he reappeared, looking better but still very tired. I suggested going out to a bar, and we did, carefully but unspokenly avoiding those we used to go to as a threesome. Neither of us had mentioned Rebecca yet, but she was there between us in everything we said and didn't say. We walked down winter streets to a place I knew had opened recently, and it was almost as if for the first time I felt I was grieving for her properly. While David had been away, it had been as if they'd just gone away somewhere together. Now he was here, I could no longer deny that she was dead.

We didn't say much for a while, and all I learnt was that David had spent much of the last two years in Eastern Europe. I didn't push him, but simply let the conversation take its own course. It had always been David's way that he would get round to things in his own good time.

'I want to come back,' he said eventually.

'David, as far as I'm concerned you never went away.'

'That's not what I mean. I want to start the project up again, but different.'

'Different in what way?'

He told me. It took me a while to understand what he was talking about, and when I did I began to feel tired, and cold, and sad. David didn't want to refine ImmunityWorks. He had lost all interest in the body, except in the ways in which it supported the mind. He had spent his time in Europe visiting people of a certain kind, trying to establish what it was about them that made them different. Had I known, I could have recommended my Aunt Kate to him – not, I felt, that it would have made any difference. I watched him covertly as he talked, as he became more and more animated, and all I could feel was a sense of dread, that for the rest of his life my friend would be lost to me.

What he believed was this. He believed that mediums, people who can communicate with the spirits of the dead, do not possess some special spiritual power, but instead a difference in the physical make-up of their mind. He believed that it was some fundamental but minor difference in the wiring of their senses which enabled them to bridge a gap between this world and the next, to hear voices which had stopped speaking, see faces which had faded away. What he wanted to do was determine where this difference lay, pin-point it and learn to replicate it. He wanted to develop a species of becky which anyone could take, which would rewire their soul and enable them to become a medium.

More specifically, he wanted to take it himself, and I understood why and as I realized what he was hoping for I felt like crying for the first time in two years.

He wanted to be able to talk with Rebecca again, and I knew both that he was not insane and that there was nothing I could do except help him.

He put his hand down on the table and I placed mine on top of it.

Room 211 was as I remembered it. Nondescript. A decent-sized room in a mid-range motel. I put my bags on one of the twin beds and checked out the bathroom. It was clean and the shower still gave a thin trickle of luke-warm water. I washed and changed into one of the two sets of casual clothes I had brought with me, and then I made a sandwich out of cold cuts and processed cheese, storing the remainder in the small fridge in the corner by the television. I turned the latter on briefly and got snow across the board, though I heard the occasional half-word which suggested that someone was still trying somewhere.

I propped the door to the room open with a Bible and dragged a chair out on to the walkway, and then I sat and ate my food and drank a beer looking down across the court. The pool was half full, and a deck chair floated in one end of it.

Our approach was very simple. Using some savings of mine we flew to Australia, where I talked Aunt Kate into letting us take minute samples of tissue from different areas of her brain, using a battery of lymph-based beckies. We didn't tell her what the samples were for, simply that we were researching genetic traits. Jenny was now married to an accountant, it transpired, and they, Aunt Kate and David and I sat out that night on the porch and watched the sun turn red.

The next day we flew home again and went straight on to Gainesville, where I had a much harder time persuading my mother to let us do the same thing. In the end, she relented, and despite claiming that the beckies had 'tickled', had to admit it hadn't hurt. She seemed fit, and well, as did my father when he returned from work. I saw them once again, briefly about two months ago. I've tried calling them since, but the line is dead.

Back at Jacksonville David and I did the same thing with our own brains, and then the real work began. If, we reasoned, there really was some kind of physiological basis to the phenomena we were searching for then it ought to show up to varying degrees in my family line, and less so – or not at all – in David. We had no idea whether it would be down to some chemical balance, a difference in synaptic function, or a virtual 'sixth sense' which some sub-section of the brain was sensitive to – and so in the beginning we just used part of the samples to find out exactly what we'd got to work with.

We drew the blinds and stayed inside, and worked eighteen hours a day. David said little, and for much of the time seemed only half the person he used to be. I realized that until we succeeded in letting him talk with his love again, I would not see the friend I knew. We both had our reasons for doing what we did.

It took a little longer than we'd hoped, but we threw a lot of computing power at it and in the end began to see results. The implications of the data we'd collated were complex, and not absolutely conclusive, but appeared to suggest that all three possibilities were partly true. My aunt showed a minute difference in synaptic function in certain areas of her brain, which I shared, but not the fractional chemical imbalances which were present in both my mother and me. On the other hand, there was evidence of a loose meta-structure of apparently unrelated areas of her brain which was only present in trace degrees in my mother, and not at all in me. We took these results and correlated them against the findings from the samples of David's brain, and finally came to a tentative conclusion.

The ability, if it truly was related to physiological morphology, seemed most directly related to an apparently insignificant variation in general synaptic function which created an almost intangible additional structure within certain areas of the brain.

Not, perhaps, one of the most memorable slogans of scientific discovery, but that night David and I went out and got more drunk than we had in five years. We clasped hands on the table once more, and this time we believed that the hand that should have been between ours was nearly within reach. The next day we split into two overlapping teams, dividing our time and minds as always between the software and the beckies. The beckies needed redesigning to cope with the new environment, and the software required yet another quantum leap to deal with the complexity of the tasks of synaptic manipulation. As we worked we joked that if the beckies got much more intelligent we'd have to give them the vote. It seemed funny back then.

November 12th, 2017 ought to have a significant place in the history of science, despite everything that happened afterwards. It was the day on which we tested MindWorks, 1.0, a combination of computer and corporeal which was probably more subtle than anything man has ever produced. David insisted on being the first subject, despite the fact that he had another cold, and in the early afternoon on that day I injected him with a tiny dose of the beckies. Then, in a flash of solidarity, I injected myself. Together till the end, we said – though, at the end, we weren't.

We sat there for five minutes, and then got on with some work. We knew that the effects, if there were any, wouldn't be immediate. To be absolutely honest, we weren't expecting much at all from the first batch. As everyone knows, anything with the version number '1' will have teething problems, and if it has a '.0' after it then it's going to crash and burn. We sat and tinkered with the plans for a 1.1 version, which was only different in that some of the algorithms were more elegant, but couldn't seem to concentrate. Excitement, we assumed.

Then late afternoon David staggered, and dropped a flask of the solution he was working on. It was full of MindWorks, but that didn't matter – we had a whole vat of it in storage. I made David sit down and ran a series of tests on him. Physically he was okay, and protested that he felt fine. We shrugged and went back to work. I printed out ten copies of the code and becky specifications, and posted them to ten different places around the world. If this worked it was going to be ours, and no one else was taking credit for it. Such considerations were actually less important to us by then, because there was only one thing we wanted from the experiment – but old habits die hard. Ten minutes later I had a dizzy spell myself, but apart from that nothing seemed to be happening at all.

We only realized that we might have succeeded when I woke to hear David screaming in the night.

I ran into his room and found him crouched up against the

wall, eyes wide, teeth chattering uncontrollably. He was
staring at the opposite corner of the room. He didn't seem to
be able to hear anything I said to him. As I stood there
numbly, wondering what to do, I heard a voice from behind
me – a voice I half-thought I recognized. I turned, but there
was no one there. Suddenly David looked at me, his eyes wide
and terrified.

'Fuck,' he said. 'I think it's working.'

We spent the rest of the night in the kitchen, sitting round
the table and drinking coffee in the harsh light. David didn't
seem to be able to remember exactly what it was he'd seen,
and I couldn't recapture the sound of the voice I'd heard, or
what it might have said. Clearly we'd achieved something, but
it wasn't clear what it might be. When nothing further
happened by daybreak, we decided to get out of the house for
a while. We were both too keyed up to sit around any longer
or try to work but felt we should stay together. Something
was happening, we knew: we could both feel it. We walked
around campus for the morning, had lunch in the cafeteria,
then spent the afternoon downtown. The streets seemed very
crowded, but apart from that nothing else weird happened.

In the evening we went out. We had been invited to a
dinner party at the house of a couple on the medical staff, and
thought we might as well attend. David and I were a little
distracted at first, but once everyone had enough wine inside
them we started to have a good time. The hosts got out their
store of somewhat elderly dope, and by midnight we were all
a little high, comfortably sprawled around the living room.

And of course, eventually, David started talking about the
work we'd been doing. At first people just laughed hysterically,
and that made me realize belatedly just how far outside the
scope of normal scientific endeavour we had moved. It also
made me determined that we should be taken seriously, and
so I started to back David up. It was stupid, and we should
never have mentioned it. It was one of the people at that party
who eventually gave our names to the police.

'So prove it,' this man said at one stage. 'Hey, is there a
ouija board in the house?'

The general laughter which greeted this sally was enough to tip the balance. David rose unsteadily to his feet and stood in the centre of the room. He sneezed twice, to general amusement, but then his head seemed to clear. Though he was swaying gently, the seriousness of his face was enough to quieten most people, although there was a certain amount of giggling. He looked gaunt, and everybody stopped talking and the room went very quiet as they watched him.

'Hello?' he said quietly. He didn't use a name, for obvious reasons, but I knew who he was asking for. 'Are you there?'

'And if so, did you bring any grass?' the hostess added, getting a big laugh. I shook my head, partly at how foolish we were seeming, partly because there seemed to be a faint glow in one corner of the room, as if some of the receptors in my eyes were firing strangely. I made a note to check the beckies when we got back, to make sure none of them could have had an effect on the optic nerve.

I was about to say something, to help David out of an embarrassing position, when he suddenly turned to the hostess.

'Jackie, how many people did you invite tonight?'

'Eight,' she said. 'We always have eight. We've only got eight complete sets of tableware.'

David looked at me. 'How many people do you see?' he asked.

I looked round the room, counting.

'Eleven,' I said. One of the guests laughed nervously. I counted them again. There were eleven people in the room. In addition to the eight of us who were slouched over the settees and floor, three people stood round the sides. A tall man, with long and not especially clean brown hair. A woman in her forties, with blank eyes. A young girl, maybe eight years old.

Mouth hanging open, I stood up to join David. We looked from each of the extra figures to the other. They looked entirely real, as if they'd been there all along. They stared back at us, silently.

'Come on, guys,' said the host nervously. 'Okay, great gag –

you had us fooled for a moment there. Now let's have another smoke.'

David ignored him, turning to the man with the long hair.

'What's your name?' he asked him. There was a long pause, as if the man was having difficulty remembering. When he spoke, his voice sounded dry and cold.

'Nat,' he said. 'Nat Simon.'

'David,' I said. 'Be careful.'

David ignored me, and turned back to face the real guests. 'Does the name "Nat Simon" mean anything to anyone here?' he asked.

For a moment I thought it hadn't, and then we noticed the hostess. The smile had slipped from her face and her skin had gone white, and she was staring at David. With a sudden, ragged beat of my heart I knew we had succeeded.

'Who was he?' I asked quickly. I wish I hadn't. In a room that was now utterly silent she told us.

Nat Simon had been a friend of one of her uncles. One summer, when she was five years old, he had raped her every day for two weeks. He was killed in a car accident when she was fourteen, and since then she'd thought she'd been free.

'Tell Jackie I've come back to see her,' Nat said proudly, 'And I'm all fired up and ready to go.' He had taken his penis out of his trousers and was stroking it towards erection.

'Go away,' I said. 'Fuck off back where you came from.'

Nat just smiled. 'Ain't ever been anywhere else,' he said. 'Like to stay as close to little Jackie as I can.'

David quickly asked the other two figures who they were. I tried to stop him, but the other guests encouraged him, at least until they heard the answers. Then the party ended abruptly. Voyeurism becomes a lot less amusing when it's you people are staring at.

The blank-eyed woman was the first wife of the man who had joked about ouija boards. After discovering his affair with one of his students she had committed suicide in their living room.

The little girl was the host's sister. She died in childhood, hit by a car while running across the road as part of a dare devised by her brother.

By the time David and I ran out of the house, two of the other guests had already started being able to see for themselves, and the number of people at the party had risen to fifteen.

After four beers my mind was a little fuzzy, and for a while I was almost able to forget. Then I heard a soft splashing sound from below, and looked to see a young boy climbing out of the stagnant water in the pool. He didn't look up, but just walked over the flagstones to the gate, and then padded out through the entrance to the motel. I could still hear the soft sound of his wet feet long after he'd disappeared into the darkness. The brother who'd held his head under a moment too long; the father who'd been too busy watching someone else's wife putting lotion on her thighs; or the mother who'd fallen asleep. Someone would be having a visitor tonight.

When we got back to the house after the party and tried to get back into the lab, we found that we couldn't open the door. The lock had fused. Something had attacked the metal of the tumblers, turning the mechanism into a solid lump of metal. We stared at each other, by now feeling very sober, and then turned to look through the glass upper portion of the door. Everything inside looked the way it always had, but I believe that even that early, before we knew what was happening, everything had already been set in motion. The beckies work like God, it would appear, in strange and invisible ways.

David got the axe from the garage and we broke through the door to the laboratory. We found the vat of MindWorks empty. A small hole had appeared in the bottom of the·glass, and there was a faint trail where the contents had flowed across the floor, making small holes at several points. It had doubled back on itself, and at several points it had also flowed against gravity. It ended in a larger hole which, it transpired, dripped through into a pipe. A pipe which went out back into the municipal water system.

The first reports were on CNN at seven o'clock the next morning. Eight murders in downtown Jacksonville, and three on the University campus. Reports of people suddenly going crazy, screaming at people who weren't there, running in terror from voices in their head and acting on impulses that they claimed weren't theirs. By lunchtime the problem wasn't just confined to people we might have come into contact with: it had started to spread on its own.

I don't know why it happened like this. Maybe we just made a mistake somewhere. Perhaps it was something as small and simple as a chiral isomer, some chemical which the beckies created in a mirror image of the way it should be. That's what happened with thalidomide, and that's what we created. A thalidomide of the soul.

Or maybe there was no mistake. Perhaps that's just the way it is. Maybe the only people who stick around are the ones you don't want to see. The ones who can turn people into psychotics who riot, murder, or end their lives, through the hatred or guilt they bring with them. These people have always been here, all the time, staying close to the people who remember them. Only now they are no longer silent.

A day later there were reports in European cities, at first just the ones where I'd sent my letters, then spreading rapidly across the entire land mass. By the time my letters reached their recipients, the beckies I'd breathed over them had multiplied a thousandfold, breaking the paper down and reconstituting the molecules to create more of themselves. They were so clever, our children, and they shared the ambitions of their creators. If they'd needed to, they could probably have formed themselves into new letters, and laid around until someone posted them all over the world. But they didn't, because coughing, or sneezing, or just breathing is enough to spread the infection. By the following week a state of emergency was in force in every country in the world.

A mob killed David before the police got to him. He never got to see Rebecca. I don't know why. She just didn't come. I was placed under house arrest, and then taken to the facility to help with the feverish attempts to come up with a cure. There is none, and there never will be. The beckies are too smart, too aggressive, and too powerful. They just take any antidote, break it down, and use it to make more of themselves.

They don't need the vote any more. They're already in control.

The moon is out over the ocean, casting glints over the tides as they rustle back and forth with a sound like someone slowly running their finger across a piece of paper. A little while ago I heard a siren in the far distance. Apart from that all is quiet.

I think it's unlikely I shall riot, or go on a killing spree. In the end, I will simply go.

The times when Karen comes to see me are bad. She didn't stop writing to me because she lost interest, it turns out. She stopped writing because she had been pregnant by me, and died through complications in childbirth. When David and I talked of her over that game of pool she was already dead. She will come again tonight, as she always does, and maybe tonight will be the night when I decide I cannot bear it any longer. Perhaps seeing her here, at the motel where David and I stayed that summer, will be enough to make me do what I have to do.

If it isn't her who gives me the strength, then someone else will, because I've started seeing other people now too. It's surprising quite how many – or maybe it isn't, when you consider that all of this is partly my fault. So many people have died, and will die, all of them with something to say to me. Every night there are more, as the world slowly winds down. There are two of them here now, standing in the court and looking up at me. Perhaps in the end I shall be the last one alive, surrounded by silent figures in ranks that reach out to the horizon.

Or maybe, as I hope, some night David and Rebecca will come for me, and I will go with them.

Michael Marshall Smith's first book, *Only Forward*, garnered excellent notices when it was published in 1994 and went on to win the British Fantasy Award in the Best Novel category. This complemented those he had already received in 1991 ('The Man Who Drew Cats') and 1992 ('The Dark Land') for the Best Short Fiction. His stories have appeared in such anthologies and magazines as *The Best New Horror*, *The Year's Best Fantasy and Horror*, *Dark Voices*, *Touch Wood*, *The Mammoth Book of Zombies*, *The Mammoth Book of Werewolves*, *The Mammoth Book of Frankenstein*, *Shadows Over Innsmouth*, *Omni* and the previous volume of *Dark Terrors*. A second novel, *Spares*, was published in 1996 and he has recently been working on various screenplays, including adaptations of Clive Barker's *Weaveworld* and Jay Russell's *Celestial Dogs*. About 'Hell Hath Enlarged Herself', the author explains: 'It's the first time I've set a story in the part of Florida where I grew up. We spent several family holidays in Sarasota, and during the last one – which must be fifteen years ago, at least – I remember being fascinated by a hotel along the front which was derelict and boarded up. It's possible that at least some of this story has been percolating slowly in the back of my mind for half my life!'

Ghost Music:
A Memoir by George Beaune

THOMAS TESSIER

I never wanted to tell this story, but there's no longer any point in sitting on it. I'd like to think that it might serve as a very small footnote to a very small entry in music history, but that seems rather unlikely.

Does anyone still remember Eric Springer?

Do you know who Mandy Robbins was?

A couple of months ago I was skimming *The Times* and saw the brief news item about the train wreck south of Cairo. The usual disaster in an under-developed country, dozens of people dead. I took it in and quickly passed on without a second thought, but a short while later I received a telephone call from an old friend in London. Did I know that Mandy Robbins was on that train, and had died in the crash? I was stunned. No one had heard from her in ages, though at various times rumour had it that she was living in a dark apartment in Buenos Aires, or a tiny cabin in a remote Norwegian fishing village, or a villa on a resort island in the Adriatic. But no one really knew, and after a while the stories dried up. We all more or less forgot about her, or we filed her away among our less happy memories – with Eric.

Mandy Robbins was en route to Luxor when the train accident occurred. Twenty years later, she was still running.

*

I live in Dutchess County now, about seventy miles north of Manhattan. I edit (and write most of) *Tonal/Atonal*, a monthly newsletter. My articles and reviews also appear in several other publications that cover twentieth-century music, and my monographs on Hartmann and Lutoslawski have sold well to libraries throughout the world. I'm working on Arvo Pärt now, and I teach a course at the local high school. It all adds up to a reasonable income and I suppose I'm happy enough in my A-frame. I own about five thousand CDs, records and tapes, as many books, a superb stereo system, and I occasionally have an affair with a divorcée.

You know, it *is* a life.

But in 1976 I was living in London and I sincerely believed in the importance of great art, literary and musical. There were classics, old and modern, and they truly mattered – perhaps more than anything else. A new composition by Berio was greeted as an event of quasi-religious significance. Art was in some ways more real than life itself, I thought. Back then, I hadn't yet given up on myself, though I was already beginning to cobble together a sideline career as a commentator rather than a composer.

Eric Springer was an old friend with more talent and better luck. I was thrilled when he wrote to say he'd be coming to stay in London for several months. We hadn't seen each other in a while, though we kept in touch with postcards. Eric's *Variations for Piano and Oboe* had been heard on a late-night FM station in California by a young producer who decided to use it in his next film. *No-Hopers* was a cult success and the soundtrack sold quite well. Eric had already earned a measure of critical praise as a promising young composer, but now he had the added pleasure of an unexpected payoff from the world of popular entertainment.

He was coming to London to write a quartet commissioned by the Claymore Foundation, and to be with the new love of his life. Mandy Robbins was then twenty-three, attempting a comeback in a career that had never quite happened. She'd been a bright young prospect as a violinist at the age of fourteen, but the assorted stresses of high expectations, touring, and family problems had combined to derail her. At eighteen, she packed it all in and took a couple of years off to put her life in order. Then she began slowly and carefully to make her way back as a performer.

By the spring of 1976 she had done well enough to have a new agent and a challenging but very sweet job: she would perform the Berg Violin Concerto at the upcoming Proms. A friend and wealthy patron offered her the free use of his house in London, and she intended to spend four months mastering the technically difficult and emotionally taxing composition. It would be her breakthrough concert. There was talk of a live recording, and a contract for studio albums later. Mandy would also be the star soloist at the début of Eric's quartet, some time in the future.

Eric and Mandy, Mandy and Eric. When I met them at Heathrow in late April of 1976 the air seemed charged with the excitement of their romance and the dazzling music they were setting out to create. It all seemed to be coming together for both of them and I was swept up in it as well – happily so. I felt privileged to be the friend at hand.

They quickly settled into their new home, a Georgian brick house in one of the narrow streets behind Edwardes Square, on the edge of Kensington and Earl's Court. The owner had spent a small fortune renovating and redecorating, and it featured a music room with a Bosendorfer grand on which Eric could help Mandy rehearse, using a piano reduction of Berg's orchestral score. There was a separate den with a spinet in the converted basement, where Eric could work on his own composition.

It was ideal for them, and by happy coincidence I was living in a tiny flat behind Olympia, a short walk from their place. We spent a lot of time together in the early going, as I showed them around London, took them on pub outings, introduced them to Indian food, and helped them find some of the less obvious sites that they were interested in seeing – like the modest house in Chelsea where Peter Warlock came to his sad and lonely end, and the rather dreary old pile that Edward Elgar had lived in, near the North End Road.

Eric and Mandy both took to London at once, they loved going for long walks around the city, and they soon began to talk about the possibility of finding an affordable place of their own after the Proms and staying on indefinitely.

I liked Mandy from day one. She was obviously intelligent, especially about music, though she wasn't nearly the compulsive talker on the subject that Eric and I were. She was petite, and still had a look of girlish prettiness about her, but you would occasionally catch a brief glimpse of adult sadness in her eyes when something was said that brought an unhappy memory to mind. I knew that she had struggled to escape a possessive father who'd attempted to control every aspect of her life and career; she was eventually successful in breaking away, but she still carried the emotional scars.

Most of the time, however, Mandy was buoyant and energetic, fun to talk to and be with, and it was very clear to me that she cared deeply for Eric – and that he felt the same about her. He had found her at exactly the right time in his life.

Eric was fast approaching thirty. He'd been something of a playboy for rather too long, and was in danger of being written off as an underachiever. He had never produced as much new music as some people felt he should. Now he was apparently making real progress at last. The movie success and the Claymore commission both helped enormously, but Mandy was the vital factor. She gave him love and a sense of stability, for what was perhaps the first time in his life. The two of them shared an ambitious vision – they wanted both greatness for each other in music, and to have a great love affair together for ever.

Well, why not? At that age we all want everything, and we can't imagine why we shouldn't get it. I was beginning to sense my own limitations, but I still believed in Eric. And the first time I saw Mandy strike the violin strings with the edge of her hand in the famous 'warm-up' of the Berg piece – a kind of firm but very delicate chopping motion, an incredibly difficult thing to do properly – I believed in her as well.

Eric and I were sitting on the small patio outside the Lord Edwarde one balmy evening a few weeks into their stay when I got the first indication that there were problems. Eric seemed to be distracted and had little to say. Mandy, who was not one for the drink anyway, had stayed home to take a hot bath; lately, she was being bothered by aching muscles in her shoulders and legs. Eric said she was rehearsing too much, and there may have been a minor disagreement between them.

I was sympathetic, but I sensed there was something else on Eric's mind. He was a tall, sturdy guy, but that evening he sat hunched over his pint in a way that suggested defeat. He looked like one of the dazed old-timers at Ward's. He had even gone for three or four days without shaving, which was not his style. We chatted fitfully for a while, and then I asked about his quartet. If there was trouble, it had to be with the music.

'Want to read some of it?'

'Of course, I'd love to.'

I'd been looking forward to the moment when Eric would show me some of his new work. He reached down and unzipped the slim briefcase he always carried with him, fished out a few sheets of music paper and handed them to me. He had a smile on his face, but there was something sour in it.

The first page bore the hand-printed title 'Quartet' and the dedication 'for Mandy'. My eyes scanned down the page and across the staves. I was amazed. It was pre-Serial, in fact it seemed to be pre-Romantic – an altogether astonishing turn back to the past for a composer like Eric. Another shock: the quartet opened with a *basse danse*. It was incredible. Nothing in his previous work had ever looked in this direction. But I was going too fast to hear it in my mind. I started over again, caught it – and a tremendous sense of confusion washed through me.

'You're quoting Warlock,' I said without looking up.

'Am I,' Eric said with a hollow laugh.

'This is his *Capriol Suite*.'

'I know.'

It continued for the next five pages, what was then the only fairly well-known piece of music composed by Peter Warlock, circa 1926. The restless flurry of notes ended abruptly in the middle of the seventh page, with a large 'X' scrawled across it, and the words SHIT SHIT SHIT.

'I don't understand,' I said.

'Neither do I.'

'Surely you don't mean to quote at this length, and here at the very beginning of your own work?'

'No, of course not.'

'Well. . .?'

'I'll tell you what's really kind of scary about it,' Eric said, staring at his pint. 'I've worked on that for weeks, ever since we got here, but it was only the other day when I realized what it was. Until then I had no idea.' He looked up at me. 'I honestly thought it was all mine.'

I let that pass for the moment because I couldn't think of a thing to say. All composers and writers are influenced by those who came before; as they mature they outgrow their influences and find their own voices, or else they come to a dead end. But this was not a case of excessive influence. Eric had Peter Warlock's music note for note, as far as I could tell.

'That's not scary. Embarrassing, maybe.'

'Yes.' He smiled sheepishly. 'It is embarrassing.'

What *was* scary, I thought but did not say, was that this was all he had to show for a month of steady work.

I told him not to listen to any other music (except the Berg that Mandy was practising) and to begin again on his quartet. We both knew that the history of great works of art is littered with false starts. Or as Edward Albee said, you nose around and nose around like a dog, until you find the right place to squat. Eric was clearly relieved when I brushed aside the incident.

Privately, I was disturbed, and I knew he was too. Why else

would he even show me those self-damning pages? And how could it be explained? Eric had been living quietly with Mandy for all of that month, up to nothing worse than a few pints at night after a long day's work – and who could begrudge him that? I understood influence, but how anybody could virtually transcribe the work of another person and not know that they were doing it is beyond me. Yet I had no doubt Eric was being truthful.

A few days later, on the weekend, the three of us went up to Portobello Road and poked around among the flea market stalls. I didn't find anything, but Eric bought Mandy a lovely silver charm of a cat, sleek and vaguely Egyptian, with a fleck of amber inset as an eye. It came on a thin chain, and Mandy immediately put it on around her neck. Mandy was very fond of cats, and if she and Eric stayed on in London they intended to get one.

We had a pleasant pub lunch in Church Street, and while Eric was at the bar buying another round I asked Mandy how her work on the Berg concerto was coming along.

'The music's fine, and I love it, but it's so demanding, and my body is behind schedule.' She sipped her spritzer (as usual, the only one that she would have). 'My legs get very sore after I've been standing for a while, and I seem to get tired quickly.' I nodded. For the concert soloist, physical training and stamina are every bit as important as they are for the athlete. 'But I'm following an excellent programme of exercises, so hopefully I'll be in peak condition by the end of August.'

'Good. I'm sure you'll be fine,' I told her. 'And how is Eric's work? He seems cheerful enough, but he hasn't said very much to me about it.'

Mandy's face brightened. 'I heard some of it last night and it was gorgeous. And I'm not just saying that, it really was the most beautiful music I've heard in ages.'

'What was?' Eric asked before I could speak. He was back at the table with two fresh pints.

'The theme you were working on last night,' Mandy said.

'Oh, yes.' Eric smiled at me, looking pleased with himself. 'She's right, too. It's the best thing I've ever done.'

'Great,' I responded. 'I can't wait to hear it.'

By the time we got back to their place Eric and I were quite jolly with beer and Mandy was tolerantly amused. I insisted that they both give me at least a brief preview of their work before I tottered off home. Mandy took out her violin while Eric poured a very ordinary Scotch for the two of us.

Some people don't like Alban Berg. They just don't get that whole second Viennese school. But I find his music heartbreaking, especially the Violin Concerto, his own farewell to life. Mandy nearly had me in tears within a few moments. She only played the final part, the adagio, but that was enough. She sat down with a wince and a groan, and put her feet up on a hassock. I told her how good she was, several times. Then Mandy and I badgered Eric to play a bit of his new music. It didn't take much. He seemed genuinely eager and he stepped briskly to the piano.

'Remember, it's just an idea I'm fooling around with,' Eric told us. 'And you must hear it in strings.'

He began to play, taking up his theme and exploring it, much as a jazz musician will improvise around a song line. It was far from developed, still spare and skeletal – but Mandy was right, it was a gorgeous idea that just hinted teasingly at rich colours and deeply moving harmonies.

Eric played for about ten minutes. Mandy and I clapped, and he grinned as he flopped down in the armchair and reached for his whisky glass. I came up with some encouraging words and somehow managed to hide the huge distress I felt.

I still wasn't quite sure what he'd been playing, but I knew that I knew it – and it wasn't Eric Springer's music.

My knowledge of twentieth-century music is far from encyclopaedic. I'm patchy on the Americans, Scandinavians, Russians, the Spanish and much of the rest of the world. But in 1976 I was really into British composers, particularly the more obscure ones lost in the enormous shadows cast by Vaughan Williams and Britten (since then I've concentrated on the Germans and East Europeans).

The next day I could still hear the theme in my head, and I began to work out what it might be. By late that afternoon, I at least had a pretty good idea of who the composer was. I dreaded speaking to Eric about it, but there was no choice in the matter. I rang and asked if I could stop by, knowing that was the time of day he usually finished working.

When I got there, Mandy was out and Eric was ready to go for a walk and a pre-dinner pint. That was fine with me, but first I had him play the theme for me again. He had developed it quite a bit in only twenty-four hours, but hearing it again merely served to confirm my suspicions. While we were out walking I spoke in a general way about the music and how it was so different from his previous work. We went to the Britannia in Warwick Road.

'Now,' I said after we'd taken our first sip of Young's, 'I have to tell you what I don't like about it.'

'Okay, fire ahead.'

'It's by Ernest Moeran,' I said. Eric stared at me as if he couldn't believe what I'd just said. 'I'm pretty sure it's from his String Trio, composed in 1931. That, or his Violin Sonata of 1923. Anyhow, I'm certain it's E. J. Moeran.'

'I've never even heard of him,' Eric insisted anxiously, his face flushed and agitated. 'And I'm damn sure I've never heard a note of his music.'

'I believe you, but. . .'

'You must be wrong, you've got to be.'

'Check it out yourself,' I said. 'And do it before you play or show that music to anyone else, because you'll be embarrassed, and you might even find yourself with legal problems.'

'Jesus.' Eric sat back, worried and subdued. 'What's going on here?'

'I don't know.'

'Who the hell is Ernest Moeran?'

'A minor English composer,' I explained. 'Born 1894, died 1950. A few of his works are of real, lasting quality. He's the kind of composer I love to find, overlooked by most people.' At that point, I hesitated. But I had to go on. 'When I first got into Peter Warlock seriously a couple of years ago, I came across Moeran. He and Warlock were very close friends.'

Eric stared at me.

I did not tell him the saddest details of all about Ernest Moeran. We never got around to them, or maybe I just didn't want to risk making matters worse for Eric. That in 1950, at the age of fifty-five, on one of his many trips to Ireland, Moeran was found dead in a river, apparently the victim of a heart attack. Or that in 1926 Moeran had a colossal failure – he could not complete work on a symphony that had been commissioned by the Hallé Orchestra. Or that his friendship with the remarkable but very strange Peter Warlock had nearly destroyed Moeran's life while he was still a young man. In fact, there were people who knew them both and who believed that the best thing that ever happened to Moeran was the mysterious death of Warlock himself in 1930.

I didn't see Eric again until the end of the following week. I knew he would need some time to sort himself out, and I had to put my own thoughts in order – or at least try. I used the time to do a bit of research on Peter Warlock, but that didn't help me understand what was happening with Eric. The only explanation I could come up with was that he had to be going through some kind of mental breakdown. That he did know the Moeran piece, as he'd admitted he knew the Warlock, and he had begun to re-compose them both in the mistaken belief that they were his own – as a result of some deep confusion or psychological crisis.

But, aside from the music itself, I had seen nothing in his habits or behaviour that would support such a theory. He appeared to be fine in all other respects, and Mandy had given no hint of troubles with him. All I could think was that something bizarre happened whenever he sat down at the piano to compose – perhaps the pressure to justify such an important commission became too great to handle, and his mind lurched off on its own, dredging up music he knew but dissociating it from its source.

Every Friday I spent a couple of hours at Bush House editing and polishing the English translations of émigré texts broadcast on the BBC World Service. It was a handy job, and it eventually led to my interest in the so-called dissident composers from the Eastern Bloc, like Gorecki.

Eric phoned, knowing I'd probably be there. He asked me to meet him at a place called the New Ambassador Club, which turned out to be a humble drinking den up one flight of stairs on Orange Street. I have no idea how Eric found such a place, or became a member, but he was at the last table at the back.

I almost didn't recognize him. The four-day stubble was now about two weeks old and had been shaved down to form an emerging goatee and a disconnected moustache. That was startling enough in itself, because Eric had never sported facial hair. But he also looked thin and gaunt, his skin was grey and his eyes were tired. Obviously he wasn't eating or sleeping properly

'All right,' he said, after fetching some ale. 'I've got a problem. I know I heard Warlock last summer at the Hartt School. Maybe it was the music, or his odd name, but I was curious to see the place where he died shortly after we got here.'

'Yes.'

'And maybe Moeran was on the same concert programme. I don't remember it, but maybe he was. That has to be what happened – how else would I pick up their music?'

'I'm inclined to agree.'

'But that kind of music doesn't even interest me,' Eric said with exasperation. 'It never has. Tone-colour, lyrical harmonies and the old modes. It's an *old* language.'

'I know,' I said. 'That's never been your style.'

'So why is that all I can do now? When I sit down and write or when I fool around on the piano, the only thing that comes out is that kind of music. And then I realize what it is, and I have to throw it out and start all over again.'

'Do some exercises in dissonance,' I suggested.

'I've tried,' Eric told me. 'But whenever I consciously try to set off in a particular direction I immediately come to a dead end. I get nowhere.' He leaned across the table and spoke in an urgent voice. 'I've been here going on two months now, and I've written nothing of my own. Not one note.'

'It sounds like writer's block,' I said sympathetically. 'I guess the only thing you can do is to keep working until you work your way out of it. And you will, sooner or later.'

Eric looked as if he didn't entirely believe me. In fact, I wasn't sure I believed it myself. Eric had another theory. The success of the movie soundtrack had somehow leached away at his self-confidence. He was afraid of not being taken seriously, of being dismissed as a popular hack. His quartet would be an easy target for that charge from people who resented his windfall, and fear of this was now blocking him creatively.

There may have been a small grain of truth in what he said, but there was also a large blob of paranoia. The music community didn't follow him that closely. Eric was just one of many young composers with true potential but a tenuous hold on the art, and he was not yet the focus of widespread interest.

'That's a stretch,' I told him. 'The movie money started to come in a couple of years ago. It's in the past now, so you can forget about it. And there's no point in worrying about what the critics will say about the quartet until you finish it. You have a massive case of self-consciousness, that's all, and the way out of it is to keep working. You'll break through.'

Eric thought about that for a few moments, and then he said, 'Tell me more about Peter Warlock.'

'This is not really about Peter Warlock,' I said. 'This is all about you, and your music.'

'I know,' Eric replied. 'Still. . .'

'Well, he was a brilliant scholar and a very good composer,' I said. 'Some of his songs are among the best in English music. He was born in 1894, and his real name was Philip Heseltine. But his music criticism offended so many people that when he came to the point of publishing his own music he decided it would be best to use a pseudonym. No one—'

'Look at that,' Eric interrupted. 'He was so worried about what people would say that he took another name.'

'Yes, but it didn't work. People soon knew that Warlock was Heseltine. By the way, nobody seems to know how he came up with that name, but he had a strong interest in the occult, and there were stories about experiments with satanism and drugs. Warlock certainly had his darker side. Some people remember him as being distinctly sinister and he was prone to extended drinking binges. E. J. Moeran was so much under Warlock's influence that he shared a place with him for a while, but eventually he realized that the lifestyle was destroying his work and ruining his health, and he had to get out. But there were other people who said that Peter Warlock was essentially warm and caring, a very good friend, and that his occasional outbursts of wildness were merely a release from the intense pressure of work. When it came to his music, it seems he was a hard taskmaster on himself.'

'Why did he kill himself?' Eric asked.

'We can't be sure he did. The gas valve was very loose, and it may be that he stretched out for a nap and a leak did him in. On the other hand, his personal life was troubled, his finances were always in bad shape, he suffered bouts of depression and he thought he was a failure. His music bucked the trends of the day – this was 1930 – and he thought he was going nowhere. He did mention suicide to a few friends, and later they regretted not taking him seriously. The inquest returned an open verdict, but that was probably an act of kindness. From all the evidence, it certainly does look like suicide.'

'He was what, thirty-six?'

'Right, and it's only just in the last few years that people started listening to him again and liking what they heard. He had an intense, charismatic personality, there's no doubt about that. Most people who met him either hated and feared him, or else they simply adored him.'

'Hmmn.' Eric shrugged. 'Sometimes I think there's a weird story behind every composer who ever lived – except Sibelius, of course.' I laughed. 'Warlock sounds as peculiar as they come, but what he has to do with me, I have no idea.'

'I'll tell you one more thing about him.'

'What?'

'He was tall, like you,' I said. 'Some people described him as Mephistophelean in appearance. I've seen a photograph of him, and they're right about that. He had a moustache and goatee, just like the ones you've sprouted.'

Events got in the way and I wasn't able to see Eric or Mandy for another two or three weeks after that. I did speak to him on the phone once and he assured me that he was at last beginning to make a little headway with his work. He sounded distracted, and I took that to mean that his mind was entirely on his music. The next time I called I got Mandy. Eric was out. He went out every day late in the afternoon and came back late at night, usually in a boozy state. When he worked, the music she heard was not music at all, just doodling at the keyboard. She was worried.

A few days later she rang and asked if I knew where he might be. She was in a state, and I got the impression that he had not been home at all the night before – or if he had, he'd gone out again. It was early evening and she couldn't stand waiting there alone, not knowing where he was or when he might return. I tried to calm her down and promised to look for him.

I didn't think there were very many places Eric might wander to, since he still wasn't terribly familiar with London. I tried his little drinking club in Orange Street first. He wasn't there but the large woman behind the bar told me that he had left about an hour ago, with a lady friend.

I tried the French and a couple of other pubs in Soho before I found him at the Colony Club. It was even drabber than the New Ambassador, but it had a better clientele – literary publishers, freelancers, the art crowd arrayed lovingly around Francis Bacon and Lucien Freud.

Eric was off in a corner at a typically rickety table with a woman dressed entirely in black. She had a long, horsy face, and long, straight blonde hair. Her name was Gillian, or Francesca. They were both moderately pissed and they each thought the other was wonderfully amusing, I most amusing of all. It took me one round of drinks and not much effort to detach Eric, and I got him into a taxi. He was humming like a tractor, but unfortunately it was nothing more exalted than the refrain from 'Lola'.

'What the hell are you doing?'

'I'm turning into Peter Warlock.' He laughed.

'No you're not,' I told him. 'You're just acting like a big child – dodging your work, leaving Mandy alone for hours on end. It's stupid, Eric, stupid and uncalled for.'

'Maybe he's taking me over.' Another laugh.

'Why would he bother?' I snapped. 'Peter Warlock is resting happily in his grave, his reputation is secure.'

It turned out to be a vicious remark, and I was immediately sorry I'd made it. We were miserably silent the rest of the way. I went in with him to say hello to Mandy. Eric smiled and gave her a kiss on the cheek, and then sloped off down to his study in the basement. Mandy was in tears, obviously not in the mood for much talk. The front room was a bit messy and I noticed that she was still moving very stiffly.

'Where was he?'

'Having a drink at a club with Francis Bacon.' It's amazing how you can find the gloss when you need it. 'Wait till tomorrow to have a chat with him. I'll do the same in a day or two. He's just having a hard time getting going with the quartet, but he'll snap out of it soon enough.'

'I hope so.'

'You'll see.'

'George, thank you so much.'

'Not at all. How're you feeling, love?'

'Otherwise?' A faint sardonic smile. 'Still sore and achy, but I'll be okay. As soon as Eric gets back to normal.'

I went straight round to the Black Hart in Earl's Court Road and had two quick shorts. There is a natural instinct to assume the best about our friends, and a concern about how much you can interfere in their lives before you go a little too far, and they shut you out. I feared greatly for Eric – that he was using his music troubles as an excuse to fritter away his time on clubbing, boozing and chatting up the dollies. He could easily wake up one morning soon and find that he'd blown the Claymore commission and lost Mandy, and I couldn't imagine how he would recover from two such devastating, self-inflicted failures.

I walked home that night trying to figure out how I might be able to get through to Eric, to shake him out of his funk without alienating him. I had no idea that it was already far beyond me. Even now, looking back twenty years later, I wonder. Weren't the signs all there, waiting to be seen? Shouldn't I have known what was really going on? But I didn't see, I didn't know – or if I did, some part of me must have been unwilling to face it.

Eric seemed subdued when I met him two days later. He had a slightly dishevelled look about him, his clothes were rumpled and his hair was brushed back in slick clumps that tended to separate and dangle down on the side of his face until he shoved them back again. Eric wanted to go for a pint but I wouldn't, so we sat in the sun at Holland Park, which only made him look more bedraggled and forlorn.

I can't remember much of what we said, but it wasn't of any special importance. I was going to Italy for a few days to do an interview with Luigi Nono. Eric gave me some very good questions to ask, which showed that his critical thinking was still in fine form, and that cheered me somewhat.

He didn't attempt to explain or apologize for the evening I brought him home from the Colony. He didn't refer to it at all, and neither did I: I've never seen any point in rehashing boorish or childish behaviour. Since then, of course, I've often wondered about everything we left unsaid.

I wish I'd given in a little and gone along to the Britannia or the Black Hart with him for a pint. But I wasn't in the mood, I was trying to discourage him from the beer, and we always want to believe there will be time for another pint, another day. But when we parted on the High Street a short while later, it was the last time I saw Eric Springer alive.

I rang them two or three times after I returned from Italy, but no one answered the phone. I meant to go around, but I had a number of assignments to catch up with, and so the days stretched into a week. It was about eleven o'clock one morning when I got the call. At first the voice was so faint that I almost hung up, thinking no one was there. But then I caught it – not much more than an exhalation.

'Mandy? Is that you?'

'Can you . . . help me.'

'I'll be right there.'

I'd never heard a human voice sound so weak and helpless. I think I ran all the way from my flat to their house. I tried the door at once, and found it unlocked. I shouted for both of them as I went into the front hallway, but got no response.

The front sitting-room was empty, and the main music room as well – I hesitated there just long enough to glance at the loose pages of sheet music scattered around the place, hoping that some of it might be Eric's quartet, but it was the Berg score. Plates of half-eaten fast food had been left on the floor and perched on the arms of chairs, looking as dry and hard as wax imitations.

I hurried downstairs to the room where Eric worked. It was dark, and there was a damp chill in the air. It reeked of stale tobacco. I turned on a table lamp and saw some ashtrays full of cigarette butts. There were a couple of virtually new pipes on a side table. Eric had never smoked, and I was sure I'd never told him that Peter Warlock did, both cigarettes and a pipe.

There were no books, tapes or records in the room, it was as simple and austere as a monk's cell. A chaise – for one frantic second I thought I saw Eric stretched out on it, the thin blanket tucked up under his chin, just as they found Peter Warlock. Eric wasn't there, but there were more loose sheets of music scattered all over the place. Each page was clean and unmarked, lined with blank staves that lanced my heart.

Just as I got back to the ground floor, I heard a noise from upstairs. I found Mandy in the main bedroom. She was curled up beneath a sheet, barely conscious. Her face was desperately pale and her hair clung to her face in sweaty snarls. She saw me, but she didn't seem to register who I was.

'Help . . . Eric. . .'

'It's all right, love,' I told her. 'Eric's not here at the moment. He must have gone out.'

'Eric. . .'

'No, it's George,' I said with a grin. I sat on the edge of the bed and stroked her face lightly. 'You're not well, are you? Have you seen a doctor?'

'George.' Her eyes found me then. 'I can't move.'

'Why—'

At that moment I noticed Mandy's legs poking out from under the sheet, and I was horrified. Her toes were curled tightly and her calves appeared to have shrivelled. I pushed the sheet up and saw the same slack and wasting flesh all along the lower part of her thighs. I could barely find words to speak.

'Mandy, what—'

It was absurd, but thoughts of Berg and his Violin Concerto suddenly swarmed in my mind. The piece Mandy had been preparing to play in the last week of the Proms. I've always thought of it as Berg's farewell to life, since it was all about both life and death, and Berg died (his own bizarre, absurd death) within a few months of completing it.

But there was another person involved. Manon Gropius, the lovely young daughter of close friends and a special favourite of Berg's. At the age of eighteen, just before Berg was commissioned to write the Concerto, Manon lost her long and heroic battle against the ravages of polio. Berg was deeply moved, and dedicated the Concerto to her – 'to the memory of an angel'.

Now, staring at Mandy's legs, I felt a confusion that seemed to boil up out of my bones and surge through me, leaving me dazed and paralysed. Finally I heard Mandy's faint voice again.

'Save Eric.'

'He's not—'

'The kitchen.'

I seemed to come back into my own body then and I raced down the stairs. I hadn't even thought of checking the kitchen at the rear of the ground floor. It had a gas stove. The door wouldn't budge. I was sure I could smell gas. As I rattled the doorknob uselessly, I noticed something hanging from it. The thin silver chain with the charm that Eric had bought for Mandy in Portobello Road, the Egyptian cat with the amber eye.

In a moment of awful certainty, I knew I'd never told Eric the single most revealing detail about Peter Warlock's death, the sign that strongly pointed to suicide rather than an accident. A few minutes before he stretched out on the chaise and tucked the blanket up beneath his chin, Warlock had taken his cat and put it safely outside the room. It was the cat's frightful wailing and mewing that eventually drew the landlady's attention.

I got Mandy out first. While the neighbours looked after her and alerted the police and fire brigade, I went back for Eric. I expected the house to blow up at any moment. I took a chair and smashed the kitchen window, unlocked the outside door, got in and turned off the gas. I waved a towel around, trying to clear the air. I had to step outside twice to overcome dizziness, but then I was finally able to go to Eric.

He was slumped back in a chair, his head pointing north, his feet crossed at the ankles and propped on the edge of the wooden table. He looked for all the world like someone who'd just dozed off while waiting for the kettle to boil.

But his lips and cheeks were as red as a tanager, and there was about his mouth the slightly bemused smile of the dead.

I visited Mandy at St Mary Abbot's Hospital, and I saw her again shortly before she left London. She recovered quickly from what the doctors said was probably a psychosomatic illness. She wasn't having any of that, and neither was I, but there seemed no point in trying to argue otherwise – with anyone.

Mandy and I, sadly, found that we had little to say to each other. It was as if we both wanted, or needed, to retreat from a terrible experience we had shared unwillingly. I felt more than a little guilty for not paying serious attention to what had been happening to her, so preoccupied was I by Eric's situation. She scratched the Proms, of course, and disappeared. I have no idea whether any of the rumours I occasionally heard about her over the years were true, but she never performed in public again.

If Eric Springer is remembered at all today – by people who never knew him – it is probably not as the promising composer of the plaintive and Webernist *Variations for Piano and Oboe*, but as the composer of a sweetened-up movie theme based on it.

NOTES:

'(his own bizarre, absurd death)'   Not long after he completed his great Violin Concerto, Alban Berg (1885–1935) suffered an insect bite on the back. From neglect or mistreatment, it formed an abscess. Berg was so poor at the time that he and his wife attempted to lance it themselves. They used toenail scissors. Berg's condition worsened steadily and he died soon after he finally entered a hospital. No effort was made to determine the exact cause of his death but it was most likely due to blood poisoning.

'To those whom God has forsaken is given a gas-fire in Earl's Court.'
                    Patrick Hamilton, *Hangover Square*
    I came across this line several years after Eric's death, and for obvious reasons it made a deep impression on me. Hamilton is probably best-known as the author of the plays *Rope* and *Gaslight*. He hated the movies that were based on them. His novel *Hangover Square* is set in Earl's Court on the eve of World War Two. It ends with the hero killing two people and then taking his own life – by gas – after leaving a note asking the police to look after his cat. Oddly enough, when the novel was filmed this character, who had nothing whatsoever to do with music, was transformed into a homicidal composer. Years earlier, Hamilton had been struck by a car and seriously injured. He recovered, but his face was disfigured. He took to wearing a grotesque artificial nose for a

while. This accident contributed enormously to the alcoholism that eventually killed him. It occurred in the narrow side street directly behind the house in which Eric Springer died, years later.

G.B.

Thomas Tessier is a playwright and poet and the author of several genre novels. These include *The Fates, The Nightwalker, Shockwaves, Phantom* (nominated for the World Fantasy Award), *Finishing Touches, Rapture, Secret Strangers* and *Fog Heart*. His short stories have appeared in numerous anthologies and can be found in the collection *The Lady Crossing and Other Tales of Panic*. Although born and now living in Connecticut, Tessier was educated at University College, Dublin, and spent seven years based in London, where he was a regular contributor to *Vogue* and involved with the publishing imprint Millington. About 'Ghost Music: *A Memoir by George Beaune*', he says: 'As is so often the case for me, London seems to be a central character in this tale.'

The Dead Cop

DENNIS ETCHISON

Standing in the red glow, Decker watched a pattern emerge at the centre of the paper. It appeared to be a horizon broken by several jagged vertical lines. A few seconds more and the lines sharpened into what might be swords or spears. He waited for something else to take form, anything at all that might provide a clue, but there were no surrounding details in this frame, either. And it was impossible to remember exactly what he had caught in his viewfinder that night.

As he leaned over the tray, squinting in the metallic fumes, he heard a ringing. He reached for the timer, then realized he had not bothered to set it for this print. The ringing came again, a faint chirping, as if a small bird had found its way into his studio on the other side of the thin wall. He slid the sheet of paper into the stop bath and opened the door, flooding the darkroom with light from the overhead windows. It was no good, anyway; the pattern had come up too fast and was already turning black.

His telephone rang again.

'Hello?'

'Pete? Thank God.'

'Hi, honey.' The glare from the panes in the skylight blinded him. 'What's wrong?'

'Nothing. I mean—I was about to hang up. I thought you'd left.'

'Not yet.'

'Are you okay?'

'Sure.'

'You sound so far away.'

He turned the receiver so the mouthpiece was closer to his
lips. The stubble on his chin caught in the tiny holes,
magnifying what sounded like a scraping in his ear. 'I was in
the darkroom.'

'Oh, sorry.'

'That's all right. I'm finished.'

'You are? Well, tell me!'

'Tell you what?'

'How did it go?'

The bare white walls took on texture, first the rows of dark
rectangles, favourite enlargements he had mounted for display
over the years, then the corkboard filled with test prints from
his new assignment: closeups of burgers and fries and soft
drinks in cups, all suspended in space on a folded paper swing.
The pale yellow fries fanned out from their container like the
severed fingers of children caught in the mouth of a
cornucopia.

'The job? It went fine.'

'Really?'

'I had trouble with the Monster Gulp. The ice melted, but
the guy from the Feed Bag wanted to be sure it looked cold.
So I had to spray the cup. The water kept beading up and
running off. I tried mineral water and corn syrup, and I finally
got it.'

'Congratulations!'

'They still have to see the proofs. Everything is supposed
to be high-key. Bigger than life.'

'I'm so proud of you! So—what were you doing? When I
called, I mean. You said you were in the darkroom.'

'Just cleaning up.'

'Oh.' She paused, as if allowing for a delay in the phone
lines. 'So you can go home now. Unless you have—something
else to work on.'

'No.'

She sighed, a white hissing like steam released inside the
plastic earpiece. 'That's good. I mean, I'll see you at home, then.'

'Okay.'

The conversation did not seem to be over. He waited.

'Oh,' she said, 'I almost forgot. The shoe repair, on Pico. They have my Ferragamos. Could you stop by? He closes at six.'

'I thought you get off at five.'

'It's Counsellors' Night. I have to stay till seven-thirty.'

His throat tensed. 'It'll be dark by then.'

'We have a lighted parking lot. It's safe. I promise.'

He didn't say anything.

'Are you okay?' she said.

'Sure. I'll get the shoes. Don't worry about it.'

'Thanks. You may as well go ahead and eat. There's half a barbecued chicken left.'

'Okay. Or I'll pick up something on the way.'

'The Apple Pan?' she said.

'Maybe the Feed Bag. I could strap on a burger.'

She laughed.

'Be careful, Cory,' he said, very seriously.

'You, too.'

'I feel fine now. Honest.'

'I *know* you do,' she said with an unnatural emphasis. 'Love you.'

'Me, too,' he said, and hung up.

He looked at his watch. It was only a little after five. If he worked fast he could print one more frame from the night-club. He would need as much contrast as possible to hold the details; #6 paper, full-strength developer, and maybe some dodging. But there was still time.

When he turned out of the parking lot on to Venice Boulevard, the traffic was bumper-to-bumper. A diffused glaze hung over the cars and trucks pointing east; in the opposite direction the light was more intense, as though bounced off aluminized reflectors somewhere above the haze while the sun prepared to sink into the ocean several miles to the west. He joined the flow eastwards, but only for a few blocks. At the first corner, a crowd of Hispanic workers gathered under the

American shield of the old Helms Bakery building, waiting with bowed heads for buses that would take them deeper into the city. He tried not to look at them as he inched forward to La Cienega, where he finally made a left, heading home.

The route was a relentless grind at this time of day, jammed with workers on their way back to Washington and Jefferson and the ghettos of South Central. Eyes shone white and fixed behind dirty windshields as large hands gripped steering wheels with grim determination. He moved over for another left at Pico so he could stop by the shoe repair shop. Then he noticed that it was already after six.

He had taken too long with the last batch of prints. There was nothing usable in the envelope; but it was important to be sure. A promise was a promise, especially to his son. He would tell his wife that he had spotted some flaw in the proofs for the Feed Bag and decided to do them over. As for Gary's pictures, at least he had tried. He hoped the boy would understand.

Beneath the Santa Monica freeway, the hard bass rhythms of gangsta rap shook his Mercedes, reverberating in the underpass like the aftershocks of a temblor. He should have taken Robertson. There was nothing to do about it now. He rolled his window up tightly and waited for the traffic to move again.

Another tense mile and the pale, white-gold lettering of the Great Western Bank building wavered into view through the mist. Now the letters spelled out the name of the new owner, a publisher whose sexually graphic magazines sold so well that he had bought the property outright. Years ago, when John Wayne served as the bank's television spokesman, a larger-than-life bronze statue of the late actor on horseback was erected by the entrance, like a sentinel protecting the Westside from attack by outsiders. The statue was still there. What would the conservative cowboy think, knowing that he now guarded an upwardly mobile pornographer's beachhead on the corner of La Cienega and Wilshire, inside the once secure boundaries of Beverly Hills?

He drove Wilshire to Rodeo, a street lined with the world's

most expensive shops, some so exclusive that they required advance credit approval before granting admission. An Asian couple left Gucci's and crossed in front of Decker's car, unaware that jaywalking was a crime in this city, while groups of young men and women with unfamiliar brand names on their jeans strolled past Fendi and Van Cleef & Arpel's, their European accents sounding oddly appropriate amid the many foreign-owned businesses here. The tourist section was only a few blocks long, but he found himself stuck behind a Grey Line bus that paused at every storefront in order to give its passengers a chance to focus their cameras through the tinted windows. By the time he came to Sunset Boulevard the lights of the Beverly Hills Hotel were on, throwing smudged shadows of tall palm trees across the pastel façade. Now, this close to home, he should have begun to unwind. But there was something about the shadows that held his attention and would not let go. He tried to ignore the angular verticals against the uneven horizon as he waited for the line of tail-lights to make their turns, then continued across and up into Beaumont Canyon.

The last mile was the hardest. After only a few days off work he was shocked to find traffic in the canyon dramatically worse, with so many trucks and oversized sport utility vehicles that he could see no more than a single car length ahead. It took twenty minutes to creep a few hundred yards. In front of him a Mexican gardener's pick-up groaned and shuddered, brakes squealing every ten feet. An Isuzu Trooper rode his bumper, its elevated headlights burning holes in his rearview mirror, then began to honk. Other vehicles took up the call until the canyon sounded like New York City at high noon. When a Range Rover cut out of line and tried a J-turn at the first cross street, downhill drivers flashed their high beams and made obscene gestures, only their thrusting fingers visible in the glare. Decker thought he heard the crunch of a fender somewhere ahead, followed by angry voices, and for the next several minutes all movement ceased. The Trooper boiled over in front of a mansion protected by an electrified fence, the gardener's pick-up vibrated as it lurched and rolled backwards, dropping leaves and clods of dirt on to Decker's hood. He cleaned his windshield with a few passes of the wipers. As the blades came to rest, he noticed a police car parked at the side of the road.

How did it get here so fast? he wondered. He saw no sign of a wreck, no broken glass. Perhaps there had not been an accident and the mere sight of the police car had caused the slowdown, its very presence a deterrent. He thought of giving the officer a wave and a smile, but the patrol car's windows were dark and misted over. He drove on past.

By the time he got home it was after eight o'clock. Cory was not there yet.

When he called her school there was no answer. He told himself that she was probably stuck in traffic on the other side of the hill.

He sat down at the kitchen table and opened the envelope.

With such badly underexposed negatives there was not much to see in the prints, despite his best efforts to retain an image. Even on high-contrast paper the frames had gone black with almost nothing in the shadows. The dodging left an opaque halo at the centre, ghostly against the surrounding darkness.

He would tell Gary that he had screwed up. It was embarrassing. The boy had only asked him to take a few publicity photos of the concert. That was easy enough. But something had gone wrong.

He tried to remember.

Somehow, in the noise and the crush of bodies, he had loaded his Leica with a slower portrait film instead of Tri-X. When he discovered his mistake later, he pushed it as far as he dared in the darkroom, but all that gave him was a series of exposures with severely blocked-up highlights and the remaining areas unprintably thin. They might make for some interesting abstract blow-ups, something that would work in a gallery show, but that was not what his son wanted. It was a shame; the night had been special. The word was that there were important people in the audience, people whose opinions could decide the band's future. So they had gone for it, jamming retro Goth at an earsplitting level, amps cranked up to the point where dogs howl and chase their tails, Gary's fingers raking the metal strings until what looked like drops of blood flew from the guitar, as the air grew heavy and began to crackle like an electrical storm. A performance that would never come again. And Decker had blown it.

He studied the prints one last time.

There was the name of his son's band under the ceiling, the letters an unreadable snowstorm of grain in the spotlights. Below, Gary and Mark and the rest of the group were only blurred shadows. Then the false horizon line that was the edge of the stage, and below that blackness. Decker remembered the audience rushing forward in a dark wave, pressing closer. They must have had their arms raised, because there were the vertical lines again, extending up from the bottom half of the frame.

He got out his magnifying glass.

Now he saw rounded silhouettes rising out of the darkness – closed fists, cheering the band on. But what were the lines *above* the hands? Though it had happened only a week ago, he had trouble remembering. The lines were so sharp they could be horns or the ears of wild animals.

He would have to ask Gary.

He picked up the phone, started to dial his son's number. He'd tell him that the pictures were no good, but maybe there was another gig coming up soon. And the next time he'd get it right.

Wait.

This was Thursday. Gary would be rehearsing. Where? At Mark's, just like every Tuesday and Thursday since junior high. He was probably there now. Decker carried the cordless phone to the living room and flicked on the lamp as he dialled Mark's number.

'Hello, this is the Fordham residence . . .'

'Hi, Jack.' Why was the lamp so dim? He found the remote, turned on the TV. 'Are Mark and Gary—?'

'No one can come to the phone, but if you'd care to leave a message, we'll return your call as soon as possible.'

Decker broke the connection.

He poured himself an inch of Scotch. Onscreen, a sitcom about a minority family was in progress. The programme had just started but the members of the family were already trading insults like a neighbourhood gang playing the dozens. He kept the sound low and sat down on the sofa.

Maybe Gary and Mark were over at the new drummer's. What was his name? Cory would know. He'd ask her, as soon as she got home. He took a sip of the Scotch and tried to relax while he waited.

Seated under the lamp, he felt detached from the rest of the room, as though it were receding even as he gazed across it, at the carpet and furniture and the photographs mounted in windowbox frames along the walls. There was the one of Cory by candlelight, then Cory and little Gary waving by the tree in the yard, Gary playing his first guitar, Gary's high school graduation. Their faces smiled back as always from the richly gradated prints, but now his own technique began to irritate him. The background areas in each image were so dark that in this light the faces appeared to be no more than pale reflections, as if he had forgotten to fix them in acid and they were now fading to black, about to disappear. Only the television family shone clearly out of the shadows, striking obvious poses and waiting for laughs from an unseen audience. Then the programme dissolved to a series of commercials.

He focused on the screen as images flickered across it, products so brightly lighted that they seemed more alive than anything else in the room. He wondered if there would be a spot for the Feed Bag, its oozing burgers and fries supported by disposable cardboard neck trays, as he had shot them for the layout this morning. But it was too soon; the drive-thru chain had only just opened, with LA as the first test market. Soon his photographs would pop up on billboards all over the city and he would have more assignments than he could handle. It was good to be working again. He felt as if he had taken off much more than a week.

He drained the Scotch and got up to pour another as a live teaser for the evening news came on. There were unconfirmed reports of another drive-by shooting. A special Eyeball Report on gang violence was promised at eleven.

Where did it happen this time? Decker wondered.

He thought uneasily of Cory and her class in the East Valley, an area known for gang activity. And tonight she had stayed late for a meeting there. He imagined his wife on the way to her car, after. Then other cars, low-riders, cruising into the empty lot and calling out, taunting her, and the doors flying open, the weapons in their dirty hands, the tight-lipped smiles and the catcalls and their brown eyes turning black as a single weak security light fickered by the back of the building . . .

It was another two-and-a-half hours till the newscast.

As he picked up the phone to call the school again, headlights flashed outside and a tall, pointed shadow fell across the windows. He hurried to the front door in time to see a car pass on the lane, the silhouette of the old pine tree sweeping the front of the house. Then there was only the darkness. He went back inside.

He decided to try the police. He punched 911 and got a busy signal. He pressed redial, as someone opened the back door.

'Cory?'

In the kitchen, she stumbled and almost fell as she stepped over the threshold. Her books and papers flapped to the floor. He ignored them and held her, gripping her arms.

'Hey,' she said, 'take it easy . . .'

'Are you all right?'

'Of course I am. You're hurting me. Pete . . .'

He hugged her.

'Hi,' she said.

He let her go. 'Hi.'

'Sorry I'm late. You wouldn't believe how many parents showed up. Have you been home long?'

He took a deep breath. 'No.'

'Did you eat?'

'Not yet.'

'You're supposed to eat, remember?'

'I was waiting for you.'

'I couldn't help it, Pete!'

'It's all right.'

'Well, I guess I can make us something. Just let me get out of these shoes . . .'

'I'm not very hungry.'

'Did you get my new heels?'

'I didn't have time. The traffic was unbelievable.'

She walked through to the living room, taking off her coat. 'Well, I'll just have to get them on the way to work. If he's open that early . . .'

'I was thinking. Maybe you should quit, Cory. It's not like we need the money.'

'It's not about the money.'

'What *is* it about?'

'Those kids. It matters to them.'

'Does it?'

'Why?' she snapped. 'Because they're Chicanos?'

'That's not what I mean.'

'What *do* you mean?'

He backed off and sank on to the couch. 'I was worried, that's all.'

She turned to him, one side of her face in shadow.

'You don't have to,' she said gently. 'Please.' She came over and stood before the couch. Now her features were lost completely to the backlight, only a few sharp strands of her hair outlined against the lamp. 'We're doing fine. You're back at work, and so am I. It's better this way. Isn't it?'

He took her hand and drew her down next to him. Cory was naïve but she meant well. Over her shoulder, he saw the TV family collapse together on to their sofa, convulsed with laughter, knowing that their day was coming. At least it was not here yet.

'Sure,' he said.

'There. See? So what are we talking about?'

Outside, at the end of the lane, the rush-hour traffic in the canyon had ended. A lone car with a broken muffler sped towards Mulholland, radial tyres screaming around the hairpin curves.

'I tried to get to Pico,' he said, 'but it's like a war zone out there.'

'I know. Ever since they closed the Sepulveda Pass.'

'When did they do that?'

She looked at him peculiarly. 'It's been a while.'

'Oh.'

She lowered her head and squeezed his hand.

'At least we've got a traffic cop now,' he said.

'Do we?' she said distantly.

'He was parked by Tremont Road. I passed him on the way up. I hope it does some good.'

'I hope so, too.' She studied his eyes. Then she said, 'Hey, when do I get to see the pictures?'

She meant the Feed Bag layout. Of course. 'It's only burgers and fries. Not exactly art.'

'Well, I'm proud of you, anyway. You know that, don't you?'

He put his arm around her shoulders and drew her close. He felt her cold skin and her warm breath against the side of his neck. They sat that way for a minute.

'I was wondering,' he said. 'What was that drummer's name?'

She pulled away. 'What drummer?'

'In Gary's band. The new one.'

'What are you talking about?'

'I thought I'd give him a call. Do you have the number?'

'No, Pete,' she said after a long pause. 'I don't.'

She stood abruptly and went into the kitchen. He wondered if there was trouble in the band, possibly a falling out that he did not know about. For the moment he decided not to pursue it. He heard her open the refrigerator and set something heavy on the table. Then it was quiet. Another TV programme began, the latest instalment of *Unanswered Questions*. Tonight's episode was about the recently-discovered missing pages from the diary of a dead film actress. The pages purportedly contained the solution to an unsolved murder. Decker found the remote control and raised the volume, as Cory said something unintelligible.

From the kitchen doorway he saw her seated at the table, the leftover barbecued chicken now in a Pyrex dish, and next to that the photos from the concert. She had removed them from the envelope.

'What are these?' she said.

'Nothing.'

'I asked you a question, Peter.'

He started towards her. 'Please, don't look at them.'

'Why not?'

'They're from Gary's last concert. At the Box Club. But they didn't come out.'

'Then,' she said, 'what are you going to do with them?'

He took the photos from her and slipped them back into the envelope. 'Burn them, I guess.'

'Good.'

She turned away and began making the dinner.

They hardly spoke for the rest of the evening. When the eleven o'clock news came on, she was already asleep. He sat up and watched the report about the drive-by shooting. Witnesses claimed it had happened in South Gate, miles from here, but no body had been found yet. In bed he listened to her breathing next to him and thought about her job in the Valley, where conditions were just as bad. The Chief of Police called it an isolated incident but he had taken the precaution of ordering a tactical alert throughout the city. That means it's spreading, thought Decker. He fell asleep dreaming of a parking lot very much like the one behind her school, or what he imagined it to be like. Something was going on there, but he could not see what it was through the fog.

In the morning he had a meeting at the ad agency. Fortunately it was not until eleven o'clock, well after the rush hour. On the way down the hill he tuned to the classical music station, but FM reception here was so weak that the strings sounded like keys scraping the side of his car. He switched to the AM band for the news. There was a late-breaking story about another disturbance, this time in the Crenshaw district. They were getting closer.

He was relieved to see another squad car on Beaumont. It was parked in roughly the same location as the one last night, between Tremont and Huffington Place. The motor was off and the tinted windows were rolled up so that once again he could not see the officer inside. But it was good to know that the LAPD had finally heeded the Westside's pleas for more protection. The canyons were especially vulnerable, with the Valley to the north and the rest of the LA basin to the south, not to mention the Mexican border beyond.

The meeting went smoothly. The rep from the Feed Bag wanted more light and colour in the photos. That would be easy enough; it was simply a matter of printing them up. Decker explained that losing the shadows would mean less depth and realism, but apparently they wanted their product to appear two-dimensional, with nothing left to draw the eye beyond the surface of the picture. No problem, he told them. He knew that he could do it in an afternoon. He also knew that he would put it off as long as possible, now that the job had become even less interesting.

He came home early enough to beat the worst of the traffic, though more than a few commuters were already starting their trek up and over the hill. He passed the electrified fence where the Trooper had overheated last night; the mansion was guarded by an iron servant with outstretched hand, its enamelled face painted an inaccurate but politically correct pink. A zippy young businessman with cell phone drifted over the line in his BMW, a divorcée chauffeured her blonde daughters in an aging Rolls Royce, a private shuttle full of tourists turned up a sidestreet in search of movie star homes. At the first big curve the traffic slowed to a second-gear crawl. Now, at this time of day, he realized how many non-residents used the canyon as a freeway alternate. Ahead he saw plumbers and electricians in company vans, day labourers in rusty Fords and Chevies, college students in unwashed Toyotas and Nissans, teenagers cruising in ragged convertibles and four-wheel drives. He was sure that none of them were from around here.

When he got home he watched the early news. A local reporter was at the site of the latest incident. In the background, gang members in knit caps and baggy clothes mugged for the camera with raised fists, some making the sign of the horns with their fingers.

He called his son's number, but there was no answer.

In the evening, *Unanswered Questions* presented Part Two of its story about the late actress's secret diary. The missing pages had turned up in an estate sale at a home once owned by an actor who died of alcoholism years ago.

Decker spent the next hour searching his house for the blow-ups from the concert, and finally decided that Cory must have thrown them out.

Perhaps there was a problem between her and the boy, something that she had kept from him. Why was she angry? He knew better than to press her on the subject. She would tell him in her own time. Meanwhile, he would let the problem work itself out, whatever it was. The prints were not that important, as long as he had the negatives.

A teaser for the Eyeball News promised more coverage of the unrest, which appeared to be escalating. Shots from several live remotes around the city featured interviews with spokesmen for various gangs, including blacks, Hispanics, Koreans, even a few tattooed skinheads.

He realized that Cory had not come home yet. It was late enough for him to feel uncomfortable but too early to panic. There was no point in calling the school with the switchboard closed. He could go there and try to find her, but what if she was already on her way?

Now there were unconfirmed reports of more trouble, including a firebombing in Culver City, only a mile or so from his studio.

He couldn't just sit here.

He left a note for her on the back door.

*

A mist had moved down from Mulholland and into the canyon. The houses were milky and indistinct behind the trees, cars glistening and silvered in the driveways. Diffused headlights swung past like lanterns in fog. He was surprised to see that the police car was still here. As far as he could tell it had not moved. For the first time he wondered if it might be a movie prop, with location shoots so common in this area. He slowed down, pausing at the curb for a better look.

The shield on the side appeared to be authentic, down to the seal of the city of Los Angeles. If it was a fake it was perfect. Too perfect. But if it was the real thing, why would the LAPD leave one of their cars in the same spot for days on end?

He tuned to an all-news station as he left the canyon. A ten o'clock curfew had just been declared for much of greater LA. Decker glanced at the dashboard clock and decided there was time.

He took Beverly Glen to Pico, turned right at 20th Century-Fox and continued up Motor. The Cheviot Hills Tennis Center was dark except for a pair of white shorts and a disembodied arm swinging a racket through the mist. The neon sign for D.B. Cooper's glowed like faint landing lights near National, and then the mist cleared and he made out the tall water tower that had always reminded him of a Martian spacecraft standing above the old MGM backlot, now owned by Sony.

If there had been a fire anywhere nearby there was no sign of it now. At the corner of Motor and Venice, two patrol cars blocked off the parking lot of the Versailles Cuban Restaurant while officers stood by the exit, checking IDs. As he approached the Helms Bakery building he slowed, preparing to turn into the tenants' lot, and discovered that the sidestreet was barricaded. An officer in a riot helmet waved him on, his eyes hidden behind the protective visor.

The next news bulletin announced a bombing in the garment district, near downtown LA.

That was where Gary had his loft.

The horizon to the east swirled with mist heavy enough to

be smoke. Decker wished for a car phone so that he could warn his son. Where was the nearest telephone booth? The gas stations at Robertson and at La Cienega were closed off with wooden sawhorses and the fast food restaurants up and down Venice had all shut down early.

He would have to drive there.

But the entrance ramp to the I-10 was blocked by more barricades. The surface streets between here and the dark heart of the city would be unpredictable. Olympic passed directly through Koreatown, and every other major east-west artery intersected at least one ethnic stronghold. La Cienega was already closed to the south, in the direction of Washington and Jefferson and the black neighbourhoods. Soon the western section would be cut off on all sides, effectively isolated.

Had Gary tried to call?

Cory would know.

If she had made it home.

He cut back up National to Pico, heading north. The mist thickened again and he had to use his wipers, sweeping away what appeared to be fine ash as well as moisture. As he neared Sunset the traffic grew congested. Beverly Glen, Benedict and Beaumont Canyons were all freeway alternates and late commuters now searched for any route still open to the Valley. Through the glass he heard blips of competing radio stations in other cars, each with a different version of the news. There had been a minor disturbance or a full-scale riot in East LA or Watts, with no serious injuries, mounting casualties or dozens dead. The police had the situation contained or the city was under siege and the Mayor had called for the National Guard. He kept his window closed and his door locked.

He knew now that he was on his own. They all were. LA was not a city but a freeway system that mixed together tribes with nothing in common except an overlapping geography, directed and distributed by the grid. That was why the traffic was out of control wherever people crossed each other's turf. They had no sense of community, no respect for the routes they were forced to share, and everything not part of one's neighbourhood was enemy territory, a no man's land to be trashed. Decker finally understood the appeal of sport utility vehicles. With their high cabs and reinforced bodies, they were like tanks ready for the battlefield. He pounded the wheel and leaned on the horn.

Halfway up the canyon he found himself idling next to the abandoned police car. He wondered if it belonged to an officer who lived on this street, or one who came here at all hours for private reasons, perhaps to visit a girlfriend. Now, against the line of descending headlights, he thought he saw someone in the driver's seat. The head was cocked at an odd angle, as if the officer were sleeping it off. But before he could get a closer look, there was a break in the bottleneck and the traffic began to move again.

Cory's car was parked in back but the house was dark. He rushed through to the living room and found her waiting by the sofa in the light of the television set. She threw her arms around his neck and clung to him. He kissed her as an Eyeball News reporter conducted a live interview. Onscreen, fire-fighters picked through the charred remains of a convenience store, while round-eyed children with dirty fingers waved at the camera from behind police barricades.

'I'm sorry,' she said. She felt his face carefully with her hands, as if he were fragile. 'I had to stay with the children. Nobody could get through, not even the buses.'

Over her shoulder, the TV coverage continued.

'What's happened?' he said.

'They're still looking for the body. The Crips say it's in Watts. The Brown Brotherhood says East LA. So far, it's just a rumour. But all the gangs are taking credit.'

'Why?'

'It was a cop. At least that's what they say. It's just an excuse to loot and burn. I go to work every day so the children will have a chance, and now they're destroying their own neigh-bourhoods! It's stupid, so stupid . . .'

'They know what they're doing.'

'What do you mean?'

'They want the city, this time.'

Her eyes were enormous in the semidarkness. 'That doesn't make sense.'

'Doesn't it?' He had hoped she would see the handwriting on the wall, but apparently she did not, even now. He started for the kitchen. 'Did Gary call?'

She did not answer.

He turned on the kitchen light, looking for the phone. 'He might be trying to get us. I tried, but there's never any answer. What did he do, change the number?'

Behind him, he heard her make a sound in her throat. When he turned around her eyes were full of tears.

'Oh, God,' she said.

'What's wrong? Did something happen to Gary?'

She regained control of herself and went to him. 'I thought you were all right. But you're not. Jack Fordham's been getting calls. He said it was a prank . . .'

'Tell me, Cory.'

He attempted to push her away but her hands tightened, forcing him to look at her.

'We'll be okay,' she said. 'You'll see. I'll take care of you . . .'

'Tell me!'

'You've been sick. You don't remember the last year, not anything at all, do you?'

'It's been a week, Cory. I've been off work for a week!'

'Pete, I want you to listen to me.'

He felt strangely calm. He knew what she was going to say, as if he had heard it before, in a dream. He saw the pictures in his mind again, of the parking lot and the gang, the confrontation. It was not about Cory, after all.

'Honey, Gary's dead.'

No, he thought, not yet. Somehow she knew what he had been dreaming. But that did not mean it had to happen. There was still time to stop it, to get the boy out of there before it was too late.

'You're lying,' he said.

He went outside and started the Mercedes, dropped into

gear and clicked on the headlights. He wiped a clear spot on
the fogged windshield and rolled forward over wet leaves, low
branches slapping the glass. For a moment all he could see
was a wall of mist. Then he heard a scream. He looked at the
rearview mirror. A shadow reached out to the car, red in the
glow of the taillights.

He unlocked the passenger door.

'Are you coming or not?' he shouted.

She stood there, her face crawling with rivulets of water,
then got in.

The canyon was empty of traffic as far as he could see. The
mist that had collected in the hills now poured down like
smoke, heavy with moisture, a glittering whiteness that his
headlights could not penetrate. He turned right, towards
Sunset and the city.

'Will you tell me where we're going?'

He ignored her. Even with the defroster on the windshield
did not stay clear. Beads of moisture began to collect on the
inside of the glass as he leaned forward, following the double
line. The fog thinned briefly and he saw the lights of houses
twinkling behind the trees. Then the white wall closed around
the car and he was driving blind again. He pressed harder on
the accelerator. With visibility so limited he felt alert to any
possibility. The familiar landmarks would only have lulled
him into an illusion of security, leaving him more vulnerable.
That was the danger of believing in surfaces, in what showed.
Now, aware of how much he could not see, he was ready for
anything. It was more than an aesthetic preference. It was a
matter of survival.

'Please,' she said, 'where—?'

'To get Gary.' He felt her shocked eyes on him, heard the
sharp intake of breath above the pulse of the wipers. 'If you
can't handle that, get out now.'

'I thought it was good that you forgot everything,' she said
softly, 'but now . . .'

A car passed them, speeding downhill from Mulholland.

'At least let me drive!'

He knew she was trying to trick him so that she could turn

around and go home. The tyres hissed over the wet pavement, trees sagged and waved in front of lampposts. Somewhere above the fog great wings flapped, marking the pace. Then the fog blew aside, like curtains parting on a stage, and in the spotlight he saw the police car.

She opened her window and leaned out, signalling for help. He pulled her roughly back into the seat.

'Forget it,' he told her. 'There's never anybody in that car.'

The flapping became a roar. The sky grew brighter and the fog blew aside, as a helicopter hovered overhead with its searchlight trained on the abandoned car.

As they pulled abreast of it he saw again the form inside, illuminated clearly now in the circle of light from above. There was a head and shoulders, leaning precariously to one side in the seat, about to topple over.

Not even the Westside is safe, he thought. They must have killed him right here, in Bel Air, but we were all too busy to notice.

'There's your dead cop,' he said. 'They don't know where he is? Well, they do now!'

He climbed out of the Mercedes and raised his face to the light, holding his arms up.

'Here!'

She ran to him and dragged him over to the police car, digging her fingers into his hair to make him see what was inside. It was a department-store mannequin dressed in a uniform with badge and hat, propped up behind the wheel. She shouted in his ear as the blades sliced the air.

'Look, Pete, it's a only a dummy! For traffic control! They call it passive law enforcement . . . !'

She was right, but what did that matter? Someone had seen it, one of the cars passing through, a gardener or a workman or a transient, and the rumours had started.

No cars had passed them going uphill. Did that mean Sunset was blocked off?

He hoped so. Because the gang would come back, the ones who had done it, to show the way so others would know who was to lead them. Then they would all come, from Compton and Inglewood and Huntington Park and South Gate, from Monterey Park and El Sereno and Silverlake and Little Saigon, swarming across the basin in a united front, a tide that would sweep away everything in its path. They had been sitting tight in their ghettos, waiting for someone to fire the opening shot so they could move in force. For years they had hit and run with small strikes, a convenience store, a mall, even picking off members of rival gangs, feeding on each other as the frustration grew. Now all that was over. Their time had come at last.

The helicopter banked and rose higher, flapping away.

'Come home with me, Pete,' he heard her say in the sudden silence.

'Who killed my son?'

'He was my son, too. It doesn't matter now. It's over . . .'

'You're wrong,' he said.

He squinted, struggling to see the details, as the mist returned. He had captured a piece of it in his viewfinder that night, just before it started . . .

Under the track lights was a banner with the name of his son's band, and below that the blur that he knew to be Gary on lead guitar. Then the horizon line of the stage, the heads of the crowd, and the thrusting verticals. He stared into the swirling particles of fog as if studying the grain pattern in a frame of film, and this time he refused to look away until he saw it all.

The pattern began to move.

Beyond the edges of the frame were bouncing heads, the bare-chested boys with shirts tied around their waists. The music assaulted his eardrums so that he had to shut his eyes but the image remained clear.

There, in the middle of the crowd, several figures were not moving to the music. They had slipped past the security guards after the set started and made their way down front. He had no trouble spotting them because they were wearing jackets with emblems on the back, their colours. He felt bodies pressing closer and hot breath on his neck, and realized that Cory was clinging to him.

He lowered the camera long enough to free himself from her. The night air chilled him. He opened his eyes and saw her standing in front of him, about to disappear into the mist.

'The name,' he said. 'What was the name of Gary's band?'

'Please . . .'

'Say it!'

'The New Goths,' she told him, and began to cry again.

Yes, he thought, that's it. The same as the emblem on the jackets. They came to the club to see who had stolen their name. That was why the weapons came out, at first only a few thin, jagged lines in his viewfinder, as still as swords at rest. When the song ended they put them away and did not take them out again until the parking lot. They were the last things Decker saw that night, the last things Gary ever saw.

Now the fog behind Cory became white, so bright that the outline of her body seemed a part of it. He saw her disembodied head turning to look behind her, as the helicopter reappeared above the horizon at the top of the canyon. The blades beat the air and the fog cleared and he saw the jagged lines of dead trees and the legs of a water tower against the sky, and then the rounded shapes of heads rising up in the beam of the searchlight.

'They forgot,' he said.

She turned back to him, confused.

He thought of how Beaumont Canyon continued on up to Mulholland and then all the way down the hill to the Valley on the other side, to Panorama City and Pacoima and San Fernando and the gang enclaves there.

'They stopped them at Sunset,' he told her. 'But they forgot about Mulholland.'

'What . . .?'

'It's too late now,' he said. 'They're here.'

They came marching down the hill, ignoring the police helicopter. He saw the blond stubble of their hair shining in the searchlight and the swastikas tattooed on their skulls, and he knew that it was not the Crips or the Bloods or the New Goths, not this time. They were skinheads, whatever they called themselves.

The helicopter boomed a warning but they kept coming, the lines of their sharp, splintered baseball bats held high. Their eyes shone like the eyes of wild animals, like raccoon eyes, yellow and terrible. When they saw Decker and his wife and the Mercedes they started running and yelling.

He pushed her behind him and stood his ground, stepping out into the centre of the pavement to meet them.

Dennis Etchison has written extensively for film and television, much of his contribution remaining uncredited. However, he *has* been credited with three British Fantasy Awards and two World Fantasy Awards, and he currently stands as one of the genre's most respected and distinguished practitioners. Since the 1960s he has been producing a steady stream of short stories – his preferred core work – many of which can be found in the collections *The Dark Country*, *Red Dreams* and *The Blood Kiss*. He is the author of four film novelizations, *The Fog*, *Halloween II*, *Halloween III: Season of the Witch* and *Videodrome* and the original novels *Darkside*, *Shadowman*, *California Gothic* and, most recently, *Double Edge*. Etchison has also edited several acclaimed anthologies, including *Cutting Edge*, three volumes of *Masters of Darkness* (collected in the omnibus volume *The Complete Masters of Darkness*), *Lord John Ten* and *MetaHorror*. About 'The Dead Cop', the author reveals that it is the first short story he has written in three years and that he is pleased to be back working in the short form: 'The idea came after seeing such a real police car with a uniformed mannequin behind the wheel, parked on my canyon street around-the-clock for several days and nights.'

Where the Bodies Are Buried 2020

Kim Newman

Spring Meadow, Illinois. Anytown, USA, in the Middle America of the mind. A night in fall, a full moon.

Chantal, consciousness uneasily nestled within the Tina simile, looked through the viewpoint character's eyes. As Tina, she stood alone in a patch of fenced-in park.

The verdigrised town founder, a crooked politician two centuries gone, posed on a pedestal. The statue was in sharp focus, richly dimensional, palpably solid.

Mimesis was generations beyond Virtual.

Dreamwelt was indistinguishable from Actual, affording complete sensory interface. Through the Tina construct, Chantal heard cicada chirrup on the backtrack; felt crisp cold, to the bone; saw breath clouding in damp whispers; smelled grass, after rain.

The indistinct receptors VR did not connect with were active. Her backbrain was absorbing infobits it would take conscious effort to scroll. A million tiny subliminals supported the dream.

Spring Meadow *tasted* real.

INITIATE TITLE SEQUENCE

Disembodied words ghosted in front of the statue, filling the night with letters of jagged green newsprint.

WHeRE tHE BodiES Are BurIEd

The words came apart like mist. She wasn't sure how to make the dream RUN. She couldn't swivel her neck – 'her' neck – to shift viewpoint.

PAUSE

'Don't try to think what it's like, Sister Chantal. Just let it happen.'

Jerome's voice seemed to come from empty air, blotting out all other sound and sense. Merely by giving the advice, he made it impossible for her to take it. Aural bleed-through wavered the dreamwelt, shattering the statue into pixels.

Behind the bead curtain of dreamnight, Chantal saw spectre-shapes. Jerome Rhodes and Roger Duroc were watching over her, monitoring her progress.

What was she doing really? Sitting on the couch or standing like Tina, a puppet jerked along by the program?

She felt the weight of the hoodset, the pull of her regular body, the gravity of realwelt.

The curtain hung still, the statue reformed.

STILL PAUSE

She felt the cold again, and heard insects. The spectres were hidden. Calming, she tried to accept the dream. She recognized that she found it hard to surrender to Mimesis.

People do this for *fun*, she reminded herself. For *entertainment*.

A smart program probed for a way around her mental block. She tried not to feel violated.

Chantal did not trust stories, but they still fascinated her. She was not sure which of her conflicting reactions was wrong.

As Tina, her viewpoint was fixed. It was like – 'don't try to think what it's *like*' – wearing a thick suit of too-tight clothes wired rigid by an armature sewn in the lining. She could feel everything, but do nothing.

Her itch to move her neck affected the dreamscene, shifting the visionfield.

180° PAN

The movement was part of the dream, not of her volition. She saw more of the square. Carefully trimmed trees. A white-painted bench. Abandoned civic buildings. A black cat – very convincing, lithely alive – slunk through bushes, cringing in moonlight. Something dark wafted across the penny-bright face of the moon.

Atmos, atmos.

Despite blurbclaims, it was not like *being* the viewpoint. Chantal wore Tina's dreambody, but was a *dybbuk*, a passenger in her – its – 'mind'.

She could resist the dream, but impetus was to carry on with the story.

Something gave.

RUN

Under the wind, chords sounded, building, suspenseful. Her heart – hers or Tina's? – pounded faster. That cat was gone, melding with liquid shadows. The moon was clear.

The viewpoint looked around. Not the smooth pan of the last movement, but quick, birdlike darts. The pan was to get the dreamer accustomed to visionfield shifts. This was how people saw realwelt; through a skull-camera mounted on a neck-gyro, blurring transitions between shaky half-hemispheres of SurroundSound CineRama.

Tina was waiting, expectant and a little afraid, for someone. There was to be a meeting at midnight. By the old clock on the town hall – something of a cliché – it was a breath away from twelve.

Tina was maybe fifteen years younger than Chantal, in her late teens. She wondered who the girl was.

The dream reacted: a 'Tina Singleton' packet opened, down-loading infodump. Flash-images of parents and friends, establishing relationships. A rolling scroll of backstory. Facts and figures about Spring Meadow. Blips of childhood, blats of school, blurts of domestic terror. Tina was a good student, popular at Spring Meadow High. Her home life was uncertain, locked between feuding parents. Sometimes, Mom – reversal of expectations – got zonked and hurt her. Dad didn't want to notice.

Technically, Mimesis was impressive. But not real, any more than reading a book or watching a motion picture. It was just a story.

The wind raised a flurry of leaves, which swirled around the statue, drifted against her legs. She snatched an oak leaf, held it up. Through the viewpoint's fingers, it seemed absolutely real. She crunched it up and threw it away.

How much information had she just converted?

The park was deserted. Chantal stubbornly sensed Jerome and Duroc, tuning in from outside dreamwelt. And something else.

Another presence.

Tina's nerves frazzed in fearful anticipé. Chantal was puzzled. This sharing of mindspace was not what she expected. Tentatively, she clicked on Tina, allowing more seepthrough.

Tina had been receiving Valentines, collaged of newsprint like blackmail notes. At first, sweet.

THeeNk*ng of U, allwAyS.

Then sinister, intimating secret knowledge.

HoW'S MoMMY's leeTle guRL?

Why didn't this twittette go to her School Confessor? There were so many safety nets.

Of course, Chantal knew why:

This is just a stupid story. Logical behaviour would spoil it.

Today's note:

MEaT ME, ToWN $quAre @ MEEDNiGHT.

Unlike the others, it was signed; in an arachnoidal scrawl:

Rob Hackwill.

The name triggered an eerie melody that rose and fell with the swirl of leaves.

Another information package appeared, sealed for the now. Chantal intuited more backstory.

Rob Hackwill was the villain, the killer, the monster. A blackmailer, tortured to death by his corrupt victims; back from the grave for revenge on hypocrite and innocent alike; an agent of the Devil Princess of Hell, tormented and tormenting; a franchise from the last century, still lurking in the collective pop-unconscious.

While preparing her thesis on the Hackwill Effect, Chantal had seen *Where the Bodies Are Buried*, the original motion picture, over and over. Before that, Hackwill had haunted her childhood nightmares. When her Confessor suggested the academic work was an attempt to deal with earlier terrors, he had not told her anything she had not intuited for herself.

Why did the first wide-release Mimesis production have to be a dremake of *Where the Bodies Are Buried?* Why not *Little Women* or *La Dolce Vita?*

Tina looked around nervoso. She was sure it was all skit. Stacey Snyder, her bestest ammi, projected she was *sooooo* funny. This was muchissimo. There would be payback in school tomorrow.

Or maybe it was Jimmy Traynor. One of the Hackwill notes was about him:

Yr SeeCret's saFE, I KnOW U ♥♥♥♥ JiMMy T.

She had no secret crush on Jimmy. No, she was lying to herself. Tina dezzed desperé that Jimmy would glom her.

Chantal was frustrated. The teenthink was difficult to follow. She tried to take over viewpoint, cutting the slango, communicating danger.

From the back of Tina's cramped mind construct, she shouted: look behind you, run away, go home, pull up the covers, call the cops! She caught herself trying to influence a fictional character. She had not expected to be fooled in quite this way. It was absurd.

Jimmy and Stacey were guilty, Tina was pozz. Stacey had snitched her crush to Jimmy. They were gagging together, in the bushes. Her heart would fraction again. There was no Secret Admirer. That scut was only in bad movies – Hah! – and daydreams. There was no Rob Hackwill.

Hadn't Tina registered the name? Didn't this town remember? There had been a dozen sequels. It was impossible that anyone wouldn't know. After thirteen murder-filled films, Rob Hackwill should be as famous in the storywelt as in the real.

Of course, the Mimesis wasn't so much sequel as remake. According to the blurb, this was supposed to 'reinvent the mythos', to take Hackwill 'back to his festering origins' and make him 'a monster for the new millennium'.

Something barrelled at her. A clawed hand grasped her shoulder. Music leaped like a jaguar. Her throat opened in scream. She was pulled around and knocked down.

Gotcha!

Even *knowing* this would happen did not make it less of a shock.

Pressed into soft grassy earth, she sensed the weight of the dark shape pinning her. She smelled a foul breath. She heard muttering.

'I know . . . Robbie knows . . . Robbie has always known . . . *where the bodies are buried!*'

Her coat ripped at shoulder-seam, sliced by a razor-edged clawnail. There was something like pain and something like warmth – few want to be hurt in a dream, though the option's there – as the nail pierced Tina's shoulder.

Why would anyone want to pay for this?

Chantal wanted STOP, but had no control. Tina could not struggle; the monster had her. Chantal was completely sucked in by the viewpoint. There was no Chantal Juillerat, S. J.; only Tina Singleton, doomed girl.

The nail grew in her shoulder-wound, scraping past bone, through ligament. Everything distorted. Pain substitute flooded her mind.

The viewpoint was on her back, looking up. The statue stood above, like a towering gravestone. A face thrust close to her, eclipsing the statue and the moon.

Sharp teeth clacked, several centimetres of enamel exposed. A single red eye gleamed.

An ice fist took her heart . . .

'The Hack is back!'

. . . and squeezed.

STOP EJECT

The dreamwelt vanished like ice on a griddle, but there were after-sensations. Chantal still felt Tina's terror.

She needed a moment to reorient.

She was on the couch, as when she had initiated **RUN**. Physically, she had not moved.

Jerome fussed at the dreamdeck. He had ordered **STOP** – didn't he think she could take it? – and was extracting the dreamsphere from its tray. Eyepieces receded into her hoodset.

It took moments for hearing to return. Her brain had to recalibrate for reality, after only minutes of Mimesis.

'Sister, art thou all right in thyself?' asked Duroc.

She nodded and lifted off the hoodset. She shook her hair out – as if she had Tina's shoulder-length blonde fall rather than her own black bob – and scanned the inside of the contraption. Transparent padding protected a neural network of wires and crystal chips.

The Mimesis Process was, in the end, only light. Dreams reached the brain through the optic nerves, duping neural receptors into interpreting nanoflashes as sight, sound, smell, taste, pain, pleasure. But it was hard to remember the tech when a monster was kissing you to death.

She waved Duroc away and looked a question at Jerome.

'I thought you were losing yourself,' he answered.

'I'd have preferred to make the decision from the inside.'

'You're right, Sister. I'm sorry.'

Both Duroc and Jerome used the archaic form, 'Sister'. At the Euro-Commission press conference in Brussels, she had been required to wear full habit for the cameras. She was embarrassed by the penguin costume, which made her a sexless nonperson. She preferred a plain dark singlepiece with a discreet Roman collar.

The floor swayed slightly: the ship easing on its moorings, not her strings being snipped. Her spinal spirit level was settling. She had her weltview back. She returned the hoodset to its cradle.

The Eunion Parliament had argued in circles about where to site the Euro-Commission on the Model-Duff Amendment. Brussels had superior facilities, but a policy of positive anti-bias against second-generation members meant they were in Prague.

The influx of Eurocracy with Czechia's two-year chairing of EU put office space at a premium. E-Com wound up with the *Gustav Meyrink*, a riverboat at permanent anchor near the Charles Bridge. Subotai, the Mongol indentured to E-Com as minion, joked that the ship constituted the Bohemian Navy.

Her quarters, one deck down, were not much smaller than her cell in Castel Sant'Angelo. Jerome, unused to the cenobite life, nagged admin into getting him a hotel suite. Duroc seemed not to mind his cabin. He had little baggage.

'Thoughts, Sister?'

Tina haunted her. And the stab of Hackwill's claw was a phantom twinge in her shoulder.

'Not yet, Duroc. This will take time. The tech has outpaced the psych. There'll have to be long-term studies.'

'That's what the Industry says,' put in Jerome. 'But they regard mass audiences as a field test. We've too much gen on Mimesis, not enough cognition.'

Jerome Rhodes was English, an Information Analyst. Chantal was Swiss, a Media Psychologist. Their skills were supposed to be complementary. They had not worked together before E-Com seconded their services.

'Then again, the Industry has been co-operative. Pyramid

are allowing us dreams well before the public. *Bodies* hasn't been theatrical in the States, much less cleared for Home Mimesis.'

He was in his late twenties, which gave her a year or so on him. He cultivated a slender boyishness she was not yet pozz – a stray Tina word – suited him. He might be a template for her in-progress/back-burnered bookfile on Information Children: a global generation whose personality, values and culture were shaped by mediamass rather than religion, family background, social class or nationality.

Something had made him **STOP** and pull her out.

'The Industry wants absolution, Jerome,' she said. 'Just as Model-Duff – offence none, Duroc – want us to condemn Mimesis. Everybody deems it in their interest to co-operate. It gets them to where they cognit they can influence us.'

Pyramid Releasing was part of the Derek Leech Group. The multi-media mogul had offered to underwrite the study, but E-Com could not directly accept credit from a source with such a stake in Mimesis, any more than from lobbyists who wanted the Model-Duff Amendment passed into Euro-Law. Leech had been working towards Mimesis since the turn of the century.

'There is Evil around,' Duroc said. 'The Reverend Model has warned us.'

Roger Duroc was a Hardline Christian Zealot, a French follower of Joseph Model, the Liechtensteinian Euro-Vangelist. A big man in his forties, he was a veteran of the Basque Insurrection of '09. While Jerome wore Oxford bags and a tartan *Gorille* jacket, Duroc dressed like a nineteenth century ascetic: black suit fastened with pegs, white shirt pinned at the throat. Like other extreme sects, Modelists abjured buttons.

With Britain's Prime Minister Morag Duff, Model proposed the Third Amendment to the Eunion's Revised Criminal Code. E-Com was supposed to give its recommendation to Parliament before the Code was enforced throughout the EU on January 1st, 2020.

'It is the work of the Devil. This is a Holy Crusade.'

She couldn't quite scan Duroc. Sometimes, he seemed to

assume comradeship with her as a fellow religious, though Modelists – especially ex-Catholics – were obliged to damn Pope Georgi as 'dangerously soft on hellfire'. Sometimes, she was sure Duroc put on an Ominous Warning act, subtly mocking those who expected 'thou' and 'thine' of him.

'The Reverend has decreed we must put away Evil Things.'

Duroc was an ex-cop: after the Europa Defence Forces, he had been with Interpol, specializing in transnational serial murder. He had put away three of the Hackwill Killers: Pietro Moschone, Nadja Thiel, Hugh Best.

Duroc's law enforcement background, not his standing in the Modelist Church, earned him his place on E-Com. Jerome's company had informal ties with media consortia, which meant he balanced Duroc. As of now, the vote was split: Duroc for, Jerome against; like any Swiss, she was neutral.

Though resident in Vatican City, she did not hold an EU passport. Whatever E-Com recommended, the Amendment would not apply in her homeland.

'It's not like Virtual Reality,' she said. 'Except in the generic way television is like theatre.'

'The Industry cognits Mimesis is the Real Thing,' said Jerome, holding the dreamsphere. It was a pleasing bauble, a flawless silver pearl. 'VR was a side-track. All you could do was chuck things at customers' heads or let them wander around CGNvironments. Remember when "interactive" was the buzz? That was Big Mistake Uno. Punters want *stories*, not choices. Once they got past redoing *This is Cinerama!* and zotzing aliens, everyfool zoned out of VR. That's why it's taken two decs to develop Mimesis. When all those Millennium VR parlours went belly-up, research funding dried. If not for Derek Leech's deep pockets, we wouldn't have the tech. And if Mimesis rockets faster than zonk cocaine, it still won't show a profit before 2050. Then again, Leech can afford it.'

'This is like being someone else, Jerome. No, not like being. Like being in someone else's head.'

The stick figure of Tina Singleton came to mind.

'Same effect reading *Pamela* two-point-five centuries back, Sister Chan. Or auditing an Oedipus or Hamlet soliloquy. The diff is it isn't just words now. You're not on the outside, empathizing. You're on the inside, sharing.'

'It's the work of the Devil,' said Duroc.

'Or Derek Leech, which Mum says is the same thing,' said Jerome. 'Then again, Leech's Cloud 9 Satellite Net carries Reverend Model's tele-ministry.'

Though there were no mirrors in the scene she had dreamed through, the viewpoint carried a self-image icon. Beneath the Hollywood cheerleader face, Chantal intuited a template with which she was familiar.

'Tina looks like Marthe Wink, don't you think?'

Marthe Wink was the Hamburg victim.

Jerome was startled. 'There are resemblances; then again, there are differences.'

Duroc said nothing.

Chantal found the file on the desk. She flipped it on and called up post-mortem glossies.

The phantom intrusion in her shoulder matched a wound in Marthe's shoulder. The gouge was a 3-D rose through the wrong side of a stereoscope, a hole ribbed with red folds.

'We mustn't be too dazzled by the tech or the aesthetic,' she said. 'Mimesis is just breaking. There's so much to cognit about how it works, what its potential might be. What we have to decide is whether it turns dreamers into murderers.'

After two years studying *Where the Bodies Are Buried* kill clusters, Chantal was still unsure of the Hackwill Effect.

In Vatican screenrooms, she refamiliarized herself with all thirteen films; meanwhile, tapping into archives, she immersed herself in seemingly every incidence of homicide that occurred during the fifteen-year run of the series.

The Hackwill Effect began as a newsnet scare patterned on long-running tabloid rumours that certain blues or heavy metal audio-tracks were conducive to suicide, but evidence accrued like coral. Some people who watched *Bodies* films went out and committed atrocities. Rob Hackwill reached out from screens to warp minds, making monsters of random members of the audience. Undeniably, there were murders. Equally undeniably, following a newsbite lead, it was claimed in court – by prosecution and defence – that murderers were under the influence of the bogeyman.

She scrolled through a mediamorass of interviews with 'Hackwill Killers'. The most interesting was the most talkative: Elizabeth Yatman gave a bookfile of detail about how Hackwill had turned her into a mass murderess. But Chantal intuited in Yatman's references an evasiveness that suggested only sketchy, second-hand knowledge of the films. No Hackwill fanatic would confuse Tina Singleton with Stacey Snyder, but Beth Yatman did.

Yatman, nearly fifty, was thriving in England's Broadmoor Facility, happily claiming 'Hackwill made me do it' to Backchat Sites, making encouraging noises to the pressure group campaigning for her release. An accomplished cook, she sent cakes to supporters, and also to Relatives of Hackwill Victims spokesfolk. RHV hardly needed to campaign for her continued incarceration.

Chantal was inclined to class the Hackwill Effect a modern instance of Loudon or Salem Hysteria, an arbitrary shifting of guilt on to something beyond self. Instead of the Devil, a string of tame horror films were singled out and blamed for atrocities conceived and executed by apparently normal people. The oldest, saddest excuse of all: 'I was only obeying orders.'

Cardinal Kevin Menzies, her supervisor, allowed her thesis to be a first public acknowledgement that the Vatican had ever considered the Hackwill Effect. She seconded the findings of a *sub rosa* 2004 inquiry which recommended Yatman's request for exorcism be ignored. Not refused, *ignored*. The plea was one of Yatman's increasingly bizarre attempts to remain Site Prime News. Besides, Rob Hackwill was not officially recognized as a demon, nor was ever likely to be.

There was still *something* about the *Bodies* films. Something unhealthy, if not unholy.

Yatman, like two other Hackwill Killers – one of whom was

never caught – murdered in and around the English backwater where Allan Keyes, writer-director of the original *Where the Bodies Are Buried*, had grown up. Leslie Conyers, victim of the unsolved Hackwill killing, was once Keyes's girlfriend. Another murderer was *called* Robert Hackwill. His name had lodged in Keyes's memory from childhood, resurfacing arbitrarily in his fiction.

Could it be something in the water?

Or maybe the popularity of the *Bodies* films was not causal to the Hackwill Killings but parallel with them. Both might be symptoms of something else.

It was not Hackwill that unnerved her: once she was past adolescence, he struck her as an obvious loser with a stale repertoire. More disturbing was the Devil Princess, Hackwill's infernal mistress. It said much about Keyes's psyche that he chose to depict Ultimate Evil as a provocative teenage fillette who wore black leather and chains or a scarlet nun's habit.

Maybe it was the mediaeval architecture around her as she worked, but at the root of the Hackwill Effect was something that made her yearn to leave the Post-Modern Papacy of Genial Georgi and take refuge in a Vatican which believed in physical war with the armies of the Devil.

While working on the thesis, she dreamed often.

Her conclusion, deleted from the final draft at Menzies's request, was that the church not rely on psychology in dealing with the resurgent Hackwill Effect, but fall back on ancient, spiritual resources.

Her now-cautious thesis was modestly posted on the Vatican branch of the World-Tree just as Morag Duff, on the point of yielding the EU chair to Czechskanzler Martina Drnkova, set down the Amendment as a parting gift to her successor.

'For century kiddettes like me, Information is Air, Chantal. We breathe it in from birth.'

Jerome had finally not called her Sister. For her, a little triumph.

'Actually, Mum's a Nouveau Luddite Won't have a flat-screen in the apartment. Never downloads newsbits.'

'You're probably reacting to her.'

'She taught me not to surrender to white noise, to scan only for what matters. Then again, usually I intuit *when* gen matters but not *why*. That, I cognit, is your job description.'

They were at a pavement café in the Ghetto. An electric brazier melted the thin snow back metres away from their table, and created a bubble of warmth. A maché golem, creaking with every move, served tall glasses of hot tea. Jerome played with his Kafka Salad, picking out chocolate roaches.

The tottering Expressionist walls and tiny alleyways were processed styro, spray-coated to mimic ancient stone. Cabalist graffiti art covered every surface. The place was less than ten years old, an exact recreation of an original razed early in the last century.

All the capitals of Eunion were becoming theme parks; even the Vatican. Sub-national congresses passed laws requiring citizens to wear 'traditional' costume in public. Australasian tourists expected it.

Nearby, *robotas* – in the original Czech sense, indentured workmen not machines – were restoring the frontage of a vandalized Synagogue Gift Shop by abrading deep-etched, luminous Anti-Semitic slogans. Throughout the Ghetto, there were rumours of a *pogrom* coming. Few Jews lived here, but misethnicists had as much contempt for the Mongols and Kurds collected in the beehive-cell apartments stacked above these streets.

A giant head popped into being above a public holo-plate. Waves of white hair around a withered angel face, eyes augmented by burning azure overlays.

'It's Roger's boss,' Jerome commented. 'The Model Man.'

Joseph Model was the most successful E-Vangelist. He synthesized salable qualities perfected by US tele-ministries of the last century, but preached Old World Puritanism and a Work Ethic that verged on Slavery. Doctrinally, an economic Calvinist; politically, a Mussolini fascist; he liked to compare himself with Savonarola, Malcolm Muggeridge and Rush Limbaugh.

The holo began speaking, simultaneously in Hebrew and Czech, about the uprising in Cadiz. Model harshly criticized EU refusal to let his relief-workers deploy in combat zones. In a rare moment of passion, Pope Georgi had described Modelist Rapid Response Teams as 'spiritual looters'. During the Basque Insurrection, RR Teams dispensed medical help and subsistence food only in exchange for signatures on lifetime contracts with the Modelist Ministry.

'I can't scan Roger,' Jerome admitted. 'Why is he with Model? He seems too clued to be a Zombie.'

'I've heard that said about me.'

'Georgi's made it snazz to be a nun, Chan. His renunciation of the doctrine of Papal Infallibility is a major break with deadhead tradition. Then again, liberalism might erode core strengths.'

'Strictly speaking, I'm a priest, not a nun. That's another Georgi reform for you.'

'I'm sorry. It's hard sometimes to rewrite the program.'

'Worry not. Many in the church have the same problem.'

Model was talking about the Amendment now, another declaration of intent with case histories. She caught the name 'Marthe Wink'.

'Scans like Roger reported back.'

She agreed.

'Then again, I imagine the Modelists have access to as much gen as we do.'

It turned out Marthe was one of a group of tech-buff teens who had rigged up their own dreamdeck and got hold of bootleg dreamspheres from the States. The night before her murder, the girl had dreamed *Where the Bodies Are Buried*. Model made much of the similarities between Tina Single-ton's encounter with Hackwill and the actual killing.

'He's distorting the story,' Jerome said. 'Tina's the view-point throughout. Hackwill doesn't kill her in the first scene, just marks her.'

Model announced that Marthe's parents were co-chairing

the revived Relatives of Hackwill Victims Group and supporting the Model-Duff Amendment. The financial recompense to which they would be entitled if the Amendment became law was unimportant, the E-Vangelist said, because the Winks were independently wealthy. They just wanted those responsible for their daughter's death to be held culpable. Any settlement received from Pyramid Releasing – Model actually named the Leech Company – would be donated to the Ministry's Spiritual War Chest.

'So if his law gets passed, Model is in line for a credit injection. Then again, he's already independently wealthy too.'

In its fifteen year existence, Modelism had become the second richest church in the world. If his petition to assume temporal leadership of Liechtenstein was allowed, Model would be in a position to challenge Rome. Cardinal Menzies, only half joking, suggested the Vatican develop First Strike capability against the day the Modelist standard went up in Vaduz.

She found Eurocash in her purse and settled the addition. Swiss francs or Australasian dollars would be more welcome, but Eurocrats could not afford to betray the currency.

Model was harping on 'malign Asiatic influences'. One of the *robotas* heaved a bucketful of styrodust and grubby frozen snow into the Model head, disrupting the holo-link. Patches of see-through speckled the head like measles. The *robota* was a Mongol, one of the Genghis Khan trail refugees produced by the Sino-Tibetan crisis. His gesture was cheered by many by-standers, but a black-suited 'missionary' at the next table looked on grimly, noting faces.

The holo-head kicked into its pre-programmed appeal for all the Faithful to dedicate their worldly goods to Modelism, noting both the Biblical imprecation to 'store up treasures in Heaven' and Liechtenstein's liberal tax regime. At the same time, Model scorned the poor, the sick, the stricken. If God made some people victims, then that was His business and should not be argued with. In His wisdom, God had set up tollgates on the road to Heaven.

'I love God so much, Jerome,' she said, surprised at herself. 'Through my life, that has been my strongest relationship. It's never gone away. I've never doubted, not for a second . . .'

Model offered sacraments of wealth and immortality. A credit card hotline number flashed on his forehead.

'. . . so why do I find it so easy to hate religion?'

In the dream, Tina survived but the Mark of Hackwill was on her shoulder. She alone in Spring Meadow knew the monster's face. Chantal was almost used to riding viewpoint now; comfortable in the dreambody, lulled along.

Mind-chewing over her midnight encounter, Tina walked down the corridor towards the lockers. The set was dressed with posters for the Junior Prom. Kids passing by wore 2019 fashions – box suits and skunk-stripes – and toted set-books, but the dreamscene was classically archetypal. Tina – tartan skirt, white blouse, ankle socks – would pass as a teen queen in any of the last eight decs.

A hand fell on her aching shoulder. Chantal's heart leaped as Tina jumped. She whirled, prepared to face Hackwill, and was relieved to see her best friend, Stacey Snyder.

'What's word, humming bird?' Stacey chirruped.

'What's tale, nightingale?' Tina replied.

Arm-in-arm, the girls walked to their lockers, turning boyheads as they passed. Chantal's own secondary school in Geneva had been shaped by US mediamass into a multi-lingual imitation of Spring Meadow High. Some of the extras wore the faces that furnished her memories.

'You scan devastaté, Teen. Hard night with Jimmy T.?'

'One hopes.'

Chantal looked side-on at Stacey. Like all the support-ing characters, she was almost totally convincing. An actress would have leased herself as a template for CGIdentity, converting her likeness and the character tics of a specific performance into a stream of infobits.

Now the dream, orchestrated by a computer-assisted Talent, was recycling information as a semi-autonomous illusion.

'Serious, girlchik. You scan like Death on Drugs.'

'I had . . . bad dreams.'

'Condolences.'

'Processed and perfected.'

Chantal was fluent in French, Italian, English, German, Latin and Japanese; and had a working knowledge of a dozen other tongues. She found Hollywood teenspeak hard to follow.

Processed and perfected.

Tina's locker, where Hackwill notes had been delivered, loomed large in visionfield. A subliminal thrum of dread built up suspense as she approached.

Stacey blithely opened her locker and pulled out her set-book. She shook it, disrupting the fog-pattern on the screen, and tapped in the code for the biology text.

'Ugh,' she said. 'It's annelids.'

Tina looked at her locker. She tapped entrycode on the keypad and the lock clicked free.

'S'matter, Teen? You got Jimmy's severed head stashed?'

Tina took out her set-book. The message icon was blinking at her. She meant to stab DELETE, but knew she would spend the day wondering. She accessed the message and the cut-up letters appeared on the set-book's screen.

2-niTE's Sta-C's NIGHT.

'What's it process, Teen?'

Tina looked at Stacey. A superimposition skull flashed on her pretty-pretty face. In Tina's head, Hackwill's laugh sounded.

'Absolute Secret, huh?'

Tina hugged Stacey, hard.

'Care, Stace. Take chance none. For me, please.'

'Nichevo, Teen. It's only anelids. I can process and perfect.'

'No, not that. Really care.'

A frozen moment: Tina pulled back and looked again at Stacey's open face, fixing it poignantly in memory.

From the original film – where the notes were on paper not screen – if not this heavy foreshadowing, Chantal knew Stacey would be Hackwill's next victim.

She told herself Stacey was a simulacrum wearing the face of a woman now auditioning for better roles, but it was still a wrench: tonight, this girlchik would die.

TRANSITIONAL FADE

Even Mimesis could not make it scan as real. When Tina shut her eyes, she was in school in the morning, warmed by sunlight glimmering through windowwalls; when she opened them a subjective blink later, it was after dark and she was outside her house, wearing a heavy coat against the cold.

Like theatre and cinema, Mimesis cut and pasted bits of narrative into scenes unfolding faster than life. The irony was that it was technically easier to provide convincing, unedited actuality, but there wasn't a market. In realwelt, too much time is wasted getting from place to place, feeding and cleaning, doing naught. This was reality edited for length, doled out in suspenseful slices.

Here, the dremake was departing from the first *Where the Bodies Are Buried*. The old film cut from the locker scene to Stacey later that day, receiving her own suggestive note, taking a lengthy – gratuitous – shower before dolling up for a date. In a dark scary house, she was stalked by Hackwill and turned limb by limb into a mannequin. A classic image from the film was her living eyes, trapped in a smooth plastic face, tears trickling down unfeeling cheeks.

Mimesis required the story be perceived from a single viewpoint. No cutting away to other characters, no privileging the audience with information withheld from the heroine. Right now, it was a first person medium. Jerome reported the Industry was experimenting with allowing the dreamer to hop from viewpoint to viewpoint, even choosing whom to ride through the plot. That was a generation or two down the line.

As Tina trotted nervously through the night, constantly scanning behind her, Chantal realized the dream was taking the easiest possible alternative. Tina was going to sneak into the dark scary house – the Old Hackwill Place, naturally – and witness the monster's torment of her friend.

When she wondered how Tina knew where Stacey was being lured, there was an annoying misty patch in the mind construct. Chantal recognized a program flaw. Whenever the dreamer spotted a logic lapse, the viewpoint threw up a strategic memory blank.

The Old Hackwill Place loomed. Tina stopped to look up at it, giving a visionfield of the major locale. It was a tridvid synthesis of every haunted house in every horror movie: from the rusted gate hanging by one hinge to the single light in a gable window, the stone eagle over the doorway to the bricked-up room in its own turret.

Beyond the house was the graveyard where Hackwill had been caught and tortured by the mob. Chantal was getting ahead of the story; presumably, that flashback would come later, when Tina got suspicious enough to track down Judge Jonathan and get the story out of him.

Chantal's impatience made Tina walk fast forward. The front door opened by itself and she stepped inside the house. A scream abused her ears.

ERROR

The scream caused some kind of playback fault. Chantal lost Tina and found herself back in realwelt. The heavy hoodset was giving her a crick in the neck.

This time, she was alone. But she had the sense someone had been in the cabin with her and just stepped out.

More authentically spooked at that than by the cliché horror house, she considered getting up and looking into the walkway outside. It ran the length of the *Meyrink*. Her visitor – if visitor there had been – should still be in sight.

Could it be Jerome? Subotai?

The hoodset was too heavy. A design fault. She didn't want to get up. She twisted around, looking for the remote, and found it clipped to her breast pocket.

She tapped **RUN**.

Tina stood, fear-frozen, in the doorway. Before her was a tableau.

On the stairs Stacey writhed, dead legs dragging. On the landing, looking down, was Rob Hackwill.

Tina watched the transformation continue. Stacey's elbows kinked the wrong way and became notched-and-pinned joints. She held fingers to her face and gasped as they became bone-like chunks of wood, strung together on wires.

Stacey looked to her friend for help.

Tina was rigid. Chantal was irritated at the dream's assumption of girly uselessness. **Tina made no move to help or comfort Stacey.**

Stacey's face stiffened and drained of colour. It was the crying mannequin image, recreated in tridvid. Chantal realized the moment was somewhat thrown away.

Mimesis distanced her from Stacey, trapping her in Tina. In the original, there was a powerful sense of loss. Not least because the actress playing Stacey was better than the inept ex-model cast as Tina. As a viewer, Chantal knew with Stacey's death that her pleasure in the balance of the film would be limited by the lack of the character.

Now Chantal was confused. She couldn't be frightened for Tina because she realized, even if the dremake diverged radically from Allan Keyes's old script, she was fundamentally safe. If the viewpoint died, the dream would end.

Suddenly, she realized she was invincible in the dreamwelt. With a surge of courage, she looked up at Hackwill, knowing him for a cardboard fiend. He had no power over her, in realwelt or this shoddy simile.

The monster stepped into the light. He moved like a

human snake, hissing through lipless smile, red eye winking. Talons grooved scratches in the banister.

Hackwill prodded the Staceyquin with a toe-point. In a tangle of loose limbs and twisted clothes, the dummy rolled downstairs. Twisted around, the head looked up, eyes pools of anger, face cracked across. A beetle crawled out of the fissure, a gratuitously icky touch.

Tina stood her ground. Chantal wondered if she had short-circuited the dream by spotting the logic lapse. Would her realization that the viewpoint could never be in mortal peril trigger a fast-forward to plot resolution?

'You think Robbie has no surprises left, don't you?' said the monster.

He stepped down to Tina and reached out. His claw-fingers lightly touched her face. His nailpoints were cold and sharp.

'We're to be great friends and collaborators, dearest. This rag doll is only the beginning. There'll be many others. And the work we have to do is such fun.'

Hackwill wasn't like Stacey. Up close, he had a different texture. There was something super-real about him, a fuzziness in the detail. He shifted through levels of reality, catching the light differently from moment to moment, like silk or falling rain. He was not like an actor in a close-fitting latex monster mask, any more than he was like a real disfigurement victim.

Hackwill leaned close to her and whistled softly through his bare teeth. She saw his red eye up close, and intuited something unique in its depth. She caught a whiff of gravemould under a strong cologne.

'We're partners, Sister . . .'

The sibilants of *ssissster* were razor kisses. Panic seized her.

Everything spun out of control.

'Come now,' Hackwill chided. 'Did you think I wouldn't recognize you, Chantal? We're old friends.'

STOP BREAK

'He calls her "Tina"', Jerome said. 'Well, he calls me "Tina" when I dream it. Then again, there are playback variants. It's to do with the interface between Mimesis and your back brain. It's always been metaphorically true; now it's literally so. Consciousness is inescapably subjective. We all see things differently: a tree, a painting, a girl.'

'Hackwill knew me,' Chantal insisted.

Jerome had dreamed through the scene carefully. He was genuinely concerned. He trusted her word. The monster had talked to her. Not to Tina, to her. Like a good information processor, Jerome was not denying the input but trying to interpret it.

In its blackwood and red velvet box, the dreamsphere was inert. Chantal's reflection distorted in its curved surface.

She was not quite ready to go back and dream the Dark Scary House scene again.

'Maybe it's a programming glitch. *Bodies* is pre-release. This is only a test impression.'

'I didn't feel alone in there.'

'You're intuiting the presence of the Talent. It's impossible to erase entirely.'

'Who is the Talent?'

'Ultimately, Allan Keyes. He's the dreamshaper. Augmented by tech-assists. Maybe he's just a marquee name, and subsidiary Talents do the actual shapework. Not everyone can be a Talent. It's inborn.'

Chantal knew about Allan Keyes. Rob Hackwill was his life's work. Obviously, he was still with the program.

'We'll have to take testimony from him.'

Jerome smiled. 'It's fixed. Pyramid are setting up a Virtual Pow-Wow. Us here, Keyes in La-La Land. Wonders of Modern Science.'

She got up and looked out of the porthole. A restaurant floated by, trailing balloons under the Charles Bridge. On each balloon was the face of the Dalai Lama over crossed Armalite-99 rifles. It was a fund-raiser for yet another Church Militant.

'Where's Duroc?' she asked.

'He left a holonote. His Interpol sources slipped him pre-release news and he's hared off to Barcelona. Dark hints, hush-hush. He says it's a relevant mission.'

'Relevant to us, or Model?'

'Mr and Mrs Wink, the Euro-Commission extends deep condolences for your loss.'

'Thank you, Sister,' said Herman Wink.

Chantal wished Duroc were here. Herman and Monika Wink, flanked by Modelist bodyguards, spoke mostly through a lawyer whose singlepiece was fastened by tiny tags.

The couple did not strike Chantal as especially upset, but people took losses in their own way. Most of the other parents were unable to give testimony, spasming with uncontrolled grief or mind-blanked by sedation. The Winks were the official spokesfolk of Relatives of Hackwill Victims. Their Pro-Amendment petition was still downloading.

'We take comfort that Marthe was of the Last Generation,' Monika Wink said. 'Her transgression was justly rewarded, but her lapse will guide others.'

Jerome covered the audio and talked to Chantal, 'I'm not understanding this. Transgression? Lapse?'

As Modelists, the Winks believed their daughter marked herself for death simply by sampling the dream. By being murdered, she had cleansed herself and would be redeemed. Model always used the analogy of investment, referring to those judged favourably by the Lord as wise savers whose investment had matured. Those who sinned were spendthrifts whose earthly poverty would extend into the afterlife. Extreme suffering of the flesh could, in certain cases, wipe out the heaviest of debts.

'It is certain Marthe dreamed *Where the Bodies Are Buried*?'

Herman nodded. Chantal thought a flicker of genuine hurt crossed Monika's face.

'This is so,' Herman admitted. 'She was led into Evil Ways by unhealthy associations. The Reverend Model has proscribed Mimesis as a Tool of the Devil, but Marthe would not see the wisdom. She was wilful.'

Marthe's murderer was still unknown and at large. I-Pol established he was the same person known to be responsible for at least sixteen other killings, throughout the Eunion, within the last two years. The newsnets inevitably tagged him as a Hackwill Killer. The murders began at about the time Pyramid announced *Bodies* would be remade in Mimesis. Three of the last five victims had, like Marthe, contact with bootlegs.

'We comfort ourselves that our daughter's death serves a high purpose, Sister,' Herman Wink said. 'This Evil Thing will be destroyed.'

'We thank you,' said Jerome.

The Winks' lawyer broke the link. The holo-projections of the witnesses and their entourage vanished.

Chantal and Jerome sat alone in the hearing room. She loosened her collar.

'They were a piece of work,' Jerome said.

She flipped on Marthe Wink's file, scrolling through the forensics, calling up pre-death clips. She had looked like her mother.

'This isn't about them Jerome. This is about Marthe. And the others.'

She was on deck, reading her breviary. After fourteen years, daily duty came easily. As a novice, she had scrubbed cell floors between masses and her secular studies. Though clerical celibacy was abolished, it was no wonder few priests married. Who had the time?

'Chan, excuse me . . .'

It was Jerome, with something important. He knew the breviary was her one inescapable daily commitment.

'Some Czechs have come aboard. They want to throw Subotai over the side.'

She had been aware, distantly, of the commotion.

'Modelists?'

'No, regular fascisti.'

'How many?'

'Three.'

They walked around the deck. The fascisti – teenagers with Rommel coats, swastika-tat scalps and top hats – had Subotai up against the rail. The E-Com cook and one of the secretaries – both Czechs who openly despised the Mongol – were watching, not making a move.

She tried to conquer her anger.

Obviously, the fascist not holding Subotai, prepared to let her comrades do the tossing-overboard for her entertainment, was leaderine. She was a heavy-set girlchik with steroid biceps and blonde Viking plaits.

Without saying anything, Chantal walked into the situation and angled a high kick at the underside of leaderine's chin, sticking the point of her pump into softness.

The fascist staggered, dizzy, gulping. Jerome was equally astonished. The girlchik growled – she had a jewel skull inset in an incisor – and Chantal ducked under an attempted wrestling-grasp. She heaved up, thumping Valkyrie sternum with her shoulder.

The leaderine went over the side with a satisfying splash, crashing through a thin ice-lily.

'As Devil Princesses go, not very impressive, *hein?*'

Chantal chided herself for enjoying the moment.

The other two let Subotai go.

'My vows oblige me to forgive you your sins, but not forget them. You may leave by the gangway and fish out your wet friend. Good day.'

The kids bolted. Subotai nodded impassive thanks and returned to whatever he had been doing.

'We were lucky,' she told Jerome. 'Modelists wouldn't have been seen off so easily. Religion gives a lot of idiots strength.'

Jerome was admiring her.

'Chan, I can't decide whether you remind me more of Audrey Hepburn in *The Nun's Story* or Diana Rigg in *The Avengers*. I'm sorry. Those references don't mean anything to you, do they?'

She laughed. He always forgot her field was pop culture.

'In Switzerland, *The Avengers* is called *Bowler Hat and Kinky Boots*. It was on all the time when I was little. And every woman with the calling has to see *The Nun's Story* when they're nine. I saw it back-to-back with *The Red Shoes* and was torn between becoming a saint or a prima ballerina.'

Duroc's head sat on the plate. Chantal and Jerome held still, so their faces were caught in the link-beams. Agitated talkers lost ears and noses over holo.

'The Hackwill Killer is in the city,' Duroc said.

'We're conferencing with Keyes tomorrow,' Jerome said. 'Can you tap in from Barcelona?'

'It is not likely,' Duroc replied. 'Thy report will be accepted.'

His face was blank. He accepted holo but Virtual Conference was too close to Mimesis. She wondered if he was tempted to sample a dream. She and Jerome dipped in and out of *Where the Bodies Are Buried* all the time, but Duroc was required by contract with the tale-ministry to abjure Mimesis. The Modelist must at least be curious. He was still human.

The head vanished.

'His cop genes are taking over,' Jerome said. 'These cases were his specialty.'

With his background, I-Pol Barcelona must be glad to have Duroc. From his involvement with the Moschone, Thiel and Best cases, he was up to speed on Hackwill Killers.

'He knows about us,' she said.

'Duroc?'

'The killer. He's following E-Com. The first murder was just after the Model-Duff Amendment was proposed. Jeanine Csathó, the Budapest victim. All the killings have been inside the Eunion. If Model-Duff becomes law, it will only be enforced within the EU.'

'Gets bigger every year. If Libya is admitted, it'll open up the rest of North Africa. The only hold-out is your place.'

'There are no Swiss victims. He's killed from Gibraltar to Greenland, from Ankara to Yeltsingrad. Why not Zürich, or Tel Aviv, or Cuba? The *day* after Bermuda came in, he killed there. It's as if he's drawing a map.'

'He doesn't want to go through passport control.'

'He'd have needed a passport to get to Bermuda before killing McCharen.'

'You're beginning to sound like a Hackwill Killer yourself. Do you really think Rob Hackwill is talking to you?'

'This is realwelt, Jerome.'

'I'm sorry, Chan. I'll have to process this. You have to admit it scans paranoid at first scroll-through.'

'You, me and Duroc. We're between two huge grinding cliffs of credit. On the one side, a hugely wealthy Industry: the Derek Leech Group is richer than most countries. On the other, the Relatives of Hackwill Victims, underwritten by the Modelist tele-ministry. These killings have been going on since the last century. If Model-Duff gets on the statutes in the EU, RHV will bring multiple suits. If cases go their way, there'll be a credit transfer bigger than the one that caused the Nikkei Crash of 2014.'

'I know all this, Chan. We have to focus on micro-issues. The Amendment. We recommend or not on its own merits. Think of the victims. Think of the victims who are still alive, who haven't been born yet.'

The idea wasn't original to Joseph Model and Morag Duff: it had been proposed in America as early as the 1990s. It was to do with blame and compensation: if murderers were shaped not born, then the forces which influence them should share culpability. If a rapist's mind was warped by pornography, then a rape victim should be able to sue pornographers. The Model-Duff Amendment proposed moral guilt be brought under a legal remit.

It was a simple, appealing idea. Yet it frightened her.

The Barcelona Victim was called Armando De Castro Oros. Duroc downloaded stats before the newsnets got them.

Hours before the scheduled Virtual Conference, Chantal was praying for guidance. No matter how she tried to clear her mind, De Castro Oros remained.

The boy was found dressed as a schoolgirl, face coated with asphyxiating plastic. Post mortem, his murderer had cracked the fast-setting mask and jammed in a chocolate beetle. The victim's tears were trapped bubbles in the plastic.

He was a Stacey. Like Victor McCharen, Saira Matsoela and Laure Petietich.

The killer was repeating victim types: Tinas, Staceys, Jimmy Traynors, Judge Jonathans, Boss Hoopers. All the characters from the dream.

There was no other connection between De Castro Oros and *Where the Bodies Are Buried*. If there was a black market dreamsphere in Barcelona, I-Pol had not found it.

Duroc was returning to Prague by way of Bermuda, where he wanted to follow up on McCharen. An American tourist, the Bermuda Victim might have been a smuggler, responsible for getting the dreamspheres into the EU in the first place.

For Chantal, prayer was a communion. Like Jerome processing random infobits, she could sometimes run through the elements of a problem and be led to a conclusion in something approaching a vision.

Not today.

Chantal would have been satisfied with a holo-link, swapping tridvid with Beverly Hills. Pyramid, wanting to impress E-Com with tech, insisted on a fancier Virtual Conference.

They were to meet Allan Keyes in Spring Meadow. Jerome, excited, explained the *Bodies* dreamwelt could be accessed as a non-narrative CGNvironment. It was a supplementary feature of Home Mimesis dreamspheres, along with a bound copy of the script and collectors' cards.

Jerome sat on the couch, adjusting his hoodset. He had already helped her plumb in.

'You won't be a *dybbuk* this time, Chan. You'll have autonomy.'

'But I'll still be Tina.'

Jerome nodded, hoodset bulbous. 'Since *Bodies* is a single viewpoint dream, so will I.'

Her eyepieces descended, blanking her vision. A test signal blipped into her brain.

'Ready?' Jerome asked.

*

She was back in the park, standing before the statue, waiting for midnight. As she slipped into the Tina simile, Chantal prepared for a mindlink that did not come. For a moment, she thought the puppet's strings were cut and she would fall in a tangle. Then, she was in control.

She was herself, but with Tina's dreambody.

By the statue stood a pretty girl in a heavy coat and a wool scarf. She smiled and shrugged.

'Weird,' Jerome commented, through the pretty girl's mouth. 'This gets stranger.'

Jerome-as-Tina looked a little different from the self-image of Chantal-as-Tina. She saw Jerome's slenderness in his simile, even an underlay of his cheekbones in the Tina face.

She wondered if Allan Keyes and the Pyramid CEO would also be forced to be Tinas. Probably not; at their end, they would have more sophisticated dreamtech and should be able to select viewpoints to suit themselves.

She looked around, dreamflesh creeping.

'What's up, Chan?'

'There's someone here.'

'They're not online yet.'

'No, not them.'

He glanced about too, and shrugged again. His distinctive smile stretched the Tina face.

'It's the first scene feeling, from the dream,' she explained. 'When Hackwill is creeping up on Tina.'

'The story isn't in RUN. For once, there's no Robbie here.'

'"There's always a Hackwill in Spring Meadow."'

'A-ha. Judge Jonathan's speech. You're a *Bodies* buff. I keep forgetting.'

Beeptone came from their coats. Jerome found his setbook before Chantal found hers. Both lit up with identical messages.

> ThE olD HaCKwill playCE.

'Do you want to walk, or . . .?'

'Skip that,' she said. They both blinked . . .

TRANSITIONAL FADE

... and were outside the Dark Scary House. Stacey, a walking mannequin, was waiting for them on the porch. She had blots of rouge on white plastic cheeks.

'Mr Rhodes, Ms Juillerat,' she said through stiff, barely-parted lips. 'I'm Medea Calm, of Pyramid Releasing. We're proud to have you in Spring Meadow.'

The similes shook hands. Medea's fingers were hard and unmoving.

'Sorry about this. I had hoped to rep myself as the Stacey of her cute scenes, not the Staceyquin. I actually look a little like the babe version. But we had a simile transfer glitch. The bugs will be worked out prontissimo. It's cutting edge tech.'

Chantal had expected a Pyramid exec to be more like the Devil Princess.

'Allan is inside, waiting.'

Medea hobbled lop-sided into the mansion. Jerome hung back a little to let Chantal in first. The hallway was as it was in the finale, hellfire burn-marks on the wall.

Someone stood in the dark at the top of the stairs.

'Allan,' said Medea-as-Staceyquin, 'Mr Rhodes and Ms Juillerat are from the Euro-Commission on the Model-Duff Amendment.'

'I've scrolled your thesis, Sister,' said Keyes. 'You make some points.'

He stepped forward into the light.

Chantal had expected Keyes to be Hackwill, but the Talent was in the simile of Japheth Jonathan, the corrupt judge who explains Hackwill's origins. Thankfully, he was not as last seen in the dream – head exploded by his own tongue swollen to the size of a watermelon – but as in his intro scene. Keyes must be about Jonathan's age, but newsims did not suggest other resemblance. The Judge was an impressively-eyebrowed character actor; Keyes was one of those nondescript Englishmen, Jerome grown not old but faint.

One of the Hackwill Victims was Keyes's own girl-friend: it must take something to continue weaving nightmares after that. Originally a novelist, Keyes had turned himself into a motion picture director and then a Mimesis Talent, extending the reign of Hackwill into fresh media.

'How does a Jesuit get to know so much about horror films?' he asked.

'My field of study is Media Influence. Genre horror is central to the discipline. The pioneer work of Martin Barker and Julian Petley in the 1990s . . .'

'But do you *like* horror? Do you like what *I* do?'

She tried to give an honest answer. 'While working on my thesis, I became so familiar with the material that I lost perspective on aesthetic or entertainment quality. But I first decided to be a Jesuit because of *The Exorcist.* As a child, I saw the original *Where the Bodies Are Buried* – it was made the year I was born – on Cloud 9 TV. It gave me nightmares for weeks, but I pleaded with my parents to let me watch it again.'

'Your thesis could do with input from the little girl you once were. I intuit you regret a weakness for the films. Because of the Hackwill Effect.'

'Pyramid Releasing does not acknowledge the existence of the so-called Hackwill Effect,' Medea cut in. 'Many studies – including your own, Sister Juillerat – question a hypotheticized causal relationship between fictional and realwelt violence.'

'Our guests aren't interested in blipquotes, Medea,' Keyes said. 'Credit them with that.'

Medea continued, 'If you lump together so-called Hackwill Killings over the last twenty-five years, including those later established as unconnected, you have at most four hundred murders. Five times that many died in the Reverend Model's Warsaw *pogrom* last year. And what about British Druids mustard-gassed by Special Branch in the solstice of '17? Joseph Model and Morag Duff should look to their own consciences.'

The lecture was pointed, but sounded strange from a life-sized broken doll.

'You've obviously given the Hackwill Effect thought,' Chantal said to Keyes. 'Yet you've continued with *Bodies*. It can't just be for the credit. Why do you do it? Why do you create only horrors?'

Keyes smiled sadly. 'What makes you think I have a choice?'

All around, hellfire exploded.

INTERFERENCE

The similes could be hurt. These flames bit harder than the pain analogues usual in dreams. Consciousness unfiltered through viewpoint, she was immersed in intense heat, blinding light, choking stench, nipping agony.

Jerome was patting out the flames on her arm. Medea had vanished, presumably breaking the link. Half of Jerome's Tina hair was singed off.

A burning beam fell between them and Keyes. He stood still in the inferno. She wondered if his simile was an empty freeze-frame. But his eyes moved.

The laughter of the Devil Princess poured out of the air, setting fires wherever it was heard. In the original, only the mansion was destroyed; in the dremake, most of Spring Meadow was consumed.

Windows burst outwards. Draughts of cold air whipped flames into spirals that entwined the two Tinas. Chantal and Jerome hugged, as if the heroine wanted to reunite her divided self.

'Another glitch?' Jerome asked.

In the fire behind Keyes, a black shape coalesced, rearing up over him, arms enfolding the Talent. Bands of clawed shadow held him fast. A single red eye shone, a crystal of fire in a man-shaped patch of night.

'*Keyes!*' she shouted.

Jerome thumped his own forehead, where the hoodset panel was in realwelt. He disappeared.

She was alone in Spring Meadow with Keyes and the

Hackwill Effect. Fire rushed to fill the space where Jerome's Tina had been.

Allan Keyes – she could swear – smiled with almost relief as the shadow and flame wrapped around him. This was the end of his private dreamstory.

STOP

Jerome was pulling the hoodset off her. Half his face was an angry red.

She looked at her hands and saw white spots where cinders had scalded her in Spring Meadow.

Subotai was checking the fixed-up link, genuinely concerned for his temporary masters.

She intuited she had just experienced the downside of cutting edge tech.

'Do we still have audio-link?' she asked Subotai.

The *robota* stood aside and gave her the handset.

Jerome was swearing profusely in English, touching his pain patches. He was burned under unsinged clothes.

'Hello,' she said to the handset. 'Ms Calm? Keyes?'

There was a commotion at the other end.

'Ms Juillerat,' came a voice. A woman, shaky.

'Medea?'

'Uh, yes. We have no rationale for that . . . uh . . . incident.'

'Is Keyes out of the dream?'

'We've cut him off. He's here . . . his body's here . . . but there's nobody home.'

It was Site Prime in the weeks leading up to Hallowe'en: Allan Keyes, the Hackwill Man, was the latest victim of the Hackwill Effect. His body might live but he was mindwiped, a human blank. Medicos theorized that if he came out of coma, he might develop from mental infancy, growing a new personality. But it was a moot point: he had suffered 78 per cent burns in the Virtual Conference; if he came round, he would probably die from paintrauma.

From the deck, Chantal looked down on grey waters. A drift of ground-hugging riot gas seeped down from the bridge, floating on the surface of the Vltava. She felt after-sting in her nostrils, even through the domino mask she wore when the pollution count was high.

Where the Bodies Are Buried had been recalled – E-Com had to surrender their dreamsphere to a notarized messenger – and Mimesis was on hold 'until bugs can be ironed out'. Whatever the truth of the Hackwill Effect, Keyes was proof that Mimesis could be hazardous to dreamers' health, mental and otherwise.

E-Com's ground was out from under them. The original unexpressed purpose of the enquiry, beyond even the Amendment, was to determine whether Mimesis be allowed unrestricted into Eunion. Now, Mimesis was withdrawn by the Industry: if Model-Duff passed, it would apply only to old-fashioned mediatech like motion pictures, tele and VR. Not newsworthy, but still a major legislative shift.

Using the railing as a *barre*, Chantal ran through ballet moves, stretching her legs until they felt real, making points of her toes. With the Troubles, she was advised not to go jogging up to the Castle and back as she had in E-Com's early days in the city. The *Meyrink* sometimes felt like a prison. She needed to maintain strength and suppleness. Exercise was a courtesy to God: it was her duty to maintain in peak condition the wonderful gift of a body her soul had been given.

As she felt the knots popping in her muscles and joints, she thought it over.

Duroc, back from his travels, was meticulously assembling an infodump about the current Hackwill Killings. He had taken their report of the Conference on board but had no ideas about it. To him, Mimesis dreams were hell equivalents even without brimstone.

Jerome thought it a glitch – bleedthrough from the narrative of *Bodies* – but Chantal was convinced there had been another presence in Spring Meadow. It was hard not to think of it as Rob Hackwill.

On the Charles Bridge, the demonstration turned ugly. Students, supporting persecuted refugees, clashed with Model-ists, and armed police were caught between them. People fell or were tossed off the bridge, splashing in gas-covered water. Throwing malcontents into the river was a traditional Prague response to trouble; just as throwing bureaucrats out of windows was a traditional Prague way of making trouble. Last night, the head of the local Modelist Congregation had been defenestrated.

She stopped her programme of kicks, and towelled her sweaty forehead. Through the domino, she breathed deeply.

The McDonald's Airport was shut down, transnational holo-links were out. After the Ghetto riots, Modelist Advance Teams combed the ruins, offering salvation with share options and low monthly payments. Subotai had heard a whisper that E-Com would have to share the *Meyrink* with a Europa Defence Force response unit straight from Cadiz.

Jerome came up on deck, looking sheepish. Turfed out of his hotel by a newsnet anchor, he was mooching around the ship, face glistening from the healing gel he had to wear until his burns faded.

'Chan, I've made my decision.'

She had expected this. The Spring Meadow Incident had shaken him. And the December deadline was approaching. She pulled off her domino so she could speak with him.

'I'm voting the Amendment be attached to the Revised Criminal Code,' he said. 'That aligns me with Roger.'

'I see.'

It didn't have to be unanimous. She still felt the enquiry should be pursued: Mimesis might even prove a side-issue to the greater question.

'As of now, I can't change my position,' she said.

'Still Swiss?'

She took the railing and kicked in the air, above Jerome's head. She had always had trick hips.

'I abstain. You know why.'

'I'm sorry, Chan.'

She went belowdecks to tell Duroc. At her knock, he unlocked his door.

Aside from the bunk, his cabin was furnished only with a

flatscreen and a knee-rest. An official holo-bust of Reverend Model hovered under the bare lightstrip. Duroc worked always under the blind gaze of his master.

He stood aside to let her in. They both had to bow slightly because of the low ceiling. Duroc blithely dipped his head through Model, but Chantal avoided the holo as if it were a solid.

Duroc, alarmingly, was stripped to the waist. His back was striped with scars, some fresh. He had a scourge in his hand, a wicked cluster of studded flails with a riding crop grip.

She had not realized Duroc was a flagellant.

On the flatscreen were images Chantal recognized. A field laid out neatly with corpses. Black-clad Modelists prowling among the dead.

'The Basque Insurrection?' she asked.

Duroc nodded.

Most who had served in the Insurrection were soured on Modelists for life. There was a famous incident in which a non-com was court-martialled for disobeying orders and intervening to cut short a massacre supervised by elders of the tele-ministry.

Duroc must be Model's only convert from the EDF. No wonder he felt the need to whip himself.

'Jerome's changed his vote. To Yes.'

Duroc nodded, understanding.

'I'll prep a formal statement for Brussels. We all put our signatures to it. Then, we can go home.'

'Hast thou changed thy vote?'

'It doesn't have to be unanimous.'

'I know.'

He looked at her. She saw something hanging back in his eyes, but could not process it.

'Yes,' she admitted, 'I have changed my vote. From Abstention to No.'

She did not ask if Duroc wished to change his Yes to Abstention or No. That would have been futile.

'I'm sorry, Sister. We must all act in accordance with our conscience.'

He looked sideways at the Model head, as if seeking higher approval.

The decision was communicated on a priority line to Brussels, and the Model-Duff Amendment was attached to the Revised Criminal Code.

On New Year's Eve, Joseph Model held a celebratory rally in Vaduz. In his speech, he personally commended Chantal Juillerat, Jerome Rhodes and Brother Roger Duroc as Good Credit Christians. He claimed their Heavenly Portfolios were maturing exceptionally well, throwing off high-yield interests. He also promised arms to the Advance Teams in Prague, and accused Tel Aviv of inciting ghetto-dwellers to murder their Modelist rescuers.

The E-Com, officially dissolved, was still in Prague. Travel restrictions were in force until the fighting died down. On New Year's Day, there was a Hackwill Killing outside the Castle. Pavel Zahradnik, a Boss Hooper, head burned to the skull. His wife signed up with RHV. The Model-Duff Amendment – no, the Model-Duff Law – was retroactive: Petra Zahradnik would have to join a queue of grieving, suing relatives.

The conglomerated lawsuit was already issued, and Pyramid's corporate attorneys were resisting attempts to bring the case to the European Court in Kiev.

Morag Duff, under fire for imposing an extension of the term between general elections to ten years, gloried in the success of her Amendment – she carefully never mentioned Model in public – and announced she would now devote herself to removing nudity from art galleries and British World Tree Sites. With lewdness and licence expunged, she claimed – repeating her last electoral slogan – 'everything will be nice again'.

Chantal kept her cabin when the EDF unit moved in, but Duroc and Jerome had to bunk together. Subotai was pounced upon in the Square and severely beaten by Modelists. He was then removed to a camp in the Carpathians, where Czechs-kanzler Drnkova claimed refugees could be protected from violent mobs. Duroc did not to take part in any of his church's activities in the city, and shutters came down whenever the soldiers talked about the militia missionaries against whom they expected to be deployed.

Cardinal Menzies communicated that she was expected back in Rome when restrictions were lifted. She passed time with her breviary, unable to shift her mind from the dead issue of E-Com to her next task, finishing her Information Children bookfile.

She still sensed, just out of sight, the creature of flame and darkness that had attacked Allan Keyes in Spring Meadow.

'What are you scanning?' Jerome asked.

On deck, the EDF were doing push-ups. Duroc, twenty years older than most of the soldier kids, was earning respect by matching them thrust for thrust.

Jerome was frustrated; he missed spending the holidays with his mother. It seemed he would not get out of Czechia before spring. Also, he was off-salary.

'I'm going through our logs, checking the hours we've put in at terminals and in meetings.'

'You think we've been rooked on our expenses?'

'Something nags.'

'Close it down, Chan. It's processed and perfected. We did our bit. Now it's up to lawyers.'

On St Valentine's Day, Subotai escaped from the Relocation Centre and made his way to Prague where, according to the newsnets, he was waylaid by the Hackwill Killer. He was a Judge Jonathan, head burst by a pressure capsule – intended for instant life-raft inflation – forced into his mouth.

Chantal was shocked and depressed. She liked and trusted the *robota*. Subotai's scattered family – and several women who repped themselves as his wives, but whose claims were instantly disproved – joined the RHV and added their lawsuits to the others. She intuited the case would not come to Kiev until the Hackwill Killer was caught.

Allan Keyes's condition remained stable.

On the *Meyrink*, it was hard to concentrate. She kept going over the logs of the E-Com. Jerome, suffering cabin fever, had taken to complaining about foreigners. The EDF – mostly Turks and Swedes – were growing nervy as their deployment was put off. Everyone was getting irritable.

Except Duroc. He exercised, read Modelist screentexts, and showed no interest in the world outside his faith.

It was Jerome who pointed out the anomaly.

'It's odd. Roger traipsed from Spain to Bermuda on the trail of the Hackwill Killer, but hasn't crossed the river to join the hunt now the murderer is in Prague. I'm surprised I-Pol haven't conscripted him to head the investigation.'

Just around midnight on March 1st, the alarum sounded. One moment, Chantal was in the *Meyrink*'s mess hall, improving her Swedish by chatting with a non-com from Malmö; then, she was surrounded by *Mary Celeste* detritus of abandoned card games and unfinished mugs of recaff.

The clattering of boots was a brief thunder. The ship actually rocked as the EDF unit assembled on one side of the deck. They yomped out, weighed down by weaponry, towards the Ghetto. She prayed for their safety. And for those they would be fighting.

Through the mess windows, she saw a glow in the sky. She had a flash of the Old Hackwill Place.

'They're burning the Ghetto,' Jerome said. 'The bloody fools. Modelist maniacs.'

Duroc was with them, showing no emotion.

Jerome turned on the Modelist. 'How can you be with those bloodthirsty credit-grubbers?'

'The Reverend Model tells us we must terminate unrewarding investments. Only radical measures will serve.'

'You can't really believe that scut!'

Duroc went up on deck.

In prayer, it came to her. The discrepancy that had been nagging was Duroc's trip to Barcelona.

She had to check first.

'Where are you going, Chan?'

She left Jerome in the mess hall and made her way down a deck.

The office was sealed but she still had a viable entry-code. She called up the logs on the terminal and scrolled them side-by-side with a newsnet chronology of the killings.

Jerome was in the doorway, puzzled. She was glad he had followed her. The ship lurched. A noise hammered: an explosion ashore, nearby. There was the popping of gunfire.

She concentrated on the screen, shutting out the macro-issues.

'Chan, what is it?'

'Look. Duroc arrived in Barcelona *before* Armando De Castro Oros was murdered.'

'He had an I-Pol tip-off?'

'No, he's the Hackwill Killer.'

There was a thump.

She turned from the screen and looked at Jerome's face. He was open-mouthed and wide-eyed, stunned. A trickle of blood came from his hairline. He stood statue-still, then pitched forwards.

Duroc, spanner in hand, stepped over Jerome and looked at her.

'I'm not a Hackwill Killer,' he said. 'There are no Hackwill Killers.'

As a teenager, ballet had led for a while to martial arts. She saw the point in the centre of Duroc's solid chest where she should kick.

She stood slowly, tense but trying to calm herself. She knew she had no chance. Besides his training as a soldier, a police-man and a fanatic, Duroc was a practised murderer. She could not hope to fight him.

'I'm doing the Lord's work,' he said, deadpan. 'As revealed to me by the Reverend Model. We must put away Evil Things.'

Was he mocking her?

He held the spanner loosely, thwacking his open palm with the heavy instrument.

Would she be a Tina or a Stacey?

He was a barrier in the doorway. That left her with one other option.

She made her move, grabbing the terminal chair and rolling it across the deck towards Duroc. It slammed him, not hurting at all, but distracting.

Chantal jumped and grasped with both hands a pipe that ran across the ceiling. She swung back and forth twice like an aerialist, feeling the *wrench* in her shoulders, then aimed herself feet-first at the porthole.

She was – thank God – wearing sensible shoes and a singlepiece. Her points punched the circle of glass out of the hole and she followed through, body like a dart, praying hips or shoulders would not catch.

Fire raked her back as she plunged through the porthole, scraping herself on the rim. Her whole body was out in cold night when her wrists were grabbed.

Her shoulders exploded. Angry ants ate at the muscles from inside. For an instant, she thought her arms had come off.

Duroc held her, but her whole weight dragged her down. She slammed against the *Meyrink*'s steel hull. Bursts of shadow and flame obscured her visionfield.

This time, she was not a viewpoint. This was realwelt, with real pain and real death.

Her weight and momentum hauled Duroc partially out of the porthole. She looked up at his face and saw only shadow. The sky above the ship was crimson-streaked.

Somewhere else, guns were going off.

Duroc held her by the wrists, but couldn't haul her up without adjusting his grip.

'You never dreamed *Where the Bodies Are Buried*,' she said, through pain. 'You told me you never even saw the old film.'

'That is true.'

'Was it the Hackwill Killers you caught? You've been recreating their crimes?'

'There are no Hackwill Killers.'

It hit her that Pietro Moschone, Nadja Thiel and Hugh Best were innocent. Roger Duroc had framed them for earlier murder clusters.

'Roger, why?'

A fireburst illuminated the side of the ship, casting their harsh shadows on the hull. In red light, she glimpsed an upside-down smile playing around Duroc's lips.

'Sister, the Lord showed me the Way. Through Joseph Model.'

He dropped her.

She plunged into the filthy Vltava and felt she touched bottom before air in her lungs buoyed her. She struggled up through thick, freezing water. The ripples above were blobbed with reflected firebursts.

When she broke the surface, her ears were roaring. She swam to the bank, found an iron ring inset in a concrete wall, and pulled herself up, sopping, on to a jetty. Her singlepiece stuck to her like a layer of clogged ice.

She wanted to curl up and get warm.

But she had left Jerome with Duroc.

She found the gangplank and ran up it, leaving dripping footsteps.

'*Duroc!*' she shouted.

A bullet spanged against the hull of the *Meyrink*. A power-boat passed by, raising a white froth of wake. Someone fired another wild shot, not at her but at the sky.

'Praise the Lord and shoot the sinners,' shouted the boatman.

She had no idea what that was about.

She looked around for a weapon as she made her way down to the office deck. All she could find was a solid-body guitar. One of the Turkish soldiers had left it behind.

The corridor was quiet. She saw Jerome's legs, stuck out of the doorway. They shifted, as he was turned over.

Heart clenched, she ran to the office.

Duroc squatted by Jerome, examining his head wound.

'He'll be all right, Sister.'

She held the guitar by the neck, hefting it like a bludgeon.

'I've called the police. They're busy.'

With all her strength, she smashed the guitar into Duroc, lifting him off the floor.

As Duroc fell backwards, Chantal stepped through the door. The lights went out and a chill fell on her. She blinked and held on to the neck of the broken guitar.

She was not in the office, with its burst porthole and dreamdeck, but back in the park in Spring Meadow. Duroc was sprawled at the base of the statue of the town founder.

He was not Duroc, but Hackwill.

Yet she was not Tina, but Chantal.

She stood over the monster, wondering whether to end it by driving the guitar neck through his heart. You could not kill Hackwill; he always came back for the sequel.

For some reason, the Modelist had been committing murders for years. Initially, he had used his position in I-Pol to frame others, tagging them as Hackwill Killers. It couldn't be the Hackwill Effect, unless it were a new strain, a Hackwill Effect By Proxy.

The monster was hurt, trying to lift himself.

'I said we had work to do, Sissster,' he said.

She held the guitar-neck out like a crucifix to ward off Evil. Duroc supported himself by clinging to the pedestal. Bloody spittle hung from his mouth.

She guessed Duroc had intervened in the Virtual Conference, projecting into the dreamwelt through the thing of shadow and fire. He was playing some immense game-plan.

And she had a horrid intuition that mass murder and E-Com and Model-Duff were merely facets of an intricate device whose purpose was not yet apparent.

Darkness and fire were contained in Duroc's thick chest, entwining his body with ropes of wavering black and red. He wore a transparent Hackwill mask. Behind it, his face was set.

She tossed the guitar-neck away and braced herself to fight.

In this waking dream, she was herself. She was still wet and hurt.

Pirouetting, she slammed her foot into his chest, imagining it a blunt knife, focusing her all into the kick.

Duroc coughed and thumped back against the statue.

Her ankle was badly jarred, but she ignored pain. Making triangular wedges of her fingers, she jabbed Duroc's torso where she had kicked, probing for broken spots.

Despite her blows, he stood up.

'I do the Lord's work,' he repeated.

He was completely shrouded in flame and shadow. Heat seared and cold stung her hands as she hit him. His Hackwill mask was illuminated from within, as if his skull were red hot beneath translucent flesh.

'May the Lord forgive you,' she said.

She punched him in the face and danced back away from him, knowing she couldn't keep this up much longer.

At the edges of the park, the dead gathered. The dead of *Where the Bodies Are Buried*: Stacey, Jimmy, the Judge, even Tina. And the dead of realwelt: Jeanine Csathó, Subotai, Marthe, McCharen, Zahradnik, De Castro Oros. Mannequin-like, the broken witnesses hobbled together.

Duroc stood still, relaxing, head hung slightly. She felt her anger fading.

Horror movie dead closed in, a shambling noose tightening around Chantal and Duroc. Allan Keyes was there, a ghost in his own dreamwelt, drifting above the grass. And the Devil Princess, hair like white flame spilling from her scarlet wimple.

The dream was running down.

'Where are we?' she asked.

'Outside, Sister,' the Devil Princess purred. 'In Spring Meadow, where the bodies are buried.'

Duroc spread his arms in surrender. Feathers of flame ran along their undersides. Fire and darkness gathered in Duroc's torso and coursed through his arms, exploding from his fingers, channelling into the dead, dissipating in the dream.

Duroc, empty, sagged at the knees, slumped at the feet of the statue. His face was pathetic, a childish plastic mask, broken across. His claws had come off too.

Rob Hackwill was only Roger Duroc dressed up.

Chantal stood over the murderer, feeling the tug of the realwelt beginning.

She knew now there was no Rob Hackwill. Just a man who had killed in the monster's name.

Suddenly, a laugh fell upon her from above, a laugh like a rain of hot pebbles. She knew instantly the cackle of the Real Rob. The pure evil of the old movies thrived. Hackwill still lurked in dreamspheres, scratching inside silver eggshell, to be born into the realwelt.

She looked up from the fallen Duroc to the greened bronze boots of the town founder. The statue creaked to life. A clawed hand raised a sword.

The burning red eye, the gnashing bloody teeth, the pouring laughter. Raised on his pedestal, Rob Hackwill ruled Spring Meadow.

Chantal fell to her knees and locked her hands in prayer.

She was back on the *Meyrink*, kneeling by the fallen Duroc, praying fiercely.

She must work swiftly.

As she tied Duroc up with cables from the dreamdeck, she worried at it in her mind. If it had been a vision, she intuited Duroc had shared it. Some of the dream had stuck in her mind and enveloped them both. Through Rob Hackwill, she was trying to tell herself something, trying to understand a mystery.

Duroc, unconscious, was heavy and awkward. He came
round while she was binding him, but did not struggle or try
to talk.

It was not over.

When she was finished with Duroc, she checked on Jerome.
He was breathing but asleep. She sat, exhausted and shivering,
against a bulkhead. Duroc watched her, as inexpressive as
ever.

'The Lord's work,' he repeated.

She tried to stop her teeth chattering.

For the first time in fifteen years, the Reverend Joseph Model
was unavailable for comment.

In the Castle, Czech I-Pol interrogated the accused. Chantal and Jerome stood in the dark beyond the mirror, watching.
Duroc was co-operative, giving convincing detail. He had
precise recall of what he claimed were 156 homicides going
back to 2010. He insistently referred to 'the Lord's work' and
respectfully claimed that the Lord's needs were revealed to
him by the teachings of the Reverend Model.

'I say, he's going to be a Model Prisoner,' snorted Jerome.

Through one-way glass, Duroc seemed to be looking at
her. He explained how he had schooled Hugh Best to make a
confession, claiming five murders. He took no delight in his
crimes but was punctilious in corroborating his claims. She
was sure even a cursory check would confirm everything he
said.

Jerome's forehead was disfigured by a splotch of hardened
healing gel. He was certainly taking his knocks.

She was all right, but her shoulders felt as if she had been
racked and her back was scraped raw. She was a real Tina.
She had faced the monster and won. She would be around for
the sequel.

All her hurt was inside.

Rob Hackwill was laughing in her dreams, exulting in a
victory she did not yet understand. And his Devil Princess
whispered to her. She sometimes looked like Stacey, some-

times like Beth Yatman. And sometimes, horribly, like Chantal Juillerat, S.J.

'It was too easy,' Chantal said. 'He got away with it for too long to be stopped by us.'

'He doesn't seem upset or unhappy.'

Duroc politely refused an offer of recaff or a cigarette. His faith required him to abjure stimulants. He explained the electro-magnetic pulse he had used to mindwipe Allan Keyes. Model called the Talent 'the author of Maximum Evil', and Duroc had been the instrument of the Lord's vengeance.

'This is like everything else he ever did. Part of his programme.'

The Ghetto was clear of Modelists. Prague was pacified for the moment, at the expense of armoured EDF goons on every corner. As Eunion servants, Chantal and Jerome would have priority when travel restrictions were lifted. For every week their flights were delayed, they were given McDonald's scrip redeemable for a Happy Meal at any airport in the world.

They were alone on the *Meyrink*. The EDF Rapid Response team was redeploying to Dublin, where the factionalized followers of so-called Anti-Pope James Bacon were fire-bombing each other.

Duroc was all over the newsnets, nicknamed 'the Scourge of God', 'Model's Murder Messiah' or 'Holy Hackwill'. He was likely to end his days in the Eunion Penal Therapy Colony on Sicily, shackled in an *oubliette*. Pyramid announced a drama-docudream about his killing spree.

In Broadmoor, Beth Yatman changed her plea from 'Hackwill made me do it' to 'God told me to'. In Kiev, the Relatives of Hackwill Victims – reconstituted as the Relatives of Victims of Religious Fanaticism – changed their lawsuit. Pyramid Releasing and Derek Leech Enterprises were no longer indicted. The new defendants were Reverend Joseph Model, the Modelist Tele-Ministry and the State of Liechtenstein.

If, under the Model-Duff Law, the case was decided in the favour of RVRF, Model and his church would be bankrupt, forced to bestow settlements on upwards of twenty-five thousand claimants. Purge survivors all over the Eunion were bringing their own suits against Model.

All because of Roger Duroc.

Jerome importuned her for spiritual advice she could not give. Her own faith was not shaky, but she sensed a precedent: if religions were responsible legally for violence done in God's name, what church would still stand in ten years' time?

On the deck of the *Meyrink*, she walked with Jerome. Suddenly, he kissed her.

'That was for coming out of the river for me. I've never thanked you.'

'I don't think Duroc would have killed you.'

'That's not what either of us thought then.'

She had been going over Duroc's bio, following everything that came out on the newsnets. It was important that she understand. It was the same old question: what makes a monster of a man?

'It started in the Basque Insurrection,' she thought out loud. 'He saw what the Modelists were capable of in that carnage, then joined their church.'

'He was a murderer. Modelism was made for him.'

'He wasn't a murderer then. He didn't kill – even in battle – until after he joined the church.'

'Model brought out something in him. Medea Calm was right. The Reverend should have looked to his own house. The Amendment is based on the theory that people can be warped by mediamass, that dreaming of Hackwill turns you into him. Duroc proved the theory sound, but established we did not have to worry about what came out of the mind of Allan Keyes but what we heard in the pulpit and read in the Bible. You can weigh fifteen supposed Hackwill Killers against thousands of murderers who fancy themselves instruments of a vengeful God. They all learned madness in a church somewhere.'

'Exactly. And I intuit that's the position Duroc wants us to take. Or, worse, the truth he wants us to face. He's spent ten years and 156 lives on his design. And he's going to bring down a church that could count itself among the world's great powers.'

'Your lot will probably canonize him.'

'If God's ministers can be brought to trial for the crimes of His followers, Modelism will only be the first church to fall.'

This morning, Cardinal Menzies had reported that the first lawsuits were being laid against the Vatican. RVRF expanded their claims, charging not only Modelists but seventeen other major churches. Georgi was not handling the impending crisis well. Menzies wanted her in Vatican City. She was their expert on what made people murder.

It began to rain, gently at first.

'I was once told raindrops were God's tears,' Jerome said. 'He has a lot to cry about.'

Prague rain was rusty, laced with pollutants from seventy-five years of unregulated factory smokestacks. The Vltava was choppy today. The deck shifted under them.

She took Jerome's hand. She needed human contact, something to fix on, some outward manifestation of God's goodness. Though His servants were flawed, Creation was a marvel.

'I'm afraid, Jerome . . .'

'Chan?'

'Churches are built on corpses. Mine most of all.'

If Kiev upheld Model-Duff, the great wealth of the Roman Catholic Church – of all churches within the Eunion – was in peril. There were incalculable economic consequences.

'I liked him, Chan. I thought he liked us. Despite all the pegs and abjuring, I truly intuited he was a solid fellow. Was he really mad all along?'

'He was trying to teach us a lesson. Maybe he would have had to be mad to try. Maybe, after all, there was a little of Rob Hackwill in him. It's all been about attributions of guilt. It's all been about where the bodies are buried.'

She gripped Jerome's hand until her knuckles hurt. Soon, she would let go, let him go, let Duroc go, let Hackwill go.

Soon, she would return to Rome, to her cell, to her faith, to fighting for her church.

Soon.

The rain began to pelt. Drops drummed the deck like liquid bullets, driving them below.

Kim Newman is a freelance novelist, critic and broadcaster who has worked extensively in the theatre and on radio and television. His non-fiction books include *Nightmare Movies*, *Wild West Movies*, *Ghastly Beyond Belief: The Science Fiction & Fantasy Book of Quotations* (with Neil Gaiman) and *Horror: 100 Best Books* (edited with Stephen Jones, and winner of the Bram Stoker Award for non-fiction). The many publications to which he has contributed film and book criticism include *City Limits*, *Empire* (as a contributing editor), *Eyeball*, *The Guardian*, *The Independent*, *Interzone*, *Monthly Film Bulletin*, *Q*, *Sight and Sound* and *Shock Xpress*. A regular film critic on TV's *Channel 4 Daily* for three years, scripts for *The Hero Strikes Back* (for Channel 4's *Signals*), *The Vault of Horror* (BBC2) and three seasons of BBC1's *Dr Terror's Vault of Horror* represent his television work. He has also written *Film in the Forties: Out of the Dark – Val Lewton* for BBC Radio 3. Newman's acclaimed novels include *The Night Mayor*, *Bad Dreams*, *Jago*, *The Quorum*, *Anno Dracula*, and its recent sequel, *The Bloody Red Baron*. Under his Jack Yeovil pseudonym there are also a string of gaming novels: *Drachenfels*, *Demon Download*, *Krokodil Tears*, *Comeback Tour*, *Beasts in Velvet*, *Genevieve Undead*, *Route 666* and *Orgy of the Blood Parasites*. A winner of the British Science Fiction Award for Best Short Fiction ('The Original Dr Shade'), he is the recipient of no fewer than four awards for *Anno Dracula*: The Children of the Night Award, presented by the Dracula Society for Best Novel; The British Science Fiction Award; the Fiction Award of the Lord Ruthven Assembly, and the International Horror Critics' Guild Award for Best Novel. The short story collections *The Original Dr Shade and Other Stories* and *Famous Monsters* represent a sampling of the author's eclectic short fiction, while the prequels to 'Where the Bodies Are Buried 2020' can be found in our anthologies *Dark Voices 5* and *6* ('Where the Bodies Are Buried' and 'Where the Bodies Are Buried II: Sequel Hook') and the first volume of *Dark Terrors* ('Where the Bodies Are Buried 3: Black and White and Red All Over'). According to the author, regular readers of the 'Bodies' series will note that 'This latest instalment is the 'where-we-came-in' conclusion of the series. It also takes the world of the "Bodies" stories, which is more or less the world of much of my recent fiction, including "The Original Dr Shade", "Organ Donors" and *The*

Quorum, up to the beginnings of the future seen in some of my earlier science fiction stories, such as "Dreamers", "Patricia's Profession" and *The Night Mayor*. The Yggdrasil swallows its tail. A *Where the Bodies Are Buried* collection is also in the works.'

The Museum on Cyclops Avenue

HARLAN ELLISON

The jaunty feather in my hatband? I knew you'd ask. Makes my old Tyrolean look rather natty, don't it? Yeah, well, I'll tell you about this flame-red feather some time, but not right now.

What about Agnes? Mmm. Yeah. What *about* Agnes.

No, hell no, I'm not unhappy, and I'm certainly not bitter. I *know* I promised to bring her home with me from Sweden, but, well, as we say here in Chapel Hill, *that* dog just ain't gonna hunt.

I'm sorry y'all went to the trouble of settin' up this nice coming-home party, and it truly is a surprise to walk back into my own humble bachelor digs and find y'all hidin' behind the sofas, but to be absolutely candid with myself and with y'all ... I'm about as blind tired as I've ever been, fourteen and a half hours riding coach on SAS, customs in New York, missing two connector flights, almost an hour in traffic from Raleigh-Durham ... you see what I'm sayin'? Can I beg off this evenin' and I *promise* just as soon as I get my sea-legs under me again with the new semester's classes and the new syllabus, I swear I *promise* we'll all do this up right!

Oh, God bless you, I *knew* you'd understand! Now, listen, Francine, Mary Katherine, Ina ... y'all take this food with you, because as soon as the door closes behind you, I'm going to hit my bed and sleep for at least twenty-four hours, so all these here now goodies will gonna rot if you don't take 'em and make y'self a big picnic t'night. Y'all wanna do that now? Excellent! Just excellent.

Thank ya, thank ya *ever* so much! Y'all take care now, y'heah? I'll see you bunch in a few days over to the University.

Bye! Bye now! See ya!

(Henry, you want to hold on for just a few minutes? I do need someone to talk to for a spell. You don't mind? Excellent.) Bye! Drive carefully, you be sure to do it! Bye, William; bye, Cheryl an' Simon! Thank you again, thank you ver—

(Thank God they're gone. Hold on just about a minute, Henry, just in case someone forgot a purse or something.)

Okay, street's clear. Damn, Henry, thought I'd croak when I walked into the house and y'all popped out of the walls. Whose dumbshit idea was this, anyway? Don't tell me yours, I can*not* afford to lose any respec' for you at the moment. I need a friend, and I need an open mind, an' *most* of all I need a smidge outta that fifth of Jack black sittin' up there on the third shelf 'tween Beckwith's *Hawaiian Mythology* and Bettelheim's *Uses of Enchantment*.

I'd get up and fetch it myself, but I'm shanxhausted, and you're the one just had the angioplasty, so I figger you got lots more energy in you, right at the moment.

They's a coupla clean glasses right there in the cabinet, unless the cleanin' woman saw fit to move things around while I was gone. Asked her not to, but you know nobody listens.

Yeah, right. *While I was gone.* Just decant me about thirty millimetres of that Tennessee sippin', and I'll regale your aging self with the source of my truly overwhelmin' anomie.

No, I'm not cryin', it's the strain and the long trip and everything that happened in Stockholm. Truly, Henry. I'm sad, I own to it; but it's been four days since the street signs changed, and I'm reconciled to it . . . say what . . .?

All right, sorry sorry, didn't mean to get ahead of it. I'll tell you. It's a not terribly complicated saga, so I can tell you everything in a short space. But hold off makin' any judgements till I finish, we agree on that?

Fine. Then: my paper was scheduled for the second day of

the Conference, I wanted a few days to see the sights, and when SAS put that Boeing 767 down at Arlanda International, my sponsor, John-Henri Holmberg, was waiting with his new wife Evastina, and John-Henri's son, Alex. And they'd brought along a Dr Richard Fuchs, a very strange little man who writes incredibly obscure books on bizarre illnesses that no one, apparently, either buys or reads. It was quite warm; John-Henri's shirt was open and he carried his jacket; Evastina kept daubing at her moist upper lip; and Alex, who's too old for them now, he was wearing short pants; it was *quite* warm. Fuchs wore gloves. Milky-white latex gloves, the kind you'd put on to examine specimens. But he was effusive in his greetings. Said he wanted me to see a monograph he'd translated into English on some quisquous aspect of Swedish mythology. Why an' wherefore this odd little man should be such a slavish devotee of my work, the semiotics of mythology, by an obscure Professor of Classics from the English Department of the University of North Carolina, is somethin' I was unable to discover. But since it was he – of everyone I met over theah – was the cause of everything that happened to me . . . I do suspect his bein' there at the airport was considerable more than merest happenstance. I'm gettin' ahead of myself. Patience, Henry.

They took me to the Royal Viking Hotel, and I unpacked and showered and napped for about an hour. But I was still restless; I was aching for sleep, but I couldn't fall off. My legs kept twitching. I couldn't stop worrying about my paper. Two days, I was supposed to deliver it to a major international conference on the latest academic rigours, an' you *know* I've never been comfortable with all this 'deconstructionist' criticism. So I was dog-tired, but instead of taking a Q-Vel for the leg cramps and catching up on some sleep, I fiddled with the manuscript. Even wound up putting a new sub-title on it: *Post-Structuralist Hermeneutics of the Theseus-Minotaur Iconography*. I could barely get my tongue around all that. Imagine what I'd've done somebody asked me what the hell it *meant*. But I knew it'd look impressive in *The Journal*.

So by the time they came to get me for the opening day's

dinner reception, I was pretty well goggle-eyed. Maybe that's why I didn't think what was happening was all that distressin'. What Shakespeare called 'how strange or odd'. I had fourteen and a half hours on the flight back to mull it, an' I can tell you *now* that it was indeed, oh my yes, it was in*deed* distressin', strange, *and* odd.

Now take it easy! I'll skip all the local colour, what it's like ridin' over cobblestone streets, and the hoe-*ren*-duss cost of livin' in Sweden – y'know how much it costs for a roll of Scotch Tape? About seven *dollars*, that's what it costs, can you believe it – and I'll cut right to the reception, and meeting Agnes. And Fuchs. And the sepulchre on Österlånggatan. And the flame feather I brought home from Stockholm instead of the most beautiful woman who ever walked the face of the earth.

We were sitting around at this big table at the reception, with a classical pianist named Baekkelund playing all sorts of twentieth-century Swedish compositions – Blomdahl, Carlid, Bäck, Lidholm, that whole 'Monday Group' – and Fuchs was sitting next to me, looking at me as if I might start blowing bubbles at any moment, and I thanked him again for runnin' to get me a champagne refill, 'bout the third or fourth time he'd done it, like as if he wanted to come into my employ as a manservant, and he smiled at me with a little face full of nasty brown teeth, and he said, 'I notice it is that you concern over my wearing of gloves.'

I hadn't realized I'd been oglin' his li'l rubber mittens, but I was just bubbly-happy enough to smart him, 'stead of just answering polite. I said, 'Well, Dr Foowks, it *has* attended my attention that the warm factor in this jammed ballroom is very possibly running towards ninety or so, and the rest of us are, how do they say it in Yiddish, we are all *schvitzin'* like sows, whilst you are covered fingertip to neck-bone. Why *do* you think that is so, suh?'

John-Henri looked uncomfortable. It was just the three of us had come to the reception – Evastina was home with the new baby, Fnork, who had reached the infant stage of catching and eating flies – and though there were others who'd come to sit at that big round table, it was more a matter of expediency in a jammed room with limited seating, than it was a desire to mingle with the three of us. (It had seemed to me, without too close an examination of the subject, that though a few people knew John-Henri, and greeted him saucily, not only did no one *speak* to Dr Fuchs, but there were several who seemed to veer clear when they espied him.)

Dr Fuchs grew tolerably serious, and soft spoke, an' he replied to what instantly became obvious to me had been an incredibly stupid, rude, and champagne-besotted remark: 'I live with a bodily condition known as hyperhidrosis, Professor Stapylton. Abnormally excessive sweating. As you have said it, *schvitzing*. I perspire from hands, feet, my underarms. I must wear knitted shirts to absorb the moisture. Underarm dress shields, of a woman's kind. I carry pocket towels, in the ungood event I must actually shake hands flesh on flesh with someone. Should I remove my latexwear, and place my palm upon this tablecloth, the material would be soaked in a widened pool in moments.' He gave me a pathetic little smile that was meant to be courageous, and he concluded, 'I see revulsion in people's faces, Professor. So I wear the gloves, is it not?'

I felt like thirty-one kinds of a blatherin' damnfool, an' I suppose it was because I had no way of extricatin' my size 11M Florsheim from my mouth, that I was so susceptible when Fuchs humiliated me even more by introducin' me to this utter vision of a woman who came blowin' by the table.

Without even a *hesitation* on his part, springs right off this 'I make people sick 'cause I'm soakin' wet all the time,' right into, 'Oh, Agnes! Come, my dear, come meet the famous American scholar and authority of mythic matters, Professor Gordon Stapylton of Chapel Hill, North Carolina, a most brilliant colleague of our friend John-Henri.'

We took one look at each other, and I knew what it was to endure hyperhidrosis. Every pore in my body turned Niagara. Even half stupored on good French champagne, I was sober enough to know I had, at last, finally, unbelievably, met the most beautiful woman in the world, the one woman I would marry and, failing that liaison, would never be able to settle for anyone else.

Her hair was the colour of the embers when the fire has died down and the companions have snuggled into their sleeping bags and you cannot fall asleep and lie there looking into that moving breathing susurrating crimson at the bottom of the campfire. Her eyes were almond-shaped, and tilted, and green. Not murky, dirty green, but the shade of excellent Chinese jade pieces, Shang dynasty, Chou dynasty. Describing more, I'd sound even more the idiot than I do right now. I tried to tell y'all what she was like, when I called the next morning, remember? When I said I was bringing home the woman I loved, her name was Agnes? Well, I was tipsy with her. then ... and I'm tipsy all over again now, just describin' her, But the *import*ant part of all this, is that we took one look t'each other, an' we couldn't keep our hands off!

Fuchs was tryin' to tell me that Agnes Wahlström was, herself, a noted scholar, a student of mythology, and curator of the *Magasinet för sällsamma väsen*, some kind of a museum, but I wasn't much listening by that time. We were swimming in each other's eyes; and the next thing I knew, I'd gotten up and taken her hand – which had a wonderful strong independent kind of a grip – and we were outside the two-hundred-year-old building with the reception up those marble staircases; and we were in a narrow service alley that ran back from the cobblestoned street into darkness alongside the hulking ugliness of the assembly hall; and I barely had an instant to speak her name before she bore me back against the alley wall, her lips on mine.

She fumbled her dress up around her hips, and undid my belt, almost batting away my hands as I tried to undress *her*. And there, in that alley, Henry, there in the darkness I found what I'd never been able to locate in nearly forty years of believing it existed: I found utter and total passion, I-don't-give-a-damn lust, a joining and thrashing that must have made steam come off us, like a pair of rutting weasels. Look, I'm sorry to be embarrassin' you, Henry, my old friend, but under this pleasant, gregarious, buttoned-down academic pose, I have been nothin' but a *lonely* sonofabitch all my life. You *know* how it was between my parents, an' you know how few relationships I've had with women who counted. So, now, you have *got* to understan' that I was crazy with her, drunk with her, inside her and steam comin' off us. Migawd, Henry, I think we banged against that alley wall for an hour, maybe more. I have *no* idea why some Swedish cop didn't hear us growlin' and pantin' and yellin' moremoremore, and come in there an' arrest us. Oh, jeezus, lemme catch mah breath. Lawd, Henry, you are the colour of Chairman Mao's Little Book! We never got back to the reception the Conference was hostin'.

We spent the night at the Royal Viking, and the next morning she was as beautiful as the night before, except the sun loved touchin' her, Henry; and we ate breakfast in the room, and her eyes were that green, and made love again for another hour or so. But then she said she had to go home and change because she had to be at the Museum, she was late already, but she'd find me at the Conference in the afternoon and we'd, well, we'd be *together*.

Can you understand what that word meant to me? We'd be *together*. That was when I called you and told you I'd be bringin' back the greatest mythic treasure ever. I had to share it with *some*one, Henry. That was four days ago, before the street signs changed.

John-Henri is a decent man, and an absolutely great friend, so his chiding me on my behaviour was maximum softly-spoke; but I was given to understand that walkin' off like Night of the Livin' Dumbbells with some gorgeous museum curator, right in the middle of where I was *supposed* to be, was unacceptable. He also confided that he'd been stuck with Dr Fuchs all night, nearly, and he was not overwhelmin'ly thrilled by *that*, either. Turned out he was less acquainted with the man in the moist mittens than I'd thought. Out of nowhere, a few weeks before I was scheduled to fly in, he suddenly showed up, ingratiating, charming, knowledgeable about

John-Henri's background, very complimentary, workin' ever
so hard to become Evastina's and John-Henri's best new
buddy-chum. Just so, just that way, out of nowhere, he
suddenly appeared in the antechamber of the Conference
Hall, right in the middle of John-Henri's polite, with-
clenched-teeth admonition that I not pull a repeat of the
previous evening's gaucherie.

Fuchs kept smilin' at me with that scupperful of brown
bicuspids, just smarmily enquiring, had I had a pleasant
evening, but not gettin' any closer to questions I'd've had to
tell him were none of his damned business.

But I couldn't get rid of him. He dogged my every step.

And I attended the sections I'd wanted to drop in on, and
my mind wasn't focused for a second on such arcane trivia.
All I could think of was sliding my hands up between Agnes's
legs.

Finally, about three in the afternoon, she arrived. Looking
absolutely wonderful, wearing a summery dress and sandals,
in defiance of the chill that was in the air. She found me at
the rear of the auditorium, slid in beside me, and whispered,
'I have nothing on under this.'

We left not more than three heartbeats later.

All right, Henry, I'll skip all that. But now pay close
attention. Five or six hours later, she seemed distracted, an' I
suggested we go get some dinner. I was goin' to pop the
question. Oh, yes, Henry, I *see* that expression. But the only
reason you got it on you, is that you know somethin' was
amiss. But if you didn't *know* that, then you wouldn't think I
was bein' precipitous, you'd agree that once having been in
the embrace of such a woman, a man would be a giant fool to
let her slip away. So just pretend you're as innocent as I was,
at that moment, and go along with me on this.

She said no, she wasn't hungry, she'd had a big salad before
she came to fetch me at the Conference, but would I be
interested in seeing the Museum? Where she was curator. I
said that would be charming. Or somesuch pseudo phrase so
she wouldn't suspect all I could think about was makin' love
to her endlessly. As if she weren't smart enough to know *all*

that; and she laughed, and I looked sheepish, and she kissed me, and we went to get the car in the hotel structure, and we drove out, about nine or so.

It was a chilly night, and very dark. And she drove to the oldest section of Stockholm, blocky ribbed-stone buildings leaning over the narrow, winding streets, fog or mist trailing through the canyons, silvery and forlorn. It was, well, not to make a cliché of it . . . it was melancholy. Somehow sad and winsome at the same time. But I was on a cloud. I had found the grail, the crown, the sceptre, the very incarnation of True Love. And I would, very soon now, pop the question.

She parked on a side-street, cobbled and lit fitfully by old electric brazier lamps, and suggested we should walk, it was invigorating. I worried about her in that thin dress. She said, 'I am a sturdy Scandinavian woman, dear Gordon. Please.' And the *please* was neither cajoling nor requesting. It was 'Give me a break, I can outwalk you any day, son.' And so we strode off down the street.

We turned a number of times, this side-street, that little alley, pausing every once in a while to grope each other, usually on my pretext that certain parts of her body needed to be warmed against the sturdy Scandinavian chill. And finally, we turned on to an absolutely shadow-gorged street down which I could not see a solitary thing. I glanced up at the street sign, and it read: *Cyklopavenyn.* Cyclops Avenue.

Now isn't that a remarkable, I thought.

She took me by the hand, and led me into the deep shadow pool of the narrow, claustrophobic, fog-drenched Cyclops Avenue. We walked in silence, just the sound of our hollow footsteps repeating our progress.

'Agnes,' I said, 'where the hell are we going? I thought you wanted me to see—'

Invisible beside me, but her flesh warm as a beacon, she said, 'Yes. *Magasinet för sällsamma väsen.*'

I asked her if we were nearly there, and she said, with a small laugh, 'I told you to tinkle before we left.' But she didn't say 'tinkle.' She used the Swedish equivalent, which I won't go into here, Henry, because I can see that you think I'm

leading this story towards her giving me a vampire bite, or
trying to steal my soul and sell it to flying saucer people . . .
well, it wasn't *any*thing sick or demented, absolutely no blood
at all, and as you can see I'm sittin' right here in front'cher
face, holdin' up my glass for a splash more of Mr Jack Daniel's.

Thank'ya. So we keep walkin', and I ask her to translate for
me what *Magasinet* etcetera et-cet-era means, and she said, it's
hard to translate into English. But she tried, and she said
Museum wasn't quite the right word, more rightly something
not quite like Sepulchre. I said that gave me chills, and she
laughed and said I could call it The Gatherum of Extraordinary Existences – as we reached a brooding shadowy shape
darker than the darkness filling Cyclops Avenue, a shape that
rose above us like an escarpment of black rock, something
hewn from obsidian, and she took a key from a pocket of the
thin summery dress, and inserted it in the lock, and turned
the key – or you could call it The Repository of Unimaginable
Creatures – and she pushed open a door that was three times
our height, and I'm six one, and Agnes is just under six feet –
or the Cyklopstrasse Keep of Rare and Extinct Beasts – and as
the door opened we were washed by pure golden light so
intense I shielded my eyes. Where the door had snugged
against the jamb and lintel so tightly there had been no
leakage of illumination, now there was an enormous rectangle
three times our height of blazing burning light. I could see
nothing, not a smidge, but that light. And Agnes took me by
the elbow, and walked me into the light, and I was *inside* the
most breathtaking repository of treasures I'd ever seen.

Greater than the Prado, more magnificent than the Louvre,
dwarfing the Victoria and Albert, more puissant than the
Hermitage, enfeebling the image of Rotterdam's Museum
Boymans-van Beuningen, it rose above us till the arching
ceilings faded into misty oblivion. I could see room after room
after channel after salon after gallery stretching away in a
hundred different directions from the central atrium where
we stood, mah mouth open and my wits havin' fled.

Because the Museum that my Agnes tended, the Sepulchre
that my Agnes oversaw, the Gallery my Agnes captained . . .

it was filled with the dead and mounted bodies of every creature I'd read about in the tomes of universal mythology.

In niches and on pedestals, in crystal cases and suspended by invisible wires from the invisible ceilings, ranked in shallow conversation-pit-like depressions in the floor and mounted to the walls, in showcases and free-standing in the passageways:

The Kurma tortoise that supported Mt Mandara on its back during the churning of the ocean by the Devas and Asuras. A matched set of unicorns, male and female, one with silver horn, the other with golden spike. The bone-eater from the Ani papyrus. Behemoth and Leviathan. Hanuman the five-headed of the Kalighat. A Griffin. And a Gryphon. Hippogryph and Hippocamp. The Kinnara bird of Indian mythology, and the thousand-headed snake Kalināga. Jinn and Harpy and Hydra; yeti and centaur and minotaur; the holy feathered serpent Quetzalcoatl and a winged horse and a Ryu dragon. Hundreds and thousands of beasts of all worlds and all nations, of all beliefs and all ages, of all peoples and of all dreams and nightmares. There, in the stunning Sepulchre on the Verg Cyklop, was amassed and arrayed and ranked all the impossible creatures that had never made it on to Noah's leaky tub. I wandered gallery to gallery, astounded, impossible sights choking my throat and making me weep with amazement that it was all, all, *all of it* absolutely true. There was even a Boogeyman and his mate. They looked as if they had lived their lives under beds and in dark closets.

'But how . . .?' I could barely find words, at long last.

'They are here, assembled all. And I am the one who caught them.'

Of all I had seen, of all she might say, *that* was the most astonishin'. *She* had brought these beasts to heel. I could not believe it. But no, she insisted, she trekked out, and she stalked them, and she caught them, and killed them, and brought them back here for display. 'For whom?' I asked. 'Who comes to this place?' And she smiled the sweetest smile, but did not reply. *Who*, I wondered, assaying the size of the rooms, the height of the ceilings, *who did the tour of this repository of miracles?*

Hours later, she took me away, and we went back to the Royal Viking, and I was too aswirl in magic and impossibilities to drench myself in her scented skin. I could not fathom or contain what I had seen. Her naked body was muscular, but more feminine than Aphrodite and Helen of Troy and the Eternal Nymph all combined. She was gorgeous, but she was the hunter of them all. Of course she had had a strong grip. From holding machete, and crossbow, and Sharps rifle, and bolas, and gas-gun. She told me of the hunts, the kills, the scent of the track, the pursuits in far lands: Petra and Angkor, Teotihuacan and Tibet, Djinnistan and Meszria, Skull Island and Malta and Knossos.

And then she said to me, 'I am very much drawn to you, Gordon, but I know you're going to ask me to come away with you, to live in America and be your wife. And I truly, deeply, am mad about even the thought of making love to you endlessly . . . but . . .'

The next day, I went looking for Cyclops Avenue. I have a skunk-sniffin' dog's sense of direction, you know that, Henry; and I actual found the street again. I recognized all the twisty turns we'd made, even lookin' different in the daylight. But I got there. And, of course, the street signs had changed. Cyclops Avenue was now Österlånggatan. The Museum was not there. Oh, it likely *was* there, but I didn't have either the proper guide or a key taken from the pocket of a summery dress to help me find it. So I went away, and I came back here, and that's my story. Except for a couple of loose ends . . .

One: What of the peculiar Dr Fuchs? Well, Agnes never said it in so many words, but I got the impression that she had taken pity on the poor little man, that he had been someone who had loved her and followed her, and whose existence meant nothing without her in it, and so she had allowed him to assist her. She said he was her 'spotter'. I didn't ask what that meant, nor what it was he spotted. (Before I left Stockholm, John-Henri called to say goodbye, and he told me he had found a pair of gloves, apparently the property of Fuchs, half-filled with foul-smelling water or sweat or some fishy liquid, but that Dr Fuchs, himself, had vanished, leaving an enormous hotel bill for John-Henri and the Conference to pay.)

And two: I'll bet you haven't forgotten, have you?

That's right, Henry, the feather.

I plucked it from the flank of an enormous roc that she had stalked and bagged and killed and stuffed. It hung from the ceiling in the Museum of Unimaginable Creatures, hung low enough so I could pluck one memento. I think, I guess, I, well I *suppose* I knew somewhere in my head or my heart, certainly not in my pants, that I was never going to get this prize, this treasure, this woman of all women. And so, in some part of my sense, I stole a token to keep my memory warm. It's all I have, one flame-red feather from the flank of the roc that tried to carry off Sinbad the Sailor.

And do you know *why* she renounced me, gave me a pass, shined me on, old Henry? I guess I begged a little, told her how good we were together and, yes, she admitted, that was so; but it was never gonna work. Because, Henry, she said . . .

I was too easy a catch. I didn't nearly put up the fight it would take to keep her hunter's interest pinned.

What's that? Do I think I'll ever see her again?

Henry, I see her all the time. This world of you and the University and houses and streets and mail-boxes and a drink in my hand . . . it's all like a transparent membrane on which a movie picthuh is bein' cast. And behind it, I see *her*. My Agnes, so fabulous. She's in a rough-bark coracle, with a canvas sail ripped by terrible winds caused by the beating of a devil roc's great feathered wings, as its spiked tail thrashes the emerald water into tidal spires. She holds a scimitar, and her jade-green eyes are wild; and I know the flame-feathered monster that seeks to devour her, capsize her, drag her down and feast on her delicious flesh – I know that poor dumb ravening behemoth hasn't got the chance of a snowball in a cyclotron. In her path, in the fury of her flesh, *no* poor dumb beast has a chance. Not even – pardon the pun – the Roc of Agnes.

Do I see her? Oh my, yes. I see her clearly, Henry. I may never see *my* world clearly again after walking the halls and galleries of the Cyclops Avenue Museum . . . but I'll always see her.

For a poor dumb beast, that vision and a goddam red feather is almost enough to get by on. Wouldja kindly, that Jack Daniel's beside you. And then maybe I will go upstairs and try to catch a little sleep. Thank ya kindly, Henry.

Harlan Ellison has been called 'one of the greatest living American short story writers' by the *Washington Post*, and the *Los Angeles Times* said, 'It's long past time for Harlan Ellison to be awarded the title: 20th Century Lewis Carroll.' In a career spanning forty years, he has won more awards for the 64 books he has written or edited, the more than 1700 stories, essays, articles and newspaper columns, the two dozen teleplays and a dozen motion pictures he has created, than any other living fantasist. His recent publications include *I, Robot: The Illustrated Screenplay* and the script for *The City on the Edge of Forever*, while over the next few years White Wolf Publishing will release a series of twenty volumes of *Edgeworks: The Collected Ellison*. About the origin of 'The Museum on Cyclops Avenue', the author has the following to say (written, amazingly, from his recovery bed four days after quadruple heart-bypass surgery in April 1996): 'As much as any story I've written – and I find that I am as secretly fond of this story as the best of the more than 1700 stories I've written over the past forty-plus years – this one speaks to the lovely quote from Bernard Malamud: 'Art lives on surprise. A writer has to surprise *himself* to be worth reading.' Susan and I were Guests of Honour (along with ex-KGB chief Boris Pankin) at the prestigious International Book Fair in Göteberg in 1992. During that trip, I wrote large portions of what became my short novel *Mefisto in Onyx*. And I realized, much later, that whether writing on the floor of the huge convention before hundreds of bewildered attendees who couldn't understand that creation occurs everywhere and doesn't always need a velvet-lined closet, or on pillows in a hotel room, that Sweden was a particularly salutary venue to produce contemporary fantasy, light and dark. So it was with a *frisson* of familiarity that I found myself, as I started writing *this* story, three years later, returning to a memory of Stockholm. Had no idea as I sat down to write, to do this 'story behind the cover' to fit an existing painting by Ron Brown for the fifth issue of my comic book, *Harlan Ellison's Dream Corridor* (quarterly, from Dark Horse), that I was embarking on a story to be told entirely in dialect by a tenured Professor of Classics from the University of North Carolina at Chapel Hill (where I'd lectured some years earlier), recollecting incidents that had happened to him in Sweden. Most peculiar. The voice, the venue, the congeries of disparate elements, the use of my close friends John-Henri Holmberg and Richard Fuchs, all in the service of explaining what was going on in this 'heroic' painting Ron Brown had done for my comic. (Every issue, I pick some piece of specially-painted or already-existing unpublished Fine Art, and I write a story from scratch to fit the vision that will be used as cover for the comic. It's a great game. I enjoy it immensely). Incidentally, only the name 'Dr Richard Fuchs' bears relation to the real, extremely charming Dr Fuchs, who is a Swedish bestselling author and a swell guy, who permitted me to make him odd and ominous for this tale. I had no idea where I was going when I started. That I began with the feather is to me another example of how secure I've become – as *all* writers must become, I believe – in trusting the talent. The onboard expertise and cleverness of the unconscious are the best helpmeets to integrating the elements of a story . . . particularly if you begin *tabula rasa*. This is one of those stories that truly told itself. I just went along for the ride.' It should be noted that 'The Museum on Cyclops Avenue' also stands as a tribute to the late Robert Bloch, as much as David J. Schow's '(Melodrama)' does elsewhere in this volume. As Ellison explains: 'I have always written my stories on Olympia office standard or portable typewriters. Bob Bloch also wrote on Olympias. When Bob died, he passed on to me two of his machines. This story was written on one of those typewriters, completed on 5 July 1995. The work goes on.'

Hunger:
An Introduction

PETER STRAUB

On the bare, sunlit stage the hungers could begin.
John Ashbery, *Faust*

I have a sturdy first sentence all prepared, and as soon as I settle down and get used to this reversal of our usual roles I'm going to give you the pleasure. Okay. Here goes. *Considering that sooner or later everybody is going to die, people know surprisingly little about ghosts.* Is that clear? Every person on earth, saint and turd, is going to wind up as a ghost, but not one of them, I mean, of *you*, people, knows the first thing about them. Almost everything written or spoken about the subject is, I'm sorry, absolute junk. It's *disgusting*. I'm speaking from the heart here, I'm laying it on the line – *disgusting*. All it would take to get things right is a little bit of common, everyday, sensible thinking, but sensible thinking is easier to ask for than to get, believe you me.

Now I see that I have already jumped my own gun, because the second sentence I intended to deliver was: *In fact, nothing ever said about ghosts even comes close to the truth.* And the third sentence, after which I am going to scrap my prepared text completely and speak from the heart, is: *A lot of us are really steamed about that.*

For! The most commonly held notion about ghosts, the grand-daddy, the notion that parades as grown-up reason cutting right to the heart of things, shakes its head, grins, fixes you in the eye with a steely little glint that asks if you're kidding, and says ghosts don't exist.

Wrong.

Sorry, wrong.

Sorry, I know, you'd feel better if you could finally persuade yourself that every account of encounters with beings previously but not presently alive is fictional. Doesn't matter how many people say they've seen the same woman in black walking back and forth in front of the window from which in 1892 the chambermaid Ethel Carroway defenestrated a newborn infant fathered by a seagoing rogue named Captain Starbuck, thousands of people might swear to having personally seen poor Ethel's shade drag itself past that window, it don't, sorry, it doesn't matter, they're all suffering from mass hysteria. They saw the curtain move in a breeze and imagined the rest. *They want you to think they're interesting.* You're too clever to fall for that one. You know what happens to people after they die, and one thing you know for sure is that they don't turn into ghosts. At the moment of death, people either (1) depart this and all other possible spheres, leaving their bodies to depart in a messier, more time-consuming fashion; or (2) leave behind the poor old skinbag as their immortal part flies heavenwards rejoicing, or plummets wailing to eternal torture; or (3) shuffle out of one skinbag, take a few turns around the celestial block, and reincarnate in another but fresher skinbag, thereupon starting all over again. Isn't that more or less the menu? Extinction, moral payback, or rebirth. During my own life, for example, I favoured (1), a good clean departure.

Now we come to one of my personal bugaboos, or I could say, anathemas, in memory of someone I am going to have to bring in here sooner or later anyhow, my former employer, Harold McNair, a man with an autodidact's fondness for big words. Mr McNair once said to me, *Dishonesty is my anathema.* One other time, he used the word *peculation.* Peculation was his anathema, too. Mr Harold McNair was confident of his personal relationship to his saviour, and as a result he was also pretty sure that what lay ahead of him, after a dignified and painless leavetaking in the big bed on the third floor, was a one-way excursion to paradise. He was, as I say, pretty sure about that. Maybe every now and then the thought came to him that a depraved, greedy, mean-spirited, weasel like himself might have some trouble squeaking through the pearly gates, no matter how many Sundays he put on his best suit and strutted over to the church on Abercrombie Road to lip-synch to the hymns and nod over the sermon – yes, maybe Harold McNair had more doubts than he let on. When it came to the biggie, when it came down to what you really have to call the crunch, he did not go peacefully, not at all. How he went was screeching and sweating and cursing, trying to shield his head from the hammer, struggling to get back on his feet, for all the world as though he feared spending eternity as a piece of bacon. And if asked his opinion on the existence of ghosts, this big-shot retail magnate would probably have nodded slowly, sucked his lower lip, pondered mightily, and opined that—

Okay, I never actually *heard* the position of my former employer in re ghosts despite our many, oft-times tediously lengthy colloquies. Harold McNair spoke to me of many things, of the anathemas dishonesty and peculation, of yet more anathemas including the fair sex, any human being under the age of nineteen or twenty, folk of the Hebraic, Afric, or Catholic persuasions, bowel irregularities, customers who take up fifteen minutes of a salesperson's time and then just sashay out without making a purchase, customers – *female* customers – who return undergarments already worn, tight shoes, lumpy potatoes, dogs of any kind, loud music, people from California or New York City, small print, warts and wens, cysts and pustules, longhairs, eggheads, per-fessers, pinkos, and people who hold hands in public. He had so much to say on these and the many other topics that excited his disapproval, even indignation, that he never got around to describing his conception of the afterlife, even while sputtering and screeching and rolling his eyes as the hammer sought

out the tender places on his tough little noggin. Yet I know
what Mr McNair would have said.

Though ghosts may fail to be non-existent, they are at least
very few in number.

Wrong! This way of thinking disregards the difference
between Ghosts Visible, like poor Ethel Carroway, who
dropped that baby from a fourth-floor window of the Oliphant
Hotel, and Invisible, and disregarding that difference is just
exactly like pretending there's no difference between Living
People Visible, like Mr Harold McNair, and Living People
Invisible, like myself, in spite of everything the way I was way
back when, not to mention most everybody else, when you
get right down to it. Most people are about as visible to other
people as the headlines on last Monday's newspaper.

I desire with my entire heart to tell you what I'm looking
at, I yearn to describe the whole of the visible world as seen
from my vantage point beside the big azalea bush on my old
enemy's front lawn on Tulip Lane, the spot I head for every
day right about this particular time. That would clear up this
whole thing about *numbers* right away. But before I get into
describing what I can see, I have to get around to introducing
myself, since that's the whole point of my being here today.

Francis T. Wardwell is my handle, Frank Wardwell as I
was known, and old Frank can feel himself getting all heated
up already about the third numbskull idea the run of people
have about ghosts, so he better take care of that one right
away before he goes any further. The third idea is – Ghosts
are ghosts because they're unhappy. Far too many people
believe that every wandering spirit out there is atoning for
some old heart-stuffed misery, which is why they suppose
Ethel drifts past that window now and again.

Ask yourself if anything is ever that simple, even in what
you call experience. Are all the criminals in jail? Are all the
innocent free? And if the price of misery is misery, what is the
price of joy? In what coin do you pay for that, laddy, shekels,
sweat, or sleepless nights?

*

Though in every moment of my youthful existence I was sustained by a most glorious secret that was mine alone, I too was acquainted with shekels, sweat, and what the poets call White Nights. No child of luxury, I. Francis Wardwell, Frank to his chums, born to parents on the ragged-most fringe of the lower middle class, was catapulted into corporeality a great distance from the nearest silver spoon. We were urban poor (lower-middle-class-poor, that is), not rural poor, and I feel deeply within myself that a country landscape such as that of which I was deprived would have yielded to my infant self a fund of riches sorely needed. (Mark the first sounding of the hunger-theme, to which we will return betimes.) Is not Nature a friend and tutor to the observant child? Does it not offer a steady flow of stuff like psychic nutrient to the developing boy? Experts say it does, or so I hear, and also that much do I recall from my reading, which was always far, far in advance of my grade level. (I was reading on the *college level* before I was out of short pants.) Old-time poets all said Nature is a better teacher than any other. In my case, blocked off by city walls from the wise friend Nature, I was forced to feed my infant mind on the harsher realities of brick, barbed wire, and peacock-feather oil slicks. That I went as far as I did is testimony to my resilient soul-strength. Forbidden was I to wander 'mongst the heather and cowslips, the foxgloves, purple vetch, tiger lilies, loosestrife, and hawkweed on country lanes; no larks or thrushes had I for company, and we never even heard of nightingales where I came from. I wandered, when I had that luxury, that is when I wasn't running my guts out to get away from a long-nosed, red-eyed, smirking Boy Teuteburg, through unclean city streets past taverns and boarding houses, and for streaky gold-red sunsets I had neon signs. The air was not, to put it good and plain, fresh. The animals, when not domestic, were rodentine. And from the seventh grade on, at a time when I suffered under the tyranny of a termaganty black-haired witch-thing named Missus Barksdale who hated me because I knew more than she did, I was forced to endure the further injustice of after-school employment. Daily had I to trudge from the humiliations

delivered upon my head by the witch-thing, Missus Barfsbot-
tom, humiliations earned only through an inability to conceal
entirely the mirth her errors caused in me, from sadistic,
unwarranted humiliations delivered upon the head of one of
the topmost students ever seen at that crummy school, then
to trudge through sordiosities to the place of my employment,
Dockweder's Hardware, where I took up my broom and
swept, swept, swept.

For shekels! In the sense of measly, greasy coins of low
denomination in little number! Earned by my childish sweat,
the honest sorrowful perspiration, each salty drop non-
accidentally just exactly like a tear (and that, Missus Doggy-
breath, is what you call a metaphor, not a methapor, as your
warty moustachy mouth misinformed the massed seventh
grade of the Daniel Webster State Graded School in the
winter of 1928), of a promising, I mean really and truly
promising lad, an intelligent lad, a lad deserving of the finest
this world had to offer in the way of breaks and opportunities,
what you might want to call and I looking back am virtually
forced to call A Shining Boy!

Who day and night had to check over his shoulder for the
approach of, who had to strain his innocent ears in case he
could hear the footfalls of, who was made to quench his
glorious shining spirit because he had to live in total awful
fear of, the subhuman, soulless, snake-like figure of, Boy
Teuteburg. Who would crouch behind garbage cans and
conceal himself in doorways, was a lurker in alleys, would
drag at his narrow cigarette with his narrow shoulders against
the bricks and squint out from under the narrow brim of the
cap on his narrow head, was a low being of no conscience or
intelligence or any other merits altogether. A Boy Teuteburg
is not a fellow for your flowery fields and rending sunsets. He
is a creature of the streets and knows no better. And such as
this, a lowly brutal creature with no promise to him at all
except the promise to wind up in jail, became yet another,
perhaps the most severe, bane of the Shining Boy's existence.

Between Daniel Webster State Graded School and Dockweder's Hardware Emporium would this young terrorist lurk

of an afternoon, stealing some worthless tit-bit here, hawking on the sidewalk there, blowing his nose by pressing two fingers against one nostril, leaning over and firing, then repeating the gesture on the opposite side, all the while skulking along, flicking his puny red eyes over the passing throng (as *Dickens* had it) in search of children younger than he, any children in actual fact, but in most especial one certain child. This, you may have divined it, was yours truly. I know for a fact that Boy Teuteburg had a singular hatred for the child-me because of what befell me when I was able to convoy myself from one place to another amidst the kidlings of my age – other little sparrows of the street (as *Blake* might put it) – to subsume myself in the shelter of a pattering throng of classmates. We all feared Boy, having suffered under his psychotic despotism for years of grade school. Our collective relief at his eventual graduation (he was sixteen!) chilled to dread when we discovered that his release from the eighth grade meant only that Boy had been freed to prowl eternally about Daniel Webster, a shark awaiting shoals of smaller fishes. (A *simile*, Missus Doggybark, a *simile*.) There he was, smirking as he tightened his skinny lips to draw on his skinny cigarette – circling. Let us say our convoy of joking lads rounds the corner on Erie Street by the Oliphant Hotel and spreads across the sidewalk as we carry on towards Third Street, home for some, Dockweder's and the broom for me. Then a stoaty shadow separates from the entrance of Candies & Newsagent, a thrill of fear passes through us, red eyes ignite and blaze, some dreary brat begins to weep, and the rest of us scatter as Boy charges, already raising his sharp and pointy fists. And of all these larking children, which particular boy was his intended target? That child least like himself – the one he hated most – myself – and I knew why. Scatter though I would 'mongst my peers, rushing first to this one then to that, my friends, their morality stunted by the same brutal landscape that had shaped our tormentor, would'st push me away, abandon me, sacrifice me for their own ends. It was me, I mean I, he searched out, and we all knew it. Soon the others refused to leave the school in my presence, and I

walked alone once more. Oft were the days when the body
that wielded the broom ached with bruises, when the eyes
within the body were dimmed with tears of pain and sorrow,
and the nose of the body contained screws of tissue paper
within each nostril, purpose of, to staunch the flow of blood.

And oft, too, were the nights when from a multiplicity of
causes young Frank Wardwell lay sleepless a-bed. His concave
boyish tummy begged for sustenance, for the evening repast
may have been but bread and sop, and the day's beating meant
that certain favoured positions brought him pain. Yet hunger
and pain were as nothing when compared to the true reason
sleep refused to grant its healing balm. This was terror. Day
came when night was done, and day brought Boy Teuteburg.
So fearsome was my tormentor that I lay paralysed with fear
'neath my blankets, hoping without hope that I might the
next day evade my nemesis. Desperate hours I spent mapping
devious alternate routes from school to store while still
knowing well that however mazy the streets I took, they
would deliver me unto Boy. And many times I sensed that he
had glided into our yard and stood smoking beneath our tree,
staring red-eyed at my unlighted window – other times I
heard him open our back door and float through the kitchen
and hover motionless outside my door. What good now was
my intellectual and spiritual superiority to Boy Teuteburg?
What good were my yearnings? Ice-cold fear was all I knew.
Mornings, I dragged myself from bed, quaking opened my
door to find Boy of course nowhere in sight, fed my ice-cold
stomach a piece of bread and a glass of water, and dragged
myself to school, hopeless as the junkman's horse.

Had I but known of the thousand eyes upon me . . .

Why does Ethel Carroway report to her window on the
fourth floor of the Oliphant Hotel at the full of the moon?
Guilt? Remorse? Grief? You shall hear of Ethel Carroway.

In life, this was a thoughtless girl, vibrant but shallow, lively
and loud, the epitome of a Visible, who felt no more guilt
than does a cast-iron pump. For months Ethel had gone about
her maid's duties in loose overblouses to conceal her con-

dition, of which even her slatternly friends were ignorant. The infant signified no more than a serious threat to her employment. She never gave it a name or fantasized about its life or thought of it with aught but distaste. Captain Starbuck had departed the day following conception, in any case a hasty, rather *scuffling* matter, no doubt to sow his seed in foreign ports. Delivery took place behind the locked door of Ethel's basement room and lasted approximately twelve hours, during which she twice had to shout from her bed that she was violently ill and could not work. (Her exact words were, 'Sick! Pukin'! Leemee 'lone!') During the process, she consumed much of a bottle of bourbon whiskey given her by another priapic guest of the Oliphant. When at last the child triumphantly bullied its way out between her legs, Ethel bit the umbilicus in two and observed that she had delivered a boy. Its swollen purple genitals were a vivid reminder of Captain Starbuck. Then she passed out. An hour later, consciousness returned on a tide of pain. Despite it all, Ethel felt a curious new pride in herself – in what she had done. Her baby lay on her chest, uttering little kittenish cries. It resembled a monkey, or a bald old man. She found herself almost regretting that she had to dispose of this creature, who had caused her so much pain. They had been through the day together, they had shared an experience that now seemed almost hallucinatory in its intensity. She wished the baby were the kitten it sounded like, that she might keep it. She and the baby were companions of a sort. And she realized that it was hers – she had made this little being.

Yet her unanticipated affection for the infant did not alter the facts. Ethel needed her job, and that was that. She had to kill the little thing. She tried to move her legs to the side of the bed, and a fresh wave of pain made her gasp. Her legs, her middle, her arms, the bed, all were soaked in blood. Her sheets would have to be burned. The baby mewed again, and more to comfort herself than it, she slid the squeaking child upwards towards her right breast and bumped the nipple against his lips until he opened his mouth and began to suck. The baby, like Ethel, was covered with blood, as well as with something that looked like dark grease. More than anything else at that moment, she wanted to wash herself off – she wanted to wash the baby, too. At least he could die clean. She moved the baby to her other breast, which had no more milk than the first. She stroked his back, and some of the blood and grease came off on her hand, so she wiped his back with a clean part of the sheet.

Some time later, she swung her feet off the bed, ignored the bolts of pain, and stood up with the baby clamped one-handed against her chest. She would give him a gift. Grimacing, she limped to the sink against the wall, turned on the hot water, put in the stopper, mixed in cold until tepid water half-filled the sink, and shut off both taps. Then she lowered the baby into the sink. As soon as his skin touched the water, his eyes flew open and appeared to search her face. For the first time, she saw their colour – a violent purple-blue, like no other eyes she had ever seen. The baby was frowning magisterially. His legs contracted under him like a frog's. The violent eyes glowered up at her, as if the baby knew what Ethel was ultimately going to do, did not at all like what she was going to do, but accepted it. She wiped him with her washcloth until he was pretty much clean, and he kept frowning up at her, scanning her face with his astonishing eyes.

She considered drowning him. Then she would have to carry his body out of the hotel, and she didn't even have a suitcase. Besides, she didn't like the idea of holding him under the water while he looked up at her with that funny old-king frown on his face. Ethel let the red-brown water drain from the sink and wrapped the baby in a towel. She set him on the floor while she refilled the sink and rubbed the washcloth over her body, wincing and gasping. When she picked him up his eyes flew open again, then closed as his mouth gaped in an enormous yawn. She limped back to bed, tore the sheets off one-handed, cast a blanket over the mattress, and lay down and fell asleep with the baby's head at the base of her neck.

It was still dark when Ethel came awake. She had no idea of the time, indeed if it were still the same night, but the quality of the darkness told her that it would soon be morning. The baby stirred on her chest, and its arms, which had worked free of the towel, jerked up and paused in the air before drifting back down. This was the hour when, except for the furnace man, the hotel was still. All the halls were empty, and a single sleepy clerk manned the desk. In an hour, the bootboys would be setting out the night's polished shoes, and a few early-bird guests would be calling down their room service orders. In two hours, Ethel Carroway was supposed to be in uniform, reporting for hall duty. She intended to do this. When it was noticed that she was in pain, she would be allowed another day off, but she had to report. So she had about an hour in which to decide what to do with the baby and then to do it.

If she smothered it in her room, she would have to transport the dead body through the basement to get it outside. The furnace man would be sure to ask her what she was doing. What you got all wrapped up there, Ethel? Some food? Lemme see. Ethel wished she had thought far enough ahead to borrow a valise from one of the other girls, but when in her life had she thought more than an hour or two ahead? She pressed the baby to her chest and stroked its head. She could not keep the body in her room. There wasn't an inch to spare and anyhow the supervisor would be sure to find it on a room check. Poor baby, she thought, it wasn't even his fault he had to die. He was a sweet baby. She rocked him in her arms, thinking how nice it would be to keep him with her and play doll-games with him when she was off-duty.

Then she saw her plan, whole. If she went towards the service stairs after leaving her room, she would avoid the realm of the furnace man. Once on the service stairs, she could go anywhere in the hotel without being seen. The halls were almost certainly empty. She could quietly reach one of the upper floors, open a window, and – let the baby fall. That would be that. Her part would be over in an instant. And the baby's death would be a matter of a second, less than that, a moment too brief for pain. Afterwards no one would be able to connect Ethel Carroway to the little body on the sidewalk. It would look as though a guest had dropped the baby, or even better, as though an outsider had entered the hotel to rid herself of an unwanted child. It would just be a mystery – a baby from nowhere, belonging to nobody, fallen from the Oliphant Hotel. Police Are Baffled. Ethel saw no flaws in this plan – as long as she could leave and return to her room unseen. And to be as certain as possible of being unseen, she had to act now.

She pulled on a night dress and wrapped herself in an old hotel bath robe. Then she swaddled her child in the towel, hugged him to her chest, and silently left her room. On the other side of the vast, dark basement, the furnace man snored on his pallet. Gritting her teeth and cradling the dozing infant, Ethel limped towards the stairs.

The second floor was much too low, and the third seemed uncertain. To be safe, she would have to get up to the fourth floor. Her legs trembled, and spears of pain shot up from the centre of her body, and she was weeping and sweating before she made it to the second floor, but for the sake of the baby she forced herself to keep climbing. When at last she reached the fourth floor, she opened the door into the corridor and leaned against it for what was no more than a minute in real time but seemed dangerously long. A cocoon of pain surrounded her entire body, and sweat stung in her eyes. Beneath the flicker of the gas lamps, the corridor was empty. Ethel carried her baby down between two rows of diminishingly numbered doors and reached the alcove that contained the guest elevators. On the far side of the alcove, two large casement windows at the front of the Oliphant looked out on to Erie Street. She hugged the baby close with one hand and struggled with a window catch for a moment before sliding it out of its latch and pushing the heavy window open. The baby's head lolled back.

Cold air streamed in through the window, and the baby tugged his brows together and scowled as if he had been surprised by an unforeseen philosophical dilemma. Impulsively, she kissed the top of his head and then hitched herself closer to the window. The metal ridge at the bottom of the casement pressed into her hip. She moved her hands to grip the baby beneath his armpits, and the towel came loose and dropped on to her bare feet. The baby drew up his legs, kicked out convulsively, drew them up again, kicked out, as if trying to reject the cold. A bright, mottled pink rose up into his cheeks and covered his face like a rash. His mouth was a tiny red beak. Freezing air rolled over them both. One of the baby's eyes shuttered itself behind a wrinkled lid in an involuntary parody of a wink. The other slid sideways and focused upon her a gaze that seemed both reproachful and distressed.

Gripping his sides, Ethel turned to face the window, extended her arms, and moved his kicking body through the casement to hold him out above the street. She could feel the thin, sturdy little ribs beneath his skin. The metal frame pressed against her belly. Ethel took a sharp inward breath and prepared to prepare to let go of the baby by loosening her grip on his sides. Instantly, unexpectedly, he slipped through her hands and dropped away into the darkness. For an instant, no more, she leaned forward open mouthed.

What happened in that instant, people, what happened to her as she watched her baby fall away towards the Erie Street sidewalk, is the reason Ethel Carroway returns to the window on the fourth floor of the Oliphant Hotel.

The remainder of her story can be quickly told. An Oliphant doorman found the dead infant half an hour after it had slipped from Ethel's hands, and as soon as the morning shift began, the entire staff knew that someone had thrown a baby from an upper-floor window. Two policemen went from room to room, and in a maid's basement chamber came upon an exhausted young woman stuffing bloody sheets into a pillowcase. She refused to answer their questions, but denied having given birth recently or at any time. A medical examination proved her denial inaccurate, and she was arrested, tried, and condemned to death. In April, 1893, Ethel Carroway departed from her earthly state at the end of the hangman's rope. During the next few years, several fourth-floor guests at the Oliphant remarked upon a peculiar atmosphere in the area of the elevators – some found it unpleasantly chilly even on summer days, some found it suffocatingly overheated in winter, and a European recitalist (the mezzo-soprano Nelly Tetrazetti, 'The Golden Bird', touring the northern states with a programme of songs related to faery legend) complained that what she called a 'nasty, nasty porridge' in the elevator alcove was constricting her voice. In 1910, the Oliphant was sold to a man who reduced services and raised prices, and in 1916 it went out of business. It stayed empty, deteriorating steadily, until 1922, when new owners renewed it and ran it as a residential hotel until 1931, when they too went broke and sold it for use as a girls' boarding school. Students of Erie Academy for Girls first reported seeing a figure in black on the fourth floor; by 1961, when the bankrupt Academy closed its doors, local lore had supplied the spectral figure with Ethel Carroway's name, and when the Oliphant reopened yet again two years later, she began putting in her continuing regular appearances, not unlike Nelly Tetrazetti, 'The Golden Bird'. Over the decades, Ethel acquired a certain modest, though significant fame. The Oliphant devotes a long paragraph of its brochure to her, an undoubtedly idealized portrait hangs over the lobby fireplace, and a bronze plaque decorates the site of the crime. Guests with amateur or professional interests in the paranormal frequently spend whole weeks in the hotel, waiting for a glimpse of her. (Unfortunately, none of these guests have ever been granted their wish.)

But Ethel Carroway does not reappear to linger before her window (her window's replacement's replacement's replacement's replacement) to increase or encourage her fame. She does it for one reason only.

She's hungry.

I have told you of bad Boy and the thousand eyes, nay the thousand thousand eyes, fixed upon the unknowing Shining Boy, myself, and alluded to a secret. As I have introduced myself, at this point now I shall in the same forthright manner introduce the matter of the wondrous secret by laying it out on the methaporical table. All through my life I possessed a crystalline but often painful awareness of my superiority to nearly all other people. To put it squarely: I almost always understood that I was better than the others. Just about *all* the others.

A fool may say this and be ridiculed. A madman may say it and be Bedlamized. What fate befalls the ordinary-seeming mortal whose extraordinary gifts, not displayed by any outward show, he dares to proclaim? He risks the ire, disbelief, and growing irritation of his peers, in humbler words, spitballs, furtive kicks and knocks, whispered obscenities, and shoves into muddy ditches. Yet – and this must be allowed – *that the mortal in question is superior, has already aroused ire, irritation, and even hatred amongst those who have so perceived him.* Why was I immediately the focus of Boy Teuteburg's sadistic and psychopathic rage? And why did my fellow-kidlings not defend me from the depredations of our common enemy? It was not only mingled relief and fear that made them cast me out, no. *What inflamed our enemy, Boy, chilled them.* It would have been the same had I never taken the generous pains of illuminating their little errors, the same had I never pressed home the point by adding, *and I know this because I am more intelligent than you.* For they already knew of my superiority. They had seen me struggle to suppress my smiles as I instructed our teacher in her numerous errors, and surely they had likewise noted the bright inner soul-light within their precocious classmate.

Now I know not to speak of these matters (except in privileged conditions such as these). In my mid-twenties I gave all of that up, realizing that my life had become a catastrophe, and that the gifts which so elevated me above the run of mankind (as the protagonists of the great *Poe* know themselves raised up) had not as it were elevated the outward circumstances of my life in the same fashion. I was condemned to the prison-house (what I thought was the prison-house) of ordinary mortal existence, the life given over to a meaningless job, dull pleasures, despairing dreams. The inward soul-light had guttered and dimmed, and would no longer draw the attacks of the envious. Life had circled me 'round and stolen what was most essentially mine.

Not all ghosts are dead, but only the dead can be counted on for twenty-twenty vision. You only get to see what's in front of your nose when it's too late to do you any good.

At that point, enter hunger.

My life had already lost its lustre before I truly understood that the process of diminishment had begun. Grade school went by in the manner described. My high school career, which should have been a four-year span of ever-increasing glories culminating in a 4.0 average and a full scholarship to a Harvard or even a College of William and Mary, ground itself into a weary repetitive pattern of Cs and Ds hurled at me by indifferent fools long incapable of distinguishing the true creative spirit from the glib, mendacious copycat. In his freshman year, under the pen name 'Orion', young Frank Wardwell submitted three meritorious poems to the school literary magazine, all of which were summarily rejected, one on the grounds that several of its noblest phrases had been copied down from poets of the Romantic movement. Did the poets own these phrases, then? And would then a young chap like Frank Wardwell be forbidden to utter these phrases in the course of literary conversations such as he never had due to the absence of like-minded souls? Yes, one gathers, to the editors of a high-school literary magazine. The doctrine that poetic utterance becomes the common property of man was alien to them.

I turned to the creation of a private journal, in which to inscribe my deepest thoughts and record my exalted and far-reaching imaginings. But the poison had already begun its work. Brutal surroundings, moral isolation, inferior teachers, these had robbed my pen of its freshness, and much of what I set down was only lamentation over my misunderstood and friendless state. In coming from the deeps to seek expression, my high-arching thoughts met the deadly ignorance that surrounded me and shrivelled from gleaming heroes with cascading blond hair into gap-toothed dwarves. And my imaginings, the tales with which I had vowed to storm this world's castles, refused to take wing. I blush to remember how, when stalled in the midst of what was to be a furious tale of awe and terror, my talent, struck down early by a vision-denying world, turned not to Great Imagination for its forms but to popular serials broadcast at the time over the radio waves. *The Green Hornet* and *Jack Armstrong, the All-American Boy*, my personal favourites among these, supplied many of my plots and even, I grant, some of my less pungent dialogue.

All my endeavours went the way of the private journal. A young person losing his life by the gradual draining away of his spirit cannot be fully aware of the damage daily done to his being. Some vestige of the inborn wonder will beat its wings and trust that flight will come, and I saw with sad and weary regularity the evidence that I was as far above my teachers and fellow students at Edna Ferber High as I had been at Daniel Webster State Graded School. Yet my well-intentioned and instructive exposures of their intellectual errors earned me no gratitude. (Did you really imagine, Tubby Shanks, you of the quill-like red hair and carbuncled neck who sat before me in sophomore English, that Joyce Kilmer, immortal author of 'Trees', was necessarily of the female gender, for the sole reason that both your mother and sister shared his Christian name? My remark that Irish scribe James Joyce then must be a side-show morphadite did not deserve the blow you addressed to my sternum, nor the wad of phlegm your acolyte, Stewart Siddley, deposited on my desk at close of day.) True, I had no more to fear the raids of Boy Teuteburg, who had metamorphosed into a sleek ratty fellow in a tight black overcoat and pearl grey snapbrim hat and who, due to a busy round of appointments in pool halls, the back rooms of taverns and the basements of garages, had no time for childish pursuits. Dare I say I almost missed the attentions of Boy Teuteberg? That I almost longed for the terror he had caused in me? And that his indifference, what might have even been his lack of recognition, aroused within me nameless but unhappy feelings on the few occasions when

we ancient enemies caught sight of one another, me, sorry, I
mean I, dragging through our native streets at the end of
another hopeless day at Edna Ferber, he emerging from an
Erie Street establishment known as Jerry's *Hotcha!* Lounge,
then his narrow still-red eye falling on mine but failing to
blaze (though the old terror did kindle in me, that time), and
then my immemorial foe sliding past me without a word or
gesture to mark the momentous event? At such times even
the dull being I had become felt the passing of a never-to-
be-recovered earlier soul-state. Then I had known of my
superiority and nurtured myself upon it; now, knowing of it
still, I knew it did not make an ounce of difference. Boy
Teuteburg had become a more consequential person than
Francis T. Wardwell. I had seen the shades of the prison-
house pulled down 'til nearly all the light was blocked.

Soon after the unmarked momentous event, two other such
pulled them fully down.

After an unfortunate incident at school involving the loss of
a petty sum on the order of six or seven dollars from a
handbag left hanging on a lunchroom chair, an incident
admittedly not the first of its kind, the meaningless coincidence that I had been seated adjacent to the chair from which
hung the forgotten reticule somehow led to my being blamed
for the loss of the insignificant sum. It was felt, quite falsely,
that I had been responsible for the earlier incidents. I
defended myself as any innocent party does, by declining to
respond to the ridiculous accusations. I did possess a small,
secret store of money, and when ordered to repay the careless
girl who had been the real source of the crime, I paid her the
wretched seven dollars from this source.

Unbearably humiliated, I chose not to subject myself to the
hostile stares and cruel whispers I would meet in the school's
halls, so for some wretched days I wandered our streets,
spending far too many quarters from my precious cache in
coffee shops and movie theatres when supposed to be in class,
and then reporting as ever to Dockweder's Hardware, where
having passed down my broom to a shifty urchin of unclean
habits, I was entrusted with the stocking of shelves, the

fetching of merchandise to the counter, and during the generally inactive hour between four-thirty and five-thirty, the manipulation of the cash register. On the fifth day after my self-imposed suspension from school, Mr Dockweder kept me after work as he ostentatiously balanced out the day's receipts, the first time I had ever seen him do so, found the *awesome*, the *majestic* sum of $1.65 missing from the cash tray, and promptly accused me of the theft. Not the ordinary boyish mistake of returning too much change to an impatient customer or hitting a wrong button when ringing up a sale, but the theft. I protested, I denied, alas in vain. Then look to the boy, I advised, I think he steals from the stock room too, fire him and the pilfering will cease. As if he had forgotten my seven years of unstinting service, Mr Dockweder coldly informed me that sums of varying amounts had been missing from the register many nights during the period when I had been entrusted with its manipulation between the hours of four-thirty and five-thirty. He demanded I turn out my pockets. When I did so, he smoothed out one of the three bills in my possession and indicated to me on its face the check mark he had placed on every one of the register's bills before leaving the counter in my charge.

Now, in all honesty, a check mark might be made on a dollar bill in a hundred different ways. I have seen every possible sort of symbol used to deface our nation's currency. Mr Dockweder, however, would accept none of my sensible suggestions – his mind and heart were closed alike. He insisted to bring me home, and as we took to the streets gripped my shoulder in an iron clamp. Once in our dwelling, he stood in the shabby parlour and denounced me. My hottest denials went unheard. In fact, I was trembling and sweating, undergoing a thousand torments, for once or twice I had dipped into the register and extracted a few coins, a quarter, a dime, a penny or two, coins I assumed would never be missed and with which I could sustain myself throughout the long day. I even *confessed* these minor lapses, thinking to improve my situation with a fine show of honest remorse, but this fearless candour did me harm. My father repaid to Mr Dockweder from his own skimpy reserve of cash the inflated sum claimed to be missing, vowed that I personally would make the amount good to him, and informed me that I would henceforth clear my head of nonsensical ideas and learn the ways of the real world. He was sick of my airs and high-faluting manners, sick of my books, my affected mode of speech, my uselessness – sick of me. From that day I should work. Work, I mean, as a dumb beast works (my father, an alcoholic welder, being one such), without hope, without education, without let-up, without meaning, and with no reward save an inadequate weekly pay-packet.

That evening, still reeling from the depth and swiftness of my fall, I let myself out of our house after the welder and his weeping wife had collapsed into bed and went staggering through our streets. What I had been, I scarcely knew; what I now was, I could not bear to see; what I was to become, I could not imagine. Life's prison-house rose up about me on all sides. In that prison-house lay a grave, and within that grave lay I. The streets took me, where I did not know or care, and at careless intervals I looked up to see before me a featureless wall, a urine stain belt-high beneath broken windows in an abandoned warehouse, heaped-up tyres in a vacant lot. These things were *emblems*. Once I caught sight of a leering moon, and once I heard the shuffle of feet close by and stopped in terror, sensing mortal danger on all sides, and glanced all round at empty Erie Street.

Bitterly, the stillborn fantasies of childhood returned to me, their former glow now corpse-grey. Never would I kneel down in fields and woods 'midst bird's-foot trefoil, daisy fleabane, devil's pulpit, Johnny-Jump-Up, jewelweed, the foxglove, and the small sundrop. Never would I hear the lowing of the kine, the tolling of bells in a country church, the far-off call of the shepherd, the chant of the lark. Mountain lakes and mountain rivers would never take me in their chilly, breath-giving grasp. The things I was to know were all but *emblems* of the death-in-life ranged 'round me now.

I raised my all-but-unseeing eyes to the façade, six storeys high, of the Oliphant Hotel, dark dark dark. Above the lobby, dimly visible behind the great glass doors, the windows hung dark and empty in the darker brick. Behind those windows slept men and women endowed with college degrees and commercial or artistic skills, owners of property, travellers in foreign lands, men and women on the inside of life. They would never know my name, and I would never be of their Visible number. All radiantly Visible themselves, they would look at me no more in daylight than at present – and if they happened to look, would see nothing!

A figure moved past an upper window, moved back, and then reappeared behind the window. Dark dark dark. A guest, I thought, wandering sleepless in the halls, and thought to turn away for my long journey home. Some small awareness held me, looking up. High above behind a casement window hovered a figure in black garb, that figure, I now observed, unmistakably a woman's. What was she doing, why was she there? Some trouble had sent one of the gilded travellers roaming the Oliphant, and on that trouble she brooded now, pausing at the window. Recognizing a fellow-being in misery akin to my own, I brazenly stepped forward and stared up, silently demanding this woman to acknowledge that, despite all that separated and divided us, we were essentially the same. White hands twisted within her black garment. We were the same, our world was the same, being dark dark dark. Perhaps the woman would beckon to me, that we could each soothe the shame of the other. For streaming from the woman was shame – so I thought. An oval face emerged from shadow or from beneath a hood and neared the glass.

You shall see me, you shall, I vowed, and stepped forward once again. The alabaster face gazed at a point some five feet nearer the hotel than myself. I moved to meet her gaze, and just before I did so, experienced a hopeless terror far worse than anything Boy Teuteburg had ever raised in me. Yet my body had begun to move and would not stop when the mind could not command it. Two mental events had birthed this sick dread: I had seen enough of the alabaster face to know that what I had sensed streaming out was something far, far worse than shame; and I had suddenly remembered what the

first sight of this figure at this window of this hotel would
have recalled to me had I been in my normal mind – the
legend of the ghost in the Oliphant. Ethel Carroway's eyes
locked on mine. They scorched my innards. I could not cry
out through my constricted throat; I could not weep from my
singed eyes. For a tremendous moment I could not move at
all, but stood where her infant had fallen to the pavement and
met her ravishing, her *self-ravishing*, glance with my own
helpless glance. When it was over – when she released me – I
turned and ran like a dog whom wanton boys have set on fire.

The following day my father commanded me to go to Mr
Harold McNair at McNair's Fine Clothing & Draperies and
enquire after a full-time position. He had recently done some
work for Mr McNair, who had spoken of a job opening
available to an eager and hardworking lad. Now that my
circumstances had changed, I must try to claim this position
and be grateful for the opportunity, if offered. I did as my
father commanded. Mr Harold McNair had indeed a position
available, the position being assistant stock-boy, hours 7.30
a.m.–6.00 p.m. Monday–Saturday, wages @ $0.45/hr, meals
not supplied. He had thought the welder's boy might be
responsive to his generosity, and the welder's boy, all that
remained of me, was responsive, yes sir, Mr McNair, sir. And
so my endless drudgery began.

At first I worked to purchase, at the employee rate, the
shirts and trousers with which an assistant stock-boy must be
outfitted; and at intervals for the next twenty-nine years I
spun long hours into dress shirts and neckties and worsted
suits as Rumpelstiltskin spun straw into gold, for a McNair's
representative must advertise by wearing the very same clothing to be sold to McNair's beloved customers. I had no
friends. The only company I knew was that of my fellow
employees, a cringing half-brained lot devoted to sexual
innuendo, sporting events, and the moving pictures featuring
Miss Jean Harlow. Later on, Wallace Beery and James Cagney
were a big hit. Even later, one heard entirely too much of
John Wayne. This, not forgetting the pages of our Sunday

newspaper wasted upon the 'funny papers', was their culture, and it formed the whole of their conversation. Of course I held myself apart. It was the old story repeated once again, as all stories are repeated again and again, eternally, just look around you. You are myself, and I myself am you. What we did last week, last year, what we did in our infancy, shall we do again tomorrow. I could take no delight in the gulf that lay between my intellect and theirs, nor could my fellow-workers. Doubtless all of them, men and women, secretly held the opinion of me expressed near the end of our Christmas party in 1959 by Austin Hartlepoole, an Accounting junior who had imbibed too freely of the fish-house punch: 'Mr Wardwell, have you always been a stuck-up jerk?'

'No,' I might have said but did not, 'once I was a Shining Boy.' (What I did say is of no consequence.)

By then I was Mr Wardwell, note. The same superior qualities that condemned me to social and intellectual isolation had seen me through a series of promotions from assistant stock-boy to stock-boy then head stock-boy, thence laterally to manager, shipping department, then upwards again to counter staff, Shirts and Ties, followed by a promotion upstairs to second floor, counter staff, Better Shirts and Neckwear, then Assistant Manager, Menswear, in time, Manager, Menswear, and ultimately, in 1959, the year soon-to-be-sacked Hartlepoole called me a stuck-up jerk, Vice-President and Buyer, Clothing Divisions. The welder's boy had done well for himself. Just outside town, I maintained a large residence, never seen by my co-workers, for myself and a companion who shall remain nameless. I dressed in excellent clothing, as was to be expected. A grey Bentley, which I pretended to have obtained at a 'price', represented my single visible indulgence. Accompanied by Nameless Companion, I regularly visited the Caribbean on my annual two-week vacation to take up comfortable rooms in the same luxurious 'resort' hotel. By the end of the nineteen-fifties, my salary had risen to thirty-five thousand dollars a year, and in my regular banking and savings accounts I had accumulated the respectable sum of fifty thousand dollars. In another, secret account,

I had amassed the even more respectable sum of five hundred and sixty-eight thousand dollars, every cent of it winkled away a little at a time from one of the worst people, in fact by a considerable degree actually the worst person, it has ever been my misfortune to know, my employer, Mr Harold McNair.

All was well until my transfer upstairs into Better Shirts and Neckwear, my 'Ascension', we called it, to the vaulted splendours of the second floor, where affluent customers did not have to mingle with the commoners examining cheaper goods below, and where Mr McNair himself, my jailor-benefactor of years before, was wont to appear from the depths of his walnut-panelled office, wandering between the counters, adjusting the display cravats, remarking upon the quality of a freshly-purchased tweed jacket or fox stole (Ladies' was sited across the floor), taking in the state of his minions' fingernails and shoes. Mr McNair, a smallish, weaselish, darkish, baldish figure in a navy suit, his solid red tie anchored to his white shirt with a visible metal bar, demanded courteous smiles, upright postures, hygienic habits. Scuffed shoes earned an errant clerk a sharply worded rebuke, unclean nails an immediate trip to the employee washroom. The dead thing I was did not object to these simple, well-intentioned codes. Neither did I object to my employer – he was but a fixed point in the universe, like his own God enthroned in his heavens. I did not take him *personally*. Not until my Ascension, when we each fell under the other's gaze.

Living Visibles like Harold McNair do not merely expect to be seen. Though they be discreetly attired, quietly spoken, and well-mannered, within they starve, they slaver for attention, and exact it however they must. In Mr McNair's case, this took the form of divisiveness, capriciousness, sanctimoniousness, and for lack of a better word, tyranny. He would favour one counter clerk, then another, therein creating enmity and rivalry and an ardent wish in two hearts to comprehend his own heart. He would elect one obscure employee for weeks of special treatment, jokes, confidences, consultations, and then without explanation drop the elected one back into obscurity, to be pecked to death by his peers.

He drew certain employees aside and whispered subtle criti-
cisms of their dearest friends. During all this, he searched for
his true, secret favourites, those whose contempt for themselves, masked behind a smooth retailer's manner, matched
his own contempt for them, masked behind the same. In time
I began to think of Harold McNair as a vast architectural
structure something like his store, a great building charmingly
appointed with fine though not ostentatious things, where a
smiling but observant guide leads you ever deeper in, deciding
room by room if you have earned the right to see the next, by
stages conducting you into chambers which grow successively
smaller, uglier, eventually even odorous, finally through foul,
reeking sties, and at last opens the final door to the central,
inmost room, the little room at the heart of the building, the
most terrible of all, and admits you to – the real Mr Harold
McNair.

He knew I was his the first time he saw me behind the
Better Shirts counter on the second floor. He may even have
known it on the day he hired me, long years previous. In fact,
he might even have considered the alcoholic welder labouring
in his basement and seen that this man's son, if he had one,
would be his as if by Natural Law. His in the sense of easily
flattered, thus easily dominated. Ready to be plucked up by a
kind word and downcast by a harsh one. Willing to please.
Able to sustain attentive silences during the Great Man's
monologues. Liable to be supine before power, abject before
insult. A thorough and spineless subordinate. A kind of slave.
Or, a slave. Long before my final promotion, I had been
shown into the final room and met the true Harold McNair.
I knew what he was and what I was. In many ways, I had fallen
under the sway of a smoother, more corrupt Boy Teuteburg,
a Boy who thought himself a noble being and wore the mask
of a dignified, modest, successful retailer.

I accepted this. But I had determined to be paid well for
the role.

My thefts began with an impulsive act of revenge. I had just
departed Mr McNair's office after a session in which the whip
lashed out more forcefully from within the velvet bag than

was customary, both before and after my employer had expressed his apocalyptic disgust for all women, those sly scented obscenities, those temples of lust, etc., etc. Making my way granite-faced through Better Gowns, I noticed an elderly temple of lust depositing her alligator bag upon the counter as she turned to scrutinize a bottlegreen silk Better Gown with Regency sleeves. A wallet protruded slightly from the unclasped bag. Customer and Saleslady conferred in re the wisdom of Regency sleeves. My legs took me past the counter, my hand closed on the wallet, the wallet dropped into my pocket, and I was gone.

Heart a-thud, I betook myself to a stall in the male employee's washroom, opened the wallet, and discovered there sixty-eight dollars, now mine. I had been rash, that I knew, but I was electric with life. All I regretted was that the money had been the temple's, not Mr McNair's. I left the stall and by reflex went to the sinks and the mirrors. As I washed my already spotless hands I caught my face in the mirror and froze – a vibrant roguish Visible a decade younger than I looked back at me with blazing eyes, my own.

Anyone in a business that receives and disburses large amounts of cash will eventually work out a method for deflecting some of the cash out of its normal course. Some few will test their method, and most of those will be found out. A dim-witted snatch and grab like mine, unobserved, is a method as good as any. During my tenure in the store, many employees located the imperfections in their methods only when the handcuffs closed around their wrists. (Mr McNair never showed mercy or granted a second chance, never.) From the moment my living eyes met mine in the washroom mirror, I was already withdrawing from the cash available an amount appropriate to my degraded role, *stealing my real salary*. All that remained was to work out a method that could never be detected.

Many, many such methods exist, though sometimes even these are detected. I will not burden you with the details of mine, save to reveal that it involved a secret set of books. It worked successfully for better than two decades and yielded a sum nearly appropriate to my continuous humiliation. Mr McNair knew that significant amounts of money were escaping his miserly grasp, but despite feverish plotting followed by the construction of elaborate rat-traps, could not discover how or where. The traps snapped down upon the necks of minor-league peculators, till-tappers, short-change artists, bill-padders, invoice-forgers, but never did it come down upon his greatest enemy's.

On the night I placed my hundred thousandth unofficial dollar in my secret account, I celebrated with a lobster dinner and a bottle of French champagne in our finest seafood restaurant (alone, this being previous to the arrival of Nameless Friend) and, once filled with alcohol and rich food, remembered that the moon was full that night, recalled also my night of misery so long ago, and resolved to return to the Oliphant Hotel. Then, I had been lost, a corpse within a grave within a prison; now, I was achieved, a walking secret who had worked his own way to the inside of life. An invisible Visible. I would stand before Ethel Carroway and be seen – I thought I knew within me what had been written upon her face.

I walked (in those pre-Bentley days) to Erie Street and posted myself against an opposite wall to await the arrival of the shade. She would show herself to me again and acknowledge that like her I stood above the common run, distinguished by the intensity of my needs. Mine was the confidence of a lover who, knowing that this night his beloved will yield, anticipates and savours each blissful, earthy pleasure to come. Each moment she did not appear was made delicious by being the moment before the moment when she would. When my neck began to ache, I lowered my chin to regard through the enormous glass doors the Oliphant's lobby, once a place of unattainable luxury. Now if I liked I could take a fourth-floor suite and present myself to Ethel Carroway on home ground. But it was right to stand where I had before, the better to mark the distance I had come. An hour I waited, another, cold and thirsty.

My head began to ache from the champagne I had taken.

My feet complained, and my faith wavered. Yet I could not leave – Ethel Carroway had put me to a test which grew the more demanding as the minutes passed. Determined not to fail, I turned up the collar of my coat, thrust my hands into its pockets, and kept my eyes upon a dark window.

Sometimes I heard people move behind, then beside me, but looking towards the sound, saw no one. The champagne worked, I thought, like a drug in my bloodstream, falsifying and deceiving, and so I focused all the harder on the blank window. Yet she would not show herself and acknowledge, by meeting my eyes with her own, my right to *be* acknowledged. Mysterious footfalls came teasingly out of the darkness on Erie Street, as if Ethel Carroway had descended to meet me, but the footfalls were many and varied, and no pale figure in black appeared to meet my consummating gaze.

I had not understood – I knew nothing of Visibles and those not, and what I took to be confidence was but its misshapen nephew, arrogance. The cynosure and focus of myriad pairs of eyes, all of which stared unseen at me, I at last surrendered after three in the morning and wandered sore-foot home through the invisible crowd of those who, unlike myself, understood exactly what had happened there and why. In the morn, I rose from my rumpled bed to steal again.

Understanding, ephemeral as a transcendent insight granted in a dream, ephemeral as *dew*, came only with exposure, which is to say, with loss of fortune and large residence, loss of Nameless Companion, of super-duper Bentley, of elegant sobersides garb, of gay Caribbean holidays on the American Plan, loss of reputation, occupation (both occupations, retailer and thief), privacy, freedom, many Constitutionally guaranteed civil rights, and ultimately, of life. As with all of you, I would have chosen these forfeited possessions, persons, states, and conditions over any mere act of understanding, yet I cannot deny the sudden startling consciousness of a certain piquant, indeterminate pleasure-state, unforeseen in the grunting violence of my last act as a free man, which surfaced hand in hand with my brief illumination. This sense of a deep but mysterious pleasure linked to my odd flash of comprehension was often the subject of my thoughts during the long months of trial and incarceration.

I had long since ceased to fear or anticipate exposure, and the incarnadine (see *Shakespeare*) excess of exposure's aftermath would have seemed a nightmarish impossibility to the managerial Mr Wardwell, stoutly serious and seriously stout, of 1960. Weekly, a handsome sum wafted from Mr McNair's gnarled, liver-spotted grip into my welcoming hands, and upon my retirement some ten stony years hence I expected at last to float free in possession of approximately two million dollars, maybe three. My employer's rat-traps continued to snap down on employees of the anathema stripe, of late less frequently due to wide-spread awareness of the Byzantinely complex modes of surveillance and inspection which universally 'kicked in' at the stage beneath the introduction of my invented figures, on account of their having been devised by the very same anathema they were designed to entrap. Had not the odious McNair decided upon a store-wide renovation to mark the new decade, I should after thirty, with luck forty, years of pampered existence in some tropic port, after sustained experience of every luxury from highestly refined to basestly, piggishestly sensual, have attained upon my death from corrupt old age an entire understanding of my frustrated vigil before the Oliphant, of the walkers and shufflers I had heard but were not there, also of Ethel Carroway and her refusal to recognize one who wrongly thought himself her spiritual equal. But he proceeded on his dubious brainstorm, and I induced a premature understanding by smashing his brains into porridge – 'nasty, nasty porridge' – with a workman's conveniently disposed ballpeen hammer.

The actual circumstances of my undoing were banal. Perhaps they always are. A groom neglects to shoe a horse, and – a king is killed. A stranger hears a whisper in an ale-house, and – a king is killed. That kind of thing. In my case, coincidence of an otherwise harmless sort played a crucial role. The dread renovation had reached the rear of the second floor, lapping day by day nearer the Accounts Room, the Art

Department, and the offices, one mine, one Mr McNair's. The tide of workmen, ladders, dropcloths, yardsticks, plumblines, sawhorses, and so forth, inevitably reached our doors and then swept in. As my employer lived above the store in a velvety lair only his inmost courtiers had seen, he had directed that the repanelling and recarpeting, the virtual *regilding*, of his office be done during normal working hours, he then enduring only the minor inconvenience of descending one flight to be about his normal business of oozing from customer to customer, sniffing, adjusting, prying, flattering. As I owned no such convenient lair and could not be permitted access to his, not even to one corner for business purposes, my own office received its less dramatic facelift during the hour between the closing of the store, six, and the beginning of overtime, seven. A task that should have taken two days thus filled ten, at the close of every which, concurrent with my official duties, I must manage the unofficial duties centred on the fictive set of books and the disposition of the day's harvest of cash. All this under the indifferent eyes of labourers setting up their instruments of torture.

Callous, adamantine men shifted my desk from port to starboard, from bow to stern, and on the night of my downfall informed me that I must immediately jump ship that they might finish, our boss having lost patience with this stage of affairs. I jumped ship and bade farewells to departing employees from a position near the front doors. By six forty-five the store was dark, save for the rear portion of the second floor. At six fifty-five I made my way through the familiar aisles to my office door, through which I observed Harold McNair, on a busybody's journey from the sultan's quarters above, standing alone before my exposed desk alone in my newly-thised-and-thatted office and contemplating the undeniable evidence of my various anathematic peculations.

The artisans should have been packing up, but had finished early; McNair should have been consulting his genius for depravity upstairs in the velvety bower, but had slithered down to ensure their obedience. Finished early, the workmen had left, unseen by me, by the back doors. We were alone in the building. As Mr McNair whirled to confront me, a combination of joy and rage distorted his unpleasant features into a demonic mask. I could not save myself – he knew exactly what he had seen. He advanced towards me, spitting incoherent obscenities. From long, weary habit, I resigned myself to what would come.

Mr McNair arrived at a point a foot from my person and continued to berate me, jabbing a knobby forefinger at my chest as he did so. Unevenly, his face turned a dangerous shade of pink, hot pink I believe it is called. The forefinger hooked my lapel, and he tugged me deskwards. His colour grew higher as he ranted on. Finally he hurled at my bowed head a series of questions, perhaps one question repeated many times, I don't know, I could not distinguish the words. My being quailed beneath the onslaught; I was transported back to Dockweder's. Here again were a marked bill, an irate employer, a shamed Frank Wardwell – the wretched boy blazed forth within the settled, secretive, ample man.

And it came to the wretched boy that the ranter before him resembled two old tormentors, Missus Barksdale and Boy Teuteburg, especially the latter, not the smooth rodent in a pearl grey hat but the red-eyed bane of childhood who came hurtling out of shop doors to pummel head and body with sharp, accurate, knife-like fists. I experienced a moment of pure psychic sensation so foreign I could not at first affix a name to it. I knew only that an explosion had taken place within. Then I recognized that what I felt was pain, everlasting, eternal pain long self-concealed. It was as though I had stepped outside my own body. Or *into* it.

Before me on my oaken chair lay a ballpeen hammer forgotten by its departing owner. The instant I beheld it, I knew what I would do. My hand found the hammer, the hammer found McNair's head. Startled, amazed, not yet terrified, Mr McNair jumped back, clamouring. I moved in. He reached for the weapon, and I captured his wizened arm in my hand. The head of the hammer tapped his tough little skull, twice. A wondrous, bright red feeling bloomed in me, and the name of that wondrous feeling was Great Anger. Mr

McNair wobbled to his knees, and I rapped his forehead and set him on his back. He squirmed and shouted, and I tattooed his bonce another half-dozen times. Finally blood began to drizzle from his ears, also from the small abrasions to his knotty head, and I struck him well and truly above the right eye. At that, his body twitched and jittered, and I leaned into my work and now delivered blow after blow while the head became a shapeless bloody brain-spattered ... *mess*. As the blows landed, it seemed that each released a new explosion of blessed pain and anger within Frank Wardwell, it seemed too that these blessings took place in a realm once known but long forgotten, a realm in which emotion stood forth as a separate entity, neither without nor within, observable, breathtaking, utterly alive, like Frank Wardwell, this entranced man swinging a dripping hammer at the corpse of his detested and worshipped enemy. And there arose in a separate portion of my mind the remembered face of Ethel Carroway gazing down at but not in fact seeing the disgraced boy – me on Erie Street, and finally, like a reward, my brief, exalted moment of comprehension arrived, with it that surge of inexplicable, almost intellectual pleasure on the memory of which I chewed so often in the months ahead. Ethel Carroway, I thought, had known this – this shock – this gasp –

Then into the office in search of a forgotten hammer came a burly tough in a donkey jacket and a flat cap, accompanied by an even burlier same, and whatever I had understood blew away in the brief cyclone that followed. Fourteen months later, approximately dogging the footsteps of Ethel Carroway, I moved like a wondering cloud out of a sizzling, still-jerking body strapped into our state's electric chair.

The first thing I noticed, apart from a sudden cessation of pain and a sensation of generalized lightness that seemed more the product of a new relationship to gravity than any actual weight loss, was the presence in the serious room of many more people than I remembered in attendance at the great event. Surely there had been no more than a dozen witnesses, surely all of them male, all reporters save but two, in there with me? During the interesting period between the

assumption of the blindfold and the emergence of the wondering cloud, forty or fifty people, many of them women,
some even children, had somehow crowded into the serious
little room. Despite the miraculous nature of my exit from my
corporal self, these new arrivals paid me no mind at all. They
parted for me without moving, that I might stay or go, as I
wished. Neither did they dwell upon the enthroned corpse of
the fiend, Francis T. Wardwell, from which steadily rose curls
and twists of white smoke as well as the mingled odours of
urine and burned meat, though this object was the undoubted
focus of the original twelve, one nervously caressing a shabby
Bible, one locking his hands over a ponderous gabardine-
enclosed gut, the rest scratching their 'observations' into their
notebooks with chewed-looking pencils. The new arrivals
stared at *them* – the Bible-thumper and the Warden and the
scribbling reporters. I mean, they were *staring* at these unre-
markable people, *lapping them up* with their eyes, visually
devouring them.

The second thing I noticed was that except for the forty or
fifty male and female shades who it had just occurred to me
shared my new state, everything in the serious room, including
the unevenly applied green paint on the walls, including the
calibrated dials and the giant switch, including the blackened
leather straps and the vanishing twists of smoke, including
even the gritty layer of road-dust tramped over the newly
washed and dazzling black-and-white mosaic floor, also
including even the bitten pencils of the scribes, but most of
all including those twelve mortal beings who had assembled
to witness the execution of Francis T. Wardwell, mortal
beings of deep, that is to say, radiant ordinariness, expansive
overflowing heartbreaking light-shedding meaning-steeped—

The second thing I noticed was that everything—

At that moment, my own hunger slammed into me, stronger,
more forceful, and far more enduring than the river of volts
which had separated me from my living self. As avid as the
others, as raptly appreciative of all you still living could not
see, I turned ravening to gaze upon the nearest mortal man.

*

Posted beside the blazing azalea bush on Boy Teuteburg's
front lawn, I observe, mild word, what is disposed so gener-
ously to be observed. After all that has been said, there is no
need to describe, as I had intended at the beginning of our
journey, all I see before me. Of course the street before me is
thronged with my fellow Invisibles, wandering this way and
that on their self-appointed rounds; of course some six or
seven fellow-Invisibles are at this moment aimlessly stretched
out upon Boy Teuteburg's high-grade lawn of imported
Kentucky Bluegrass, enjoying the particularly nice skies we
have at this time of year while awaiting the all-important,
significance-drenched arrival upon the trembling stage of a
sweet mortal being, Tulip Lane resident or service personage.
These waiting ones in particular, like myself, resemble those
eager ticket-buyers who, returning to a favourite play for the
umpty-umpth time, clutch their handbags or opera glasses in
the dark and lean forward towards the rising curtain, breath
suspended, eyes wide, hearts already trilling, as the actors
begin to appear in their accustomed places, their dear, familiar
words to be spoken, the old dilemmas faced once again, and
the plot to spin, this time perhaps towards a conclusion equal
to the intensity of our attention. Will they get it right, this
time? Will they see? No, of course not, *they* will never see,
but we lean forward in passionate concentration as their
aching voices lift again and enthral us with everything they do
not know.

Boy is an old Boy now, in his eighties I believe, though it
may be his nineties – distinctions of this sort no longer compel
– and wonderfully, an honoured personage. He ascended,
needless to say without my vote, into public life as a city
councilman near the time of my own 'Ascension' to the
second floor, and continued to rise until a convenient majority
elected him Mayor shortly before my demise, and upon that
plateau he resided through four terms, or sixteen years, after
which ill health (emphysema) restrained him from further
elevation. His mansion on Tulip Lane contains, I am told,
many rooms – seventeen, not counting two kitchens and ten
bathrooms. But I do not bring myself here to admire the

mansion of my old adversary, now confined, I gather, to an upper floor and dependent on a wheelchair and a ready supply of oxygen. I certainly do not report to Tulip Lane at this time of the day to gloat. (Even Boy Teuteburg is a splendid presence now, a figure who plants his feet on the stage and raises his brave and frail voice.) I come here to witness a certain moment.

At this time of the day, a little girl opens the door of the room beyond the window next the azalea. She is Boy Teuteburg's youngest grand-child, the only offspring of the failed second marriage of his youngest child, Sherrie-Lynn, daughter of his own failed second and final marriage. Her name is Amber, Jasmine, Opal, something like that – Tiffany! Her name is Tiffany! Tiffany is five or six, a solemn, dark-haired, rather smudge-eyed child generally attired in a practical one-piece denim garment with bib and shoulder straps, like a farmer's overall, but white, and printed with a tiny, repeated pattern, flower, puppy, or kitten. Food stains, small explosions of catsup and the like, provide a secondary layer of decoration. Beneath this winning garment Tiffany most often wears a long-sleeved cotton turtleneck, blue or white, or a white cotton T-shirt, as appropriate to the season; on her feet are clumsy but informal shoes of a sort that first appeared about a decade ago, somewhat resembling space boots, somewhat resembling basketball sneakers; in Tiffany's case, the sides of these swollen-looking objects sport pink check marks. Tiffany is a sallow, almost olive-skinned child in whom almost none of her grandfather's genetic inheritance is visible. Whitish-grey streaks of dust (housekeeping has slacked off considerably since Mayor Teuteburg's retirement to the upper floor) can often be seen on her round, inward-looking little face, as well as upon the wrinkled sleeves of her turtleneck and the ironic pastoral of the white overall.

Smudgy of eye; streaky with white-grey dust; sallow of skin; dark hair depending in wisps and floaters from where it had been carelessly gathered at the back, and her wispy bangs unevenly cut; each pudgy hand dirt-crusted in a different fashion, one likely to be trailing a single foot-long blonde hair, formerly her mother's; introspective without notable intelligence, thus liable to fits of selfishness and brooding; round of face, arm, wrist, hand, and belly, thus liable for obesity in adulthood; yet withal surpassingly charming; yet gloriously, wholly beautiful.

This smudgy little miracle enters the room at the usual hour and, as is her habit, marches straight to the television set located immediately beneath our window, tucks her lower lip between her teeth – pearly white, straight as a Roman road – and snaps the set on. Blaring music erupts from the speakers. It is time for the adventures of Tom and Jerry. By now, most of those Invisibles who had been sprawled out on the Kentucky Blue have joined me at the window, and as matters proceed, some of those who have found themselves out on Tulip Lane will wander up, too. Tiffany backpedals to a point on the floor well in advance of the nearest chair. The chairs have been positioned for adults, who do not understand television as Tiffany does and in any case do not ever watch in wondering awe the multiform adventures of Tom and Jerry. She slumps over her crossed ankles, back bent, clumsy shoes with pink check marks nearly in her lap, hands at her sides, sallow face beneath the uneven bangs dowsing the screen. Tiffany does not laugh and only rarely smiles. She is engaged in serious business.

Generally, her none-too-clean hands rest all anyhow on her flowered denim knees, on her pink-checked feet, or in the little well between the feet and the rest of her body. At other times, Tiffany's hands explore unregarded on the floor about her. These forays deposit another fine, mouse-grey layer of dust or grime on whatever parts of the little probing hands come in contact with the hardwood floor.

During the forays, the small person's face maintains a soft immobility, the soft unconscious composure of a deep-diving rapture; and the conjunction of softness and immobility renders each inner delight, each moment of identification or elation, each collusion between drama and witness, in short, you people, each emotion that would cause another child to roll giggling on the floor or draw her smeary fists up to her cheeks, each emotion is rendered *instantly visible* – written in subtle but powerful runes on the blank page that is Tiffany's face. As the eerie tube-light washes over this enchanted child's features, her lips tighten or loosen; an adult frown redraws her forehead; mysterious pouches 'neath her eyes swell with horror or with tears; a hidden smile tucks the corners of her mouth; joy leaps candle-like into her eyes; the whole face irradiates with soul-pleasure. I have not even mentioned the dreamy play brought over the wide cheeks and the area beneath the eyes by thousands of tiny muscle-movements, each invoking the separate character, character as in fictional character, of a piquant, momentary shadow.

And from time to time, a probing hand returns to base and alights on a knee, a space-shoe, wanders for a second through the dangling wisps, hesitates, and then, with excruciating patience, approaches the opening mouth and, finger by finger, enters to be sucked, tongued, warmed, above all, cleaned of its layers of debris. Tiffany is eating. She will eat anything she finds, anything she picks up. It all goes into her mouth and is absorbed into Tiffany. Cookie-crumbs, maybe; mostly dust; loose threads from who knows what fabric; now and then a button or a coin. When she is through with her fingers she might graze over the palm. More often, she will extend a newly washed forefinger and push it into a nostril, there to probe and tease until the glistening morsel is extracted, this morsel to be brought unhesitatingly to the portals of the mouth and slipped within, then munched reflectively until it too has been absorbed into the Tiffany from whence it came.

We watch so intently, we crowd so close, thrusting into the azalea, breasting the window, that from time to time she yanks her eyes from the screen, having heard some dim version of what I twice heard on Erie Street, and glances at our window. She sees but a window, a bush. Instantly, she returns to the screen and her ceaseless meal. I have given you Ethel Carroway letting fall her child, and I have given you myself, Frank Wardwell, battering in a tyrant's brains; but no riper spectacle have I summoned to this stage than Tiffany. She embraces and encompasses living Ethel and living Frank, and exactly so, my dear ones, does Tiffany embrace and encompass you.

Peter Straub has published a string of popular bestselling novels, including *Julia*, *If You Could See Me Now*, *Ghost Story*, *Floating Dragon*, *Shadow Land*, *The Talisman* (with Stephen King), *Koko* and *Mystery*. The latter title won the World Fantasy Award, as did his novella, 'The Ghost Village'. A British Fantasy Award went to *Floating Dragon*, while a more recent novel, *The Throat*, picked up a Bram Stoker Award. His latest novel is *The Hellfire Club*, and he is currently working on 'Mr Clubb and Mr Cuff', a novella loosely based on Herman Melville's *Bartleby the Scrivener*, which is set to appear in a new anthology entitled *Murder for Revenge*. Other stories are collected in *Wild Animals* and *Houses Without Doors*. The story behind the story of 'Hunger: An Introduction' is a fascinating one, as the author reveals: 'The story came about when I agreed to edit one of the yearly Horror Writers of America anthologies, this one devoted to ghost stories, published in a signed, limited edition by Thomas and Elizabeth Monteleone's Border-lands Press and a mass market paperback by Pocket Books. Shortly after I began reading the boxes full of submissions forwarded to me by Martin H. Greenberg and Richard Gilliam, each carton scrupulously alphabetized within various recommendation categories, it occurred to me that I need not follow the conventional protocol of contributing an Introduction explaining the continuing appeal of this kind of story, my own hypothetical positions about ghosts and ghost stories, alluding to the noble tradition of this kind of thing, and concluding with a grandiloquent distribution of praise to my contributors, and by impli-cation myself for having selected them. I realized that I could write a longish story – a story pretending to be an Introduction – expressing, however obliquely, my own odd take on the matter. I could write a ghost story from the point of view of a former human being translated into ghost-hood recently enough for him to still care about communi-cating the One Big Thing he had learned since his change of status. So I wrote my mock-introduction during the day and waded through the HWA submissions at night. Both of these processes were hugely enjoyable. Sometime during the second or third day, while writing the words "If misery is the price of misery, what is the price of joy?" I felt the narrator, Mr Francis Wardwell, seize the pen, and from then on Mr Wardwell was in charge, spilling out words in his own self-justifying, enraged, ultimately resolved manner. He wanted to say his One Big Thing, and, while rapturously meditating on the spectacle of an unbeautiful but beautiful little girl named Tiffany mining her nose with a forefinger and eating the products, he finally did. I thought the anthology turned out well, too, a nice, also nicely abrasive, mixture of voices and moods. To my surprise, none of the people who felt obliged to review the book seemed to have any understanding of my own contribution to it. Expecting an Introduction of the usual sort, they were either baffled by the story's irrelevance to what followed it or content to draw the conclusion that this story was about hunger. Yes, yep, you bet, it is about hunger, uh, huh, that's the truth, and I'm delighted to have this furious diatribe of Mr Wardwell's, the rant of a man who saw what there was to see too late, made available again in this collection.'